●●●POWER ENGINEERING

Third Class
Part B2

Edition 2.0
2015

PanGlobal
TRAINING SYSTEMS

Published by PanGlobal Training Systems Ltd.
Publisher of Power Engineering Training Systems Courseware

The material in this series is aligned with Third Class Syllabus, dated January 2014.
For more info visit http://www.sopeec.org/Syllabus/SyllabusThirdClass.pdf

Address all inquiries to:
PanGlobal Training Systems
1301 – 16 Ave. NW, Calgary, AB, Canada. T2M 0L4

This curriculum is approved by the SOPEEC, Standardization of Power Engineering Examinations Committee and ACI, Canadian Association of Chief Inspectors as meeting the standard for preparation for the National Third Class Syllabus.

This curriculum is endorsed by the Canadian Institute of Power Engineers (IPE).

Cover image courtesy of TransAlta Corporation. The image is a section of the 575-megawatt (MW) gas-fired facility at Transalta's Sarnia Regional Cogeneration Plant, located in Sarnia, Ontario.

We would like to acknowledge all Power Engineering Instructors who contributed to Edition 2.0 of the 3rd Class with special thanks to the Power Engineering instructors of SAIT, NAIT & BCIT for their formal reviews.

Printed by Data Group
Third Class - Part B2
Edition 2.0, February 2015
ISBN13: 978-1-926900-01-8

For information on this and other products visit our website located at **www.powerengineering.org**
Any technical or editorial errors may also be reported on our website by using our electronic Corrections Submissions Form or faxing suggested corrections to 1-403-284-8863.

**1301 16th Ave. NW
Calgary, Alberta
T2M 0L4**

Third Class
Part B2
Edition 2.0

Table of Contents

CHAPTER 1

Steam Turbine Principles & Design

LEARNING OUTCOME

When you complete this chapter you should be able to:

Describe designs, operating principles and major components of steam turbines.

LEARNING OBJECTIVES

Here is what you should be able to do when you complete each objective:

1. Explain impulse turbine operating principles. Describe convergent and divergent nozzles, and the pressure-velocity profiles through an impulse section.

2. Explain reaction turbine operating principles and describe the pressure-velocity profiles through reaction blading.

3. Explain pressure, velocity, and pressure-velocity compounding of impulse turbines. Describe the pressure-velocity profiles and the purpose and applications of each.

4. Explain the purpose, general operating principles and arrangement for each of the following turbine types: condensing, condensing-bleeder, backpressure, extraction, topping, mixed-pressure, cross-compounded, tandem compounded, double flow and reheat.

5. Describe the designs of typical turbine casings and state the purpose and location of casing fittings, including drains and sentinel valves. Describe the designs and principles of casing/shaft seals.

6. Describe the designs and applications of disc and drum rotors. Describe methods of rotor and casing blade attachment and explain blade-sealing arrangements.

7. Explain thrust in a large turbine and describe methods to offset thrust, including thrust bearings, dummy piston, and thrust-adjusting gear.

8. Identify typical designs and components for small and large industrial turbines. Explain typical size/capacity rating specifications and explain typical applications.

9. Explain the use and design of reducing gears attached to steam turbines.

OBJECTIVE 1

Explain impulse turbine operating principles. Describe convergent and divergent nozzles, and the pressure-velocity profiles through an impulse section.

IMPULSE TURBINE OPERATING PRINCIPLES

If steam at high pressure expands through a stationary nozzle, the pressure of the steam drops and the velocity of the steam increases. The steam leaves the nozzle as a high-speed jet. If this high velocity steam is then applied to a properly shaped turbine blade the steam direction will change and some of the steam's momentum will be transferred to the blade. This produces an impulse force on the blade, which tends to cause movement. If the blade is attached to the rotor of a turbine and there is no restriction to movement, the rotor will rotate on its shaft.

Figure 1 illustrates this principle.

Figure 1	Impulse Turbine Blade Section

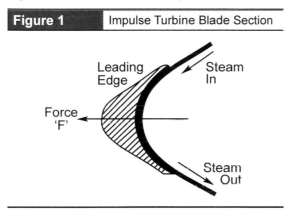

Impulse Turbine Nozzles & Buckets

In a turbine there are many blades (often referred to as 'buckets" in an impulse turbine) attached to the rotor and many nozzles attached to the casing. Figure 2 is a cutaway sketch of a few nozzles and buckets. The nozzles supply the high velocity steam to the buckets, which occupy the entire circumference of the rotor "wheel". The buckets convert the kinetic energy of the steam into mechanical energy, causing the shaft to rotate in the direction shown.

Figure 2	Impulse Turbine Nozzles and Buckets

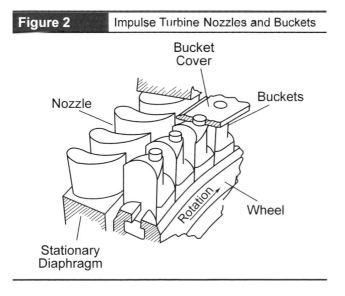

Two disadvantages of this simple impulse turbine are:

- the extremely large centrifugal forces on the buckets, due to the high rotational speeds, and
- large friction losses, due to the high velocity of the steam.

STEAM NOZZLES

Nozzles are usually constructed of Monel metal, formed over special dies. Monel is a nickel-copper alloy with high tensile strength. The shape of each nozzle is individually designed to ensure optimum expansion of the steam at the specified pressure and temperature. Passages that direct steam to the nozzles are located outside the casing. These are referred to as the steam chest.

There are two nozzle designs for steam turbines:

- Convergent
- Convergent-divergent

Convergent Nozzle

Figure 3 shows the shape of convergent nozzles.

The convergent shape of the nozzle causes the steam pressure to drop and the steam velocity to increase. These nozzles are used for relatively small pressure drops. In a well designed convergent nozzle, the pressure should drop to a specific exit pressure, called the "critical pressure", which is 0.577 times the inlet pressure. If the exit pressure is less than the critical pressure, any extra energy achieved simply goes into the formation of eddy currents (ie. turbulence) at the nozzle exit, rather than increasing steam velocity.

Figure 3	Convergent Nozzle

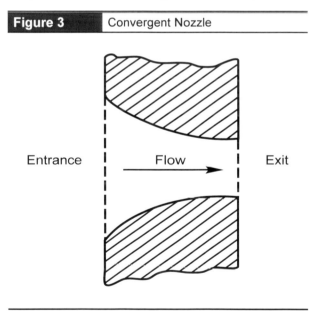

Convergent-Divergent Nozzle

Figure 4 shows the shape of a convergent-divergent nozzle.

This nozzle design is used when larger pressure drops are required. When properly designed, the pressure at the nozzle throat (the narrowest part of the nozzle, at the outlet of the convergent section) should be at the critical pressure. The pressure then continues to drop in the divergent section of the nozzle. The increasing area of this section accommodates the increase in steam volume as the pressure decreases. The velocity increases across the entire nozzle. The convergent-divergent nozzle produces the required steam velocity without producing eddy currents.

Figure 4	Convergent-Divergent Nozzle

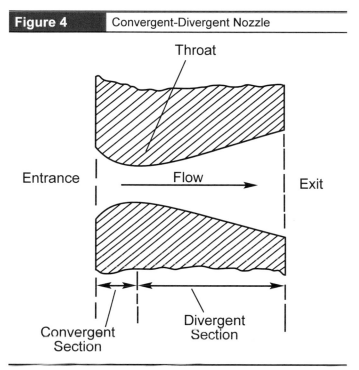

IMPULSE TURBINE PRESSURE-VELOCITY PROFILE

Figure 5 shows a profile of the nozzle and blade arrangement in a simple impulse turbine.

The graph in the figure shows how the pressure and the velocity change as the steam passes through the stationary nozzles and then the moving blades.

- Note that the **velocity** increases sharply in the nozzles, then drops in the blades (ie. the kinetic (velocity) energy of the steam is transferred to the blades).

- Meanwhile, the **pressure** drops in the nozzles, then remains constant through the blades. This is the distinguishing feature of the impulse turbine.

Figure 5	Impulse Turbine Pressure-Velocity Profile

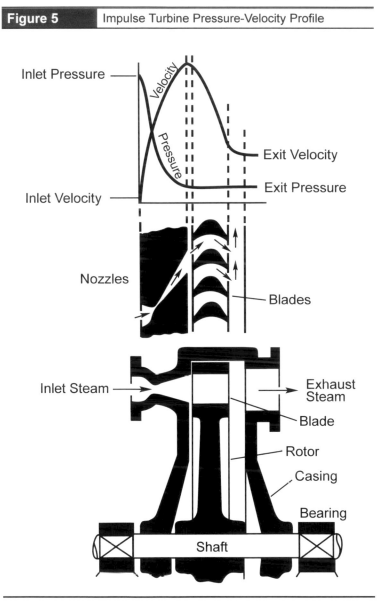

OBJECTIVE 2

Explain reaction turbine operating principles and describe the pressure-velocity profiles through reaction blading.

REACTION TURBINE OPERATING PRINCIPLES

If the moving blades of a turbine are shaped so that steam expands and the pressure drops as it passes through them, then a reaction force will be produced on the blades. This reaction effect can be illustrated by considering a container filled with high-pressure steam (or gas), as shown in Figure 6. If there is no escape opening for the steam, the pressure will be the same on all walls of the container and the container will remain at rest. However, if the container has an escape opening, the steam will escape through the opening and the pressure will drop at that point. As a result, there will be an unbalanced pressure on the wall opposite to the opening and a corresponding reaction force "R" will be produced, causing the container to move.

Figure 6	Reaction Effect

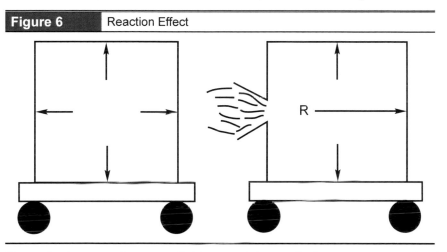

Figure 7 shows a diagram of this principle applied to a rotating wheel. The reaction forces caused by the steam leaving the ends of the wheel, cause the wheel to rotate around the center.

Figure 7	Reaction Causing Rotation

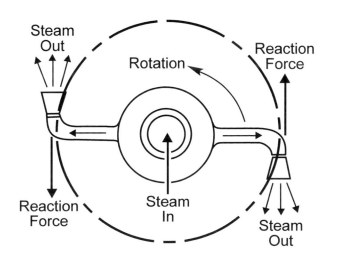

Reaction Blading

A reaction turbine has rows of stationary blades alternating with rows of moving blades. The stationary blades, due to their shape, act as nozzles. The moving blades, with the same basic shape as the nozzles, receive an impulse from the steam, but also produce a reaction force.

- The steam expands first in the stationary blades, gaining velocity as the pressure drops.
- It then enters the moving blades where its direction of flow is changed, producing a force on the blades.
- At the same time, the blade shape reduces the pressure of the steam and the expansion creates a further force (reaction) on the blades.
- This sequence is repeated in each row of stationary and moving blades.

Figure 8 shows the basic shape of reaction blades.

They are characterized by a large entrance angle (almost 90°) and a small discharge angle. The leading edge is rounded, in comparison to the sharp leading edge of impulse blades. The blade has a long, tapered trailing edge, with the convex side becoming almost straight.

Figure 8	Reaction Blade

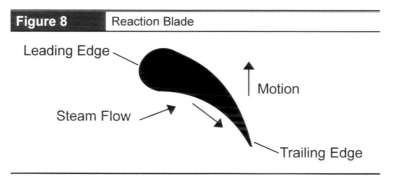

REACTION TURBINE PRESSURE-VELOCITY PROFILE

Figure 9 shows the blade arrangement and the pressure and velocity changes of the steam in a reaction turbine.

- The steam **pressure** can be seen to decrease across both the stationary blades and the moving blades.
- The absolute **velocity** (ie. the velocity of the steam relative to the moving blades) increases in the stationary blades, but decreases in the moving blades.

The distinguishing feature of the reaction turbine is the pressure drop across the moving blades. In other words, there is a pressure difference between the inlet and the outlet of the moving blades.

| Figure 9 | Reaction Turbine Pressure-Velocity Profile |

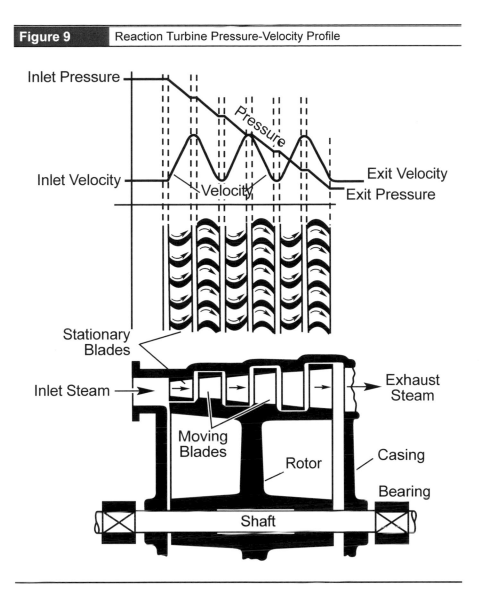

The nature of the pressure drops in a reaction turbine presents two problems, which must be overcome in the design.

- Because there is a difference in pressure across the moving blades, the steam will tend to leak around the edges and tips of the blades. For this reason, blade clearances must be kept to a minimum.

- The pressure drop across the moving blades causes an unbalanced thrust on the rotor, in the direction of steam flow, and some arrangement must be made to balance this thrust.

OBJECTIVE 3

Explain pressure, velocity, and pressure-velocity compounding of impulse turbines. Describe the velocity/pressure profiles and the purpose and applications of each.

IMPULSE TURBINE STAGING

In an impulse turbine, in order for the steam to transfer all of its kinetic energy to the moving blades, the steam must leave the moving blades at the lowest possible velocity. The lowest velocity occurs when the blade velocity is equal to half the steam velocity.

If the steam expands from inlet pressure down to the final exhaust pressure in a single set of nozzles (ie. in a single stage), the velocity of the steam leaving the nozzles could be about 1100 m/s. Therefore, to be most efficient the blade velocity would need to be about 550 m/s. This would require excessively high rotational speed and the resulting high centrifugal forces would likely cause mechanical damage. Also, the high steam velocities would cause high friction losses in the nozzles and blading.

To avoid these problems, the steam and blade velocities may be reduced, using one or more of the following methods:

- Pressure Compounding
- Velocity Compounding
- Pressure-Velocity Compounding

Pressure Compounding

Pressure compounding reduces steam and blade velocity by causing the steam pressure to drop in two or more stages. Two or more impulse stages are used, in series, inside a single casing. One pressure-compounded stage consists of a set of stationary nozzles, followed by a rotor disc with moving blades. The rows of moving blades are separated from each other by partitions or diaphragms, into which the nozzles are set.

Figure 10 shows the nozzle and blade arrangement for a pressure-compounded impulse turbine with two stages.

- In the first stage, the steam passes through the first set of nozzles, where the pressure drops and the velocity increases.
- The steam then passes through the moving blades, during which the pressure remains nearly constant, but the steam velocity drops to near zero.
- In the second stage, the second set of stationary nozzles causes a further drop in pressure while the velocity again increases to the maximum.
- Then the second set of moving blades reduces the steam velocity while the pressure remains constant.

The advantages of pressure-compounded turbines are:

- increased efficiency, due to decreased friction losses,
- reduced centrifugal forces, and
- for a given rotational speed they can be designed for a wide range of inlet steam conditions.

Figure 10 Pressure Compounded Impulse Turbine, Pressure-Velocity Profile

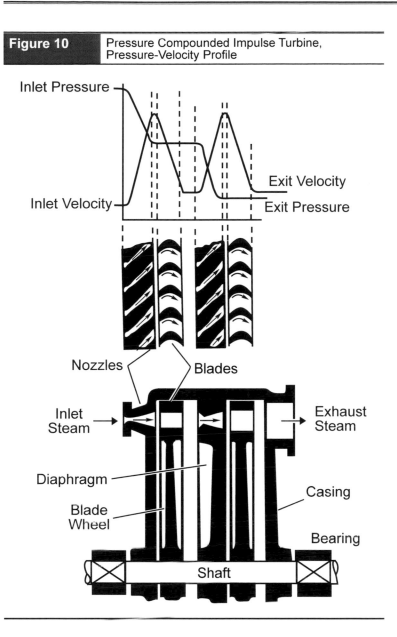

Velocity Compounding

Figure 11 shows velocity-compounding, which reduces the steam velocity in stages.

It consists of one set of stationary inlet nozzles, a rotor containing two sets of rotating blades, and a set of stationary blades between the rotating blades. The total pressure drop occurs in the stationary inlet nozzles and the pressure then remains constant across the three sets of blades. The first set of rotating blades reduces the steam velocity by approximately one half. The stationary blades then redirect the steam, with little loss of velocity, to the second set of rotating blades. As the steam passes through the second set of rotating blades, the velocity drops to the exit velocity.

Reducing the steam velocity in two stages results in the speed of the rotating blades (and, therefore, of the shaft) being one half the speed of a simple, single-stage impulse turbine (assuming the same overall pressure drop). Also, the second set of rotating blades are approximately twice the size of the first set. Since the same volume of steam passes through both sets of blades (since the pressure is constant) and the velocity is lower entering the second set, the larger size allows for the same impulse force to be applied to the second set.

Figure 11	Velocity Compounded Impulse Turbine, Pressure-Velocity Profile

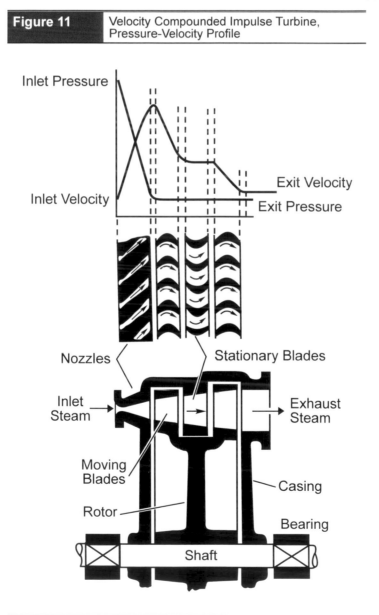

Pressure-Velocity Compounding

A pressure-velocity compounded turbine reduces both the steam pressure and steam velocity in stages. It consists of two or more velocity-compounded sections (stages) in series on the same shaft, within one casing.

Figure 12 shows the pressure-velocity compounding arrangement, with two stages.

As the graph shows, the total pressure drop, from inlet to exhaust, is divided between two nozzle sets, with half the pressure drop in the first set of nozzles and the rest in the second set of nozzles. The velocity increases to maximum in each set of nozzles and then drops in two steps through the following sets of blades. The pressure-velocity graphs are virtually identical for the two stages.

The main advantage of pressure-velocity compounding is that high steam pressures can be utilized to obtain relatively low rotational speeds.

Figure 12	Pressure Velocity Compounded Impulse Turbine Profile

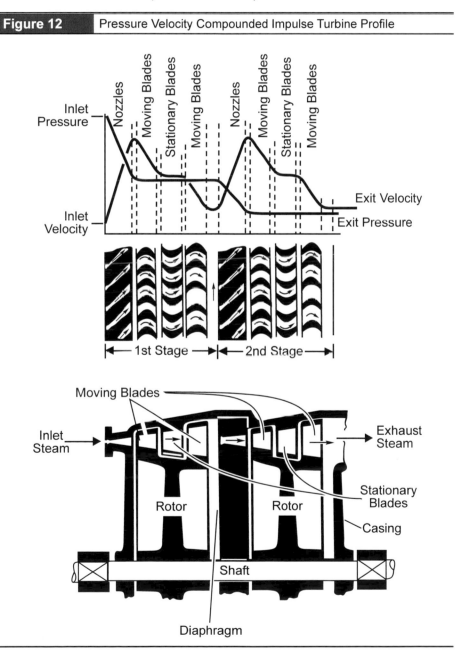

VELOCITY & PRESSURE STAGES

On very large impulse turbines, it is common to employ another arrangement of velocity-pressure compounding, in which a velocity-compounded first stage is followed by several pressure-compounded stages.

Figure 13 shows this arrangement.

One velocity-compounded stage is followed by four pressure-compounded stages. As the graph shows, in the velocity stage the pressure drops partially in the nozzle, while the velocity increases to maximum. The velocity then drops to a minimum in two steps through the rotating-stationary-rotating blades.

Each pressure stage consists of a set of nozzle shaped, stationary blades, followed by a set of moving impulse blades. In each set of stationary blades the velocity increases and the pressure decreases. Then, in each set of moving blades the velocity drops to a minimum, while the pressure doesn't change. Overall, the pressure drops in five stages before reaching the exhaust pressure.

Note that the velocity stage is designed for a greater pressure drop than each of the remaining stages. Therefore, the velocity leaving the first nozzle is much higher than the velocity at the subsequent stages.

This design allows for higher steam pressures to be used and obtains greater work and efficiency from the energy available in the steam.

| Figure 13 | Impulse Turbine with Velocity and Pressure Stages, Profile |

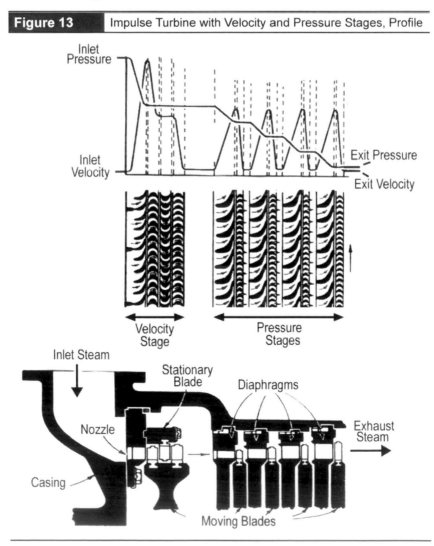

OBJECTIVE 4

Explain the purpose, general operating principles and arrangement for each of the following turbine types: condensing, condensing-bleeder, backpressure, extraction, topping, mixed-pressure, cross-compounded, tandem compounded, double flow and reheat.

TYPES OF TURBINES

There are several ways to classify steam turbines, including the following:

- Type of blading: impulse, reaction
- Type of compounding: velocity, pressure, or a combination of both.
- Direction of steam flow along the axis: single flow or double flow
- Exhaust condition: condensing, non-condensing
- Steam flows to/from the turbine: extraction, bleeder, reheat, topping, etc.

Several of these terms may be used simultaneously to describe a single turbine. Eg, a large turbine might be described as a *"pressure-velocity compounded, double flow, non-condensing, extraction, impulse"* turbine.

The types of blading and compounding have been previously described, so this Objective will describe many of the other classifications and terminology.

Single Flow vs. Double Flow

A single flow turbine is one in which the steam flows in one direction only (in relation to the turbine shaft) between inlet and exhaust.

In a double flow turbine, the steam flows in two directions (again relative to the turbine shaft). The blading is designed so that the rotation created by both sets is in the same direction. The exhausts from each end of the casing join together outside the casing and direct the exhaust steam to a common, low-pressure user. One advantage of this design is the elimination of end thrust (due to pressure differential across blades), since the blade thrust on one half of the turbine is counteracted by the blade thrust on the other half. Another advantage is the large number of stages that can be used without the need for the excessively large disc or casing diameters that common to large condensing turbines where the low pressure at the condenser inlet results in a large steam volume.

Figure 14 demonstrates four designs, with a brief description beneath each one.

Figure 14	Four Turbine Designs

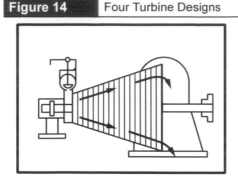

SINGLE-FLOW CONDENSING is the most widely-used type. This work-horse requires the least steam for a given power.

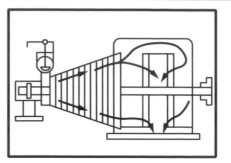

DOUBLE-FLOW CONDENSING makes possible higher powers and speeds than single-flow condensing type. This is done by double-flowing the low-pressure stage(s).

AUTOMATIC EXTRACTION and/ or induction combines the best features of straight condensing and non-condensing turbines. Automatically supplies process steam or accepts excess steam at a given pressure.

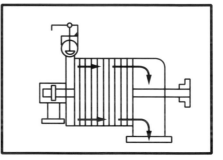

NON-CONDENSING or back-pressure is used to satisfy process steam requirements at selected pressure levels.

(Courtesy of United Technologies – Elliott)

Figure 15 illustrates several turbine arrangements in relation to the steam headers in a power plant. Each one can be described in relation to its location and its purpose or application in the plant.

Non-Condensing (Back Pressure) (see Figure 15, Turbine "A")

A non-condensing turbine is used when the exhaust steam from the turbine can be used for process or heating purposes. It is used primarily in process plants, where it receives steam from a higher pressure header and exhausts directly into a lower pressure header. Usually a regulating station is used to maintain the low pressure header, and thus the turbine exhaust, at a constant pressure. Since the turbine exhaust is controlled at a pressure above atmospheric pressure, this turbine is often referred to as a backpressure turbine. The turbine may also have bleed points (points at which steam is drawn off before the turbine exhaust), in which case it is called a backpressure, bleeder turbine.

Condensing Turbine (see Figure 15, Turbines "B" and "I")

A condensing turbine is used when there is no process use for the exhaust steam and/or maximum power is required from a limited amount of available steam. The low exhaust pressure allows the turbine to extract maximum energy from the steam. A typical application is the driver for an electric generator. Condensing turbines exhaust steam at less than atmospheric pressure into a condenser where the steam is then condensed by cooling. The condensate is usually returned to the boiler as feed water.

| Figure 15 | Turbine Types |

HP Steam Supply Header

HP Steam Supply Header

HP Process Header

LP Process Header

Steam to Condenser

I — LP Condensing

A	B	C	D	E	F	G
Non-Condensing	Condensing	Condensing Bleeder	Condensing Mixed Pressure	Condensing Double Extraction	Non-Condensing Single Extraction	Condensing Mixed Pressure Extraction

Bleeder Turbine (Figure 15, Turbine "C")

In a bleeder turbine, steam is removed (ie. bled) from the turbine at some intermediate point or points between the inlet and the exhaust. The amount of bled steam (up to about 20% of the total steam) is not usually controlled, but simply changes as the load on the turbine changes. If the turbine is a condensing turbine, the bleeding reduces the steam flow into the condenser, allowing for smaller exhaust size and reducing condenser losses. Non-condensing turbines may also have bleed points, in which case they are called backpressure, bleeder turbines. Bleed steam is generally used for heating purposes, such as feedwater heating.

Mixed Pressure Condensing Turbine (Figure 15, Turbine "D")

In a mixed pressure condensing turbine additional steam is added to the turbine part way between the inlet and exhaust. For example, excess process steam from a low-pressure process header may be applied to the low-pressure part of the turbine. Similarly, high-pressure steam, at boiler pressure, may be added to the high-pressure section of the turbine. This design allows some flexibility in turbine load capability, with extra steam being added if the load demands more power from the turbine. An example would be when the electrical load on a turbine-driven generator increases beyond a certain limit, requiring more turbine power.

These are commonly used in gas turbine combined cycle power plants (where steam is generated at high, intermediate and low pressures) to extract maximum heat from the gas turbine exhaust. The high pressure steam drives a steam turbine. The low pressure steam is commonly used to heat the deaerator and excess low pressure steam goes to the last stages of the steam turbine. Intermediate pressure steam may also go to the steam turbine, but is commonly injected into the gas turbine combustors to reduce the temperature for NO_x control.

Extraction Turbines (Figure 15, Turbines "E", "F", and "G")

Extraction turbines are used primarily in process plants, where steam from the turbine may be used at a specific pressure for process or heating purposes and this pressure is available at some point between the turbine inlet and exhaust. A controlled amount of steam is extracted at one or more points, to provide the pressure required by the user. Extraction turbines may be condensing ("E") or non-condensing ("F"). They also may have a single extraction point (see "F") or two extraction points at two different extraction pressures (see "E"), in which case they are called double extraction turbines.

Topping Turbines (Figure 15, Turbine "H")

A topping turbine is a backpressure turbine with the specific purpose of taking steam from a high-pressure header and reducing it to a lower pressure that is used by a process or by turbines that requires lower inlet pressures. One example of their use is when old, low-pressure boilers are replaced with new high-pressure boilers, but part of the process still requires the original steam pressure. The topping turbine can provide lower pressure steam, while also driving an electrical generator. In effect, the electrical generation is a by-product of the steam system.

COMPOUNDED TURBINES

Not to be confused with pressure and velocity compounding, the term "Compounded Turbines" refers to the arrangement of two separate turbines in which the exhaust steam from one becomes the inlet steam for the other. In other words, the steam flow through the turbines is in series. Compounding is used in relatively large systems, where the design conditions and demands would prohibit using a single turbine. For example, the required physical size and/or rotational speeds may be prohibitive.

There are two basic arrangements, called cross-compounding and tandem compounding. However, there are many possible arrangements within each, involving LP, IP, and HP turbine sections. The following are some typical examples.

Cross Compounding

Cross compounded turbines are separate turbines, each with its own shaft and each attached to its own load.

Figures 16 shows one cross-compound arrangement, in which each turbine drives an electrical generator and the exhaust from the first, high-pressure turbine becomes the supply to the larger, low-pressure turbine. The LP turbine is single flow.

Figure 16	Cross-Compounded Turbine

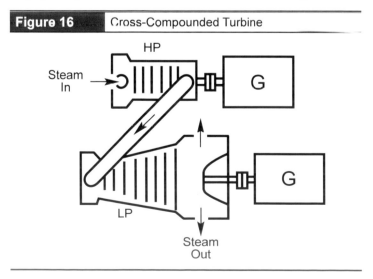

Figure 17 is also a cross-compound turbine, but the LP turbine is double flow, with the steam entering at the center and flowing toward each end.

| **Figure 17** | Cross-Compound Turbine with Double Flow Low Pressure Turbine |

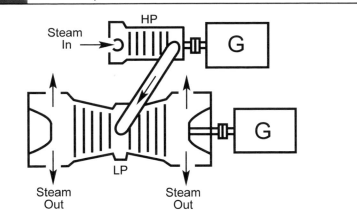

In cross-compounded turbines, the high-pressure turbines generally operate at a higher RPM than the low-pressure turbines. Often there are reducing gears involved to produce the required speed for the driven equipment, especially generators.

Tandem Compounding

Tandem compound turbines, as shown in Figure 18, have the shafts of the LP and HP turbines coupled together. The LP turbine is then coupled to the load. The power of both turbines is thus applied to a single load. Though not shown in Figure 18, in some arrangements, because of the different speeds of the two sections, there may be a reducing gear between them.

| **Figure 18** | Tandem-Compound Turbine |

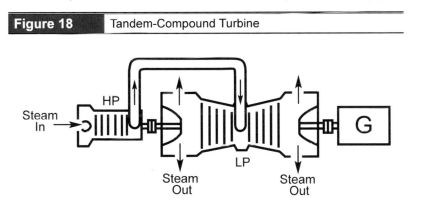

A popular arrangement for very large turbine units is a combination of tandem and cross compounding. For example, the HP and IP turbine sections may be in tandem. The IP exhaust then crosses over to an LP section, which is also in tandem with a second LP section.

REHEAT TURBINES

In some larger turbines, the steam loses enough heat energy in the HP stages of the turbine that its efficiency in the following stages would be very low. More importantly, the steam temperature leaving the HP section is close enough to the saturation temperature that there is danger of condensation in the LP turbine. Therefore, to maintain maximum efficiency and avoid condensation, the entire steam flow is extracted part way through the turbine, reheated to near its original temperature in an external heat exchanger (usually the reheater section of a steam generator), then returned to the turbine, immediately downstream of where it was extracted. Turbines that use this technique are called Reheat Turbines.

Figure 19 shows the same compounded turbine from Figure 18, but with a Reheater between the LP and HP sections. Reheat is not restricted to compound turbines only.

Figure 19	Compound Turbine with Reheat

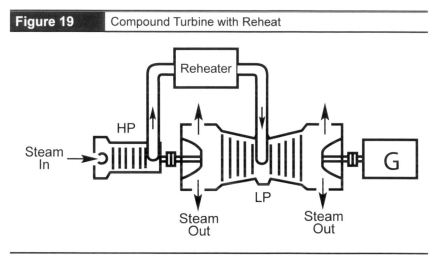

OBJECTIVE 5

Describe the designs of typical turbine casings and state the purpose and location of casing fittings, including drains and sentinel valves. Describe the designs and principles of casing/shaft seals.

TURBINE CASINGS

The turbine casing, often referred to as the shell, contains the nozzles, stationary blade diaphragms, bearing cases, and all external components. The casing must operate under high pressure and temperature conditions. It must resist distortion under these conditions and during start-up and shutdown when temperatures and pressures change drastically. The casing design must ensure that the very small running clearances of the blading and labyrinth glands remain within allowances, and that the alignment of the turbine rotor remains true. The most common design of casing is the horizontally-split casing.

Split Casings

Although there are barrel casings in some very large, high pressure turbines, the horizontally split casing is by far the most common. Horizontally split casings (occasionally referred to as cylinders) easily facilitate assembly and inspection, with a top half that "simply" bolts down onto the bottom half.

Figure 20 shows the lower section of a horizontally split casing. The center line support allows the casing to expand and contract evenly while maintaining alignment at all times.

Figure 20	Turbine Lower Casing & Support

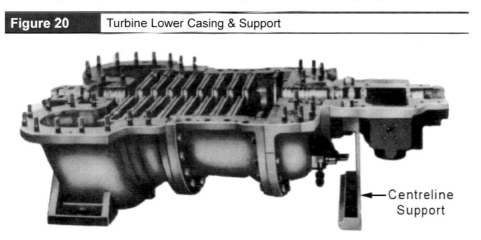

Centreline Support

The casings are made of relatively thick metal to withstand the high pressures and temperatures. In some cases the wall thickness is made gradually thinner towards the exhaust, LP end of the turbine. Casing metals differ, depending on the size, operating pressure and temperature of the turbine. For given operating conditions, the metal must have sufficient strength and be able to resist erosion and deformation during years of operation.

Large diameter casings, for low-pressure turbines, are usually constructed of welded plate. Smaller diameter, low-pressure casings are made of cast iron, which may be used for temperatures up to about 230°C. Casings for intermediate pressures are made of cast carbon steel, able to withstand temperatures up to about 425°C. High pressure, high temperature casings for temperatures above about 550°C, are made of cast alloy steel, one example being 3% chromium and 1% molybdenum.

Casing joints are made steam tight by carefully machining the flange faces, eliminating the need for gaskets. Dowel pins are often used to secure exact alignment of the flange joint and bolt holes. Boring mills are used to machine the inside of the casing, making grooves to contain the diaphragms (for impulse turbines) or stationary blades (reaction turbines). The casing is also machined for shaft seals and bearing housings.

In high-pressure casings, the flanges must be very thick. Consequently, they will heat up more slowly than the casing walls, which could cause distortion and leakage. To overcome this problem, the flanges are often heated by steam, which flows through channels machined in the flanges or through axially drilled holes.

Double Casings

Double casings are used for very high steam pressure applications. The high pressure is applied to the inner casing, which is open at the exhaust end, directing the turbine exhaust to the outer casing. The pressure differential across the high pressure casing is reduced (compared to a single casing design) and, more importantly, so is the temperature differential. Therefore, the thermal stresses on casings and flanges are greatly reduced.

Figure 21 shows a double shell HP turbine casing in which the inner and outer shells (casings) are both horizontally split. In some designs, the outer casing may a barrel design that slides over the inner casing.

Figure 21	Double-Shell HP Casing

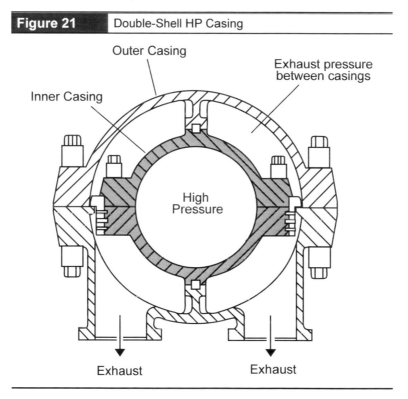

CASING DRAINAGE

Increased steam pressure and the higher temperatures of modern turbines have decreased the percentage of moisture in the exhaust steam. The maximum allowable wetness is generally about 14%. The shape of the casing allows free water to drain to the condenser, but special draining grooves are also arranged in the casing to help remove the water more effectively. A typical example of this draining arrangement is illustrated in Figure 22.

Figure 22	Cylinder Casing Drains

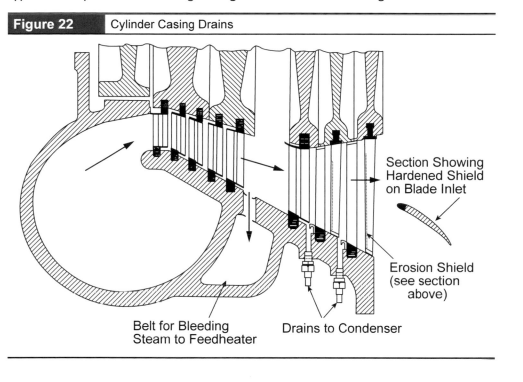

Section Showing
Hardened Shield
on Blade Inlet

Erosion Shield
(see section
above)

Belt for Bleeding
Steam to Feedheater

Drains to Condenser

SENTINEL VALVES

Figure 23 illustrates a small, non-condensing steam turbine, with all the normal external attachments, including those on the inlet and discharge lines.

One of the more important attachments is the sentinel valve, located on the highest point of the casing. Its main purpose is not to relieve steam and directly prevent overpressuring of the turbine, but to warn the operator that casing pressure is abnormally high. It does so, at a predetermined pressure setting, by relieving steam to atmosphere and producing a high-pitched whistle sound. This gives the operator both a visual and an audible warning of the high pressure.

The most useful application is during a turbine startup, when the operator may have forgotten to open the discharge valve fully. Backpressure turbines are commonly warmed up by opening the discharge valve slightly to allow the turbine casing to be warmed by the exhaust steam. Once warmed to exhaust temperature, the inlet valve is cracked open to finish heating the turbine. Then, when bringing the turbine up to speed, the operator will be informed by the sentinel valve if the exhaust valve is not fully open.

When the turbine casing and exhaust piping are not designed for the full inlet pressure, the exhaust line is fitted with a relief valve, capable of discharging the full-load steam flow.

Figure 23	Small Turbine Attachments

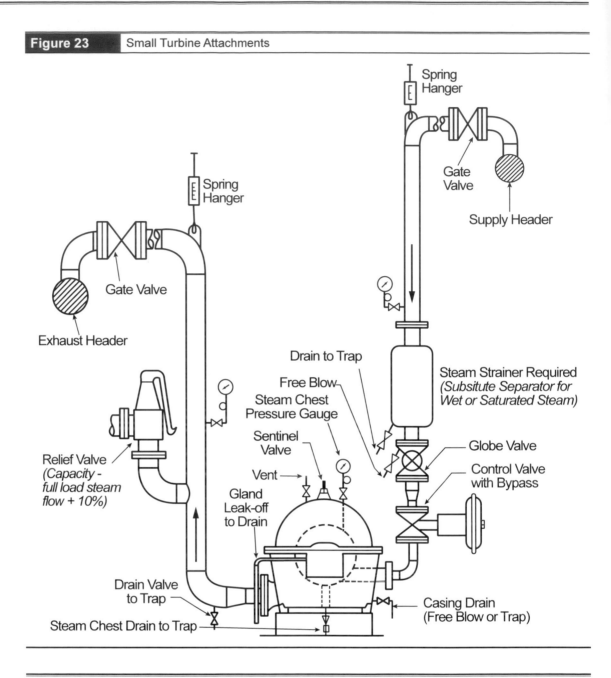

SHAFT SEALS

Shaft seals must be provided on steam turbines to prevent steam leakage where the shafts extend through the casings. In condensing turbines, where the pressure in the low-pressure section is less than atmospheric, the seals must prevent the leakage (ingress) of ambient air into the casing.

Carbon Ring Seals

On small, single-stage turbines, the most common form of sealing is carbon rings. Usually several rings are placed within a seal housing, as shown in Figure 24, that forms part of the turbine casing.

Each ring is formed by three segments, which butt tightly together and are held by the force of a garter spring around the circumference. The spring allows some radial movement, but the housing prevents axial movement.

The rings are susceptible to wear, causing leakage, but are relatively easy to replace during a turbine overhaul. Small foreign particles may become lodged between the segments, also causing leakage. Heat is generated when the rings ride on the shaft and, so carbon rings are generally limited to shafts less than 150 mm in diameter. Each carbon ring is fitted with a keyway, so a key in the bearing housing prevents the carbon rings from rotating with the shaft.

Figure 24	Carbon Ring Seal

Labyrinth Seals

A "labyrinth" may be defined as "a maze of paths separated by high hedges through which passage is very difficult". For sealing in large turbines, labyrinth seals are commonly used. A labyrinth seal consists of several rings, 1 to 2 mm thick, separated by a small space and surrounding the casing openings through which the shaft passes. In some cases, rings may also be attached to the shaft. Labyrinth seals are also used at the center openings of stationary blade diaphragms, where the shaft passes through, since steam leakage across a diaphragm reduces turbine efficiency.

Each labyrinth ring is tapered toward the outer periphery, forming a sharp edge with a minute clearance to the shaft (or casing). The sharp edge ensures better sealing and provides less rubbing surface if the shaft is slightly eccentric. With several rings in succession, the steam has a difficult time passing through the small clearances of the "labyrinth".

Within a large turbine there are several seals, located at strategic points, so that the total pressure drop across a given seal is minimal. Minimal pressure drop promotes seal efficiency.

The rings are made of either brass, stainless steel, or other metal alloys.

Figure 25 illustrates only two of many different labyrinth arrangements. In the right hand design, note the springs, which hold the stationary labyrinths against the shaft. The labyrinth is machined in sections (similar to the carbon seals discussed earlier) so they can be installed and removed. The sections will butt against each other after the labyrinth is worn in. The space between the knife edges and the shaft will be very small and there will be no actual contact between them.

Figure 25	Different Types of Labyrinth Seals

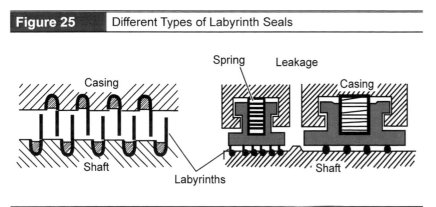

When the pressure drop across a turbine section is considered too excessive for a single section of labyrinths, a series of labyrinth sections are used, with steam pockets (spaces) between them. These pockets carry any leakage steam away from the seal, discharging it to an external location, such as feed water heater extraction lines or to the turbine exhaust. In a condensing turbine, similar pockets are usually available to carry away any ingress air that gets past the outside set of labyrinth seals at the exhaust end of the casing.

Since air leaking into the glands of a condensing turbine can become mixed with the leak-off steam from the glands, the leak-off usually goes to a separate, small condenser from which the condensate is discarded. Also, condensing turbines usually use gland seal steam to ensure air cannot leak into the condenser. This steam is supplied through a gland steam regulator at very low pressure (about 10 to 20 kPa). This steam originates from upstream of the turbine trip valve, so gland steam is available before startup. This stops air infiltration and allows a vacuum to be established.

A further refinement for labyrinth seals is the addition of grooves in the rotating shaft. Some of the labyrinth rings in a set are longer than the others and fit down into these grooves, creating an even more difficult path for escaping steam. These labyrinths are called "stepped", as opposed to the normal "straight" design.

Water Seals

Neither the carbon rings nor labyrinth seals prevent all leakage. If a positive, leak-proof seal is required, a water seal, as shown in Figure 26, may be installed. The water seal consists of an impeller on the turbine shaft, which rotates in a casing that is filled with water. The water is thrown out from the impeller and forms a leak proof water barrier. Water seals are mainly applied to low-pressure glands to guard against air infiltration, but they may also be applied as the final seal for high pressure and intermediate pressure glands.

The water seal cannot operate properly at low speed. Therefore, during startup gland steam must be applied for sealing until the turbine speed is high enough for the impeller to produce sufficient pressure for sealing. Water seals are supplied with clean, cool condensate from the condensate extraction pump discharge. The water may be supplied directly or via a head tank with an automatic level control. Labyrinth packing is attached to the casing to reduce water leakage and also to reduce steam leakage, in case of water seal failure.

Figure 26	Water Sealed Gland

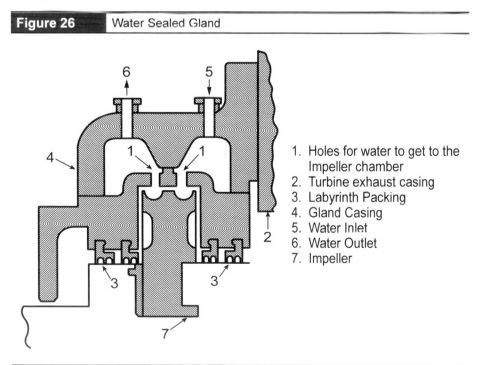

1. Holes for water to get to the Impeller chamber
2. Turbine exhaust casing
3. Labyrinth Packing
4. Gland Casing
5. Water Inlet
6. Water Outlet
7. Impeller

OBJECTIVE 6

Describe the designs and applications of disc and drum rotors. Describe methods of rotor and casing blade attachment and explain blade-sealing arrangements.

DISC ROTORS

The rotors of impulse turbines (or impulse sections of a large turbine) generally consist of a relatively small diameter shaft, with thin, large diameter discs (often called wheels) mounted onto the shaft. The moving blades are attached around the circumference of these discs.

Note: One might think that the large disc areas available to the steam would cause axial thrust on the turbine shaft. This is not the case, since there is no pressure drop across the moving blades of an impulse turbine and, therefore, no pressure drop across the individual discs.

There are two methods of producing disc rotors. They may consist of individual discs, mounted on the central shaft, or they may be machined from a solid forging as a single, solid rotor that includes the shaft and discs in one forging. Figure 27 shows a typical, disc rotor with individually mounted discs.

Figure 27	Disc Type Rotor

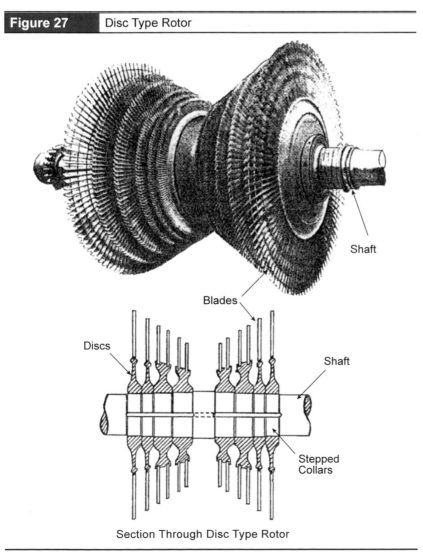

Section Through Disc Type Rotor

This rotor has separately forged discs. The wider, central section of each disc (the hub) is shrunk or keyed onto the shaft. Though not always the case, the shaft in Figure 27 is machined with "steps" to accommodate the discs, which have slightly different central diameters. Suitable clearances are left between the hubs of the discs to allow for disc expansion along the line of the shaft. The outer circumference of each disc has a machined groove, which is used to attach the blades.

Shrinking the discs onto the shaft allows for a continuing tight fit, even when operating temperatures may cause uneven expansion between the shaft and the discs. To accommodate shrinking, the center opening of the disc is made slightly smaller (about 0.1%) than the shaft diameter. The disc is heated and expanded, then slid into position on the shaft and allowed to cool. In cooling, the disc "shrinks", forming a very tight fit to the shaft.

Figure 28 shows a solid, forged and machined disc rotor, with the left half shown as a cutaway. This design is typical for large, high-pressure rotors, machined from a solid forging of nickel alloy steel. The result is a strong, fully balanced rotor, with no need to worry about discs becoming loose. However, it is an expensive construction method, since about 50% of the initial forging is wasted by machining. Again, blades are attached to slots in the circumference of each disc.

Figure 28	Solid Forged Disc Rotor

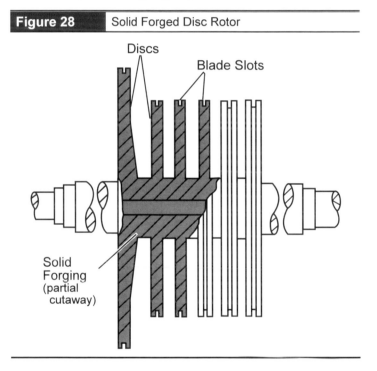

DRUM ROTORS

Unlike impulse blades, reaction blades have a pressure drop across them. With the moving blades attached to the rotor a disc design would create a large axial thrust on the rotor. Therefore, reaction turbines use a drum rotor design, to eliminate surface areas that could cause thrust.

Figure 29 shows one drum rotor design in which the drum is hollow and made in two parts.

To ensure good balance and reduce weight, the main part of the drum is machined inside and outside and is open at one end. The second part of the rotor is the drum end cover with shaft. This end cover is installed with a shrink fit and then welded in place.

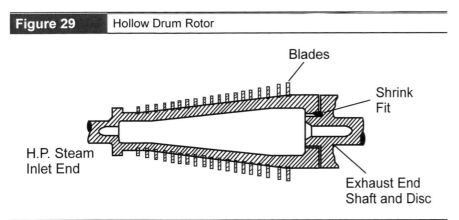

Figure 29   Hollow Drum Rotor

Figure 30 shows another design in which the drum rotor is constructed in sections.

This fairly light, but rigid, rotor consists of discs welded together at their circumferences to form a semi-hollow drum. This design produces greater resistance to centrifugal forces, which is an an advantage for large diameter turbines that operate at high speeds.

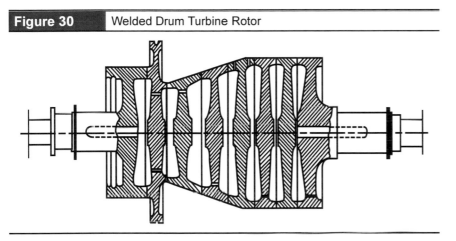

Figure 30   Welded Drum Turbine Rotor

BLADE ATTACHMENT & SEALING

The stationary blades or nozzles in an impulse turbine are mounted in diaphragms, as shown in Figure 31. The diaphragm is constructed in two halves, one being mounted in the upper turbine casing and the other half in the lower casing (look back at Fig. 20 to see eight diaphragms in the lower casing).

The diaphragms are secured in the casing by keys. The nozzles fit in machined slots in the circumference of the diaphragm and are held tight by rivets and screws.

Figure 31	Diaphragm and Nozzles

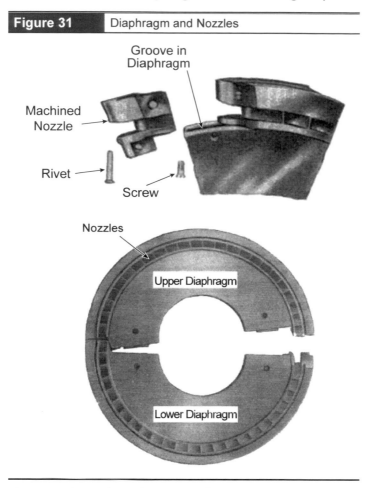

Figure 32 shows how the moving blades of an impulse type turbines are usually machined from a solid bar with the roots and spacers being part of the solid piece. This construction eliminates the need for distance pieces (packers) when attaching the blades to the disc.

Tangs are formed at the tips of the blades so that shrouding may be attached to the outside circumference of the blades. The shrouding is made from several metal strips that are punched with holes to correspond with the tangs. The strips are placed over the tangs, which are then splayed out to secure the strips tightly. To allow for expansion, the shrouding is installed as several sections.

In an impulse turbine, the purpose of the shrouding is mainly to strengthen the assembly and stabilize the ends of the blades. This allows for longer blades and greater clearances.

| Figure 32 | Stages in the Manufacture of HP Impulse Type Moving Blades |

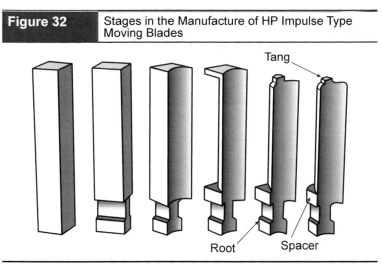

In a pressure-compounded impulse turbine, the diaphragms that hold the stationary nozzles have labyrinth seals adjacent to the rotor shaft. This prevents steam leakage along the shaft, due to the pressure difference across the nozzles. As well, seals adjacent to the stationary nozzles may be used to help direct steam flow in the high pressure stages, ensuring efficient use of the steam.

Figures 33 and 34 show methods of attaching blades in a reaction turbine. The stationary blades are fitted into grooves in the casing halves, using keys or serrations to lock them in place. A locking strip on one side of the root tightens the blades solidly in the grooves.

| Figure 33 | Drum Type Rotor with Shrouded Blades |

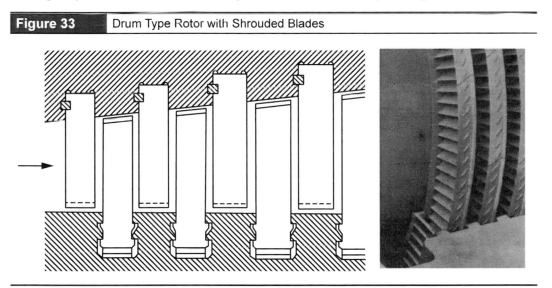

Blade sealing in reaction turbines (see Fig. 34) is intended to retard steam leakage across the blade tips, due to the pressure differential across the blades. The knife edge design of the sealing strips permits very close running clearances without the worry of significant damage if contact does occur. Sealing strips are generally made of chrome-iron alloy; they are rolled to shape and held in grooves by soft steel caulking strips.

Figure 34 shows a section of HP reaction blading with knife-edge seals and radial fins. On the rotating blades the radial fins minimize leakage between the blade tips and the casing, while the single knife-edge seals minimize leakage between the rotating and stationary blades. The double knife-edge seals at the ends of the stationary blades minimize leakage between the blade tips and the rotor.

Figure 34	Typical Reaction Blade Sealing

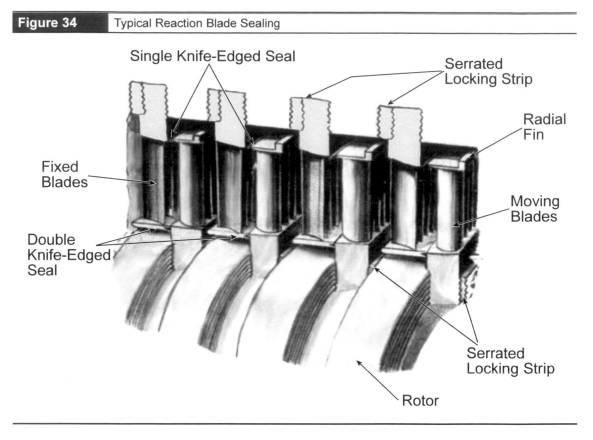

OBJECTIVE 7

Explain thrust in a large turbine and describe methods to offset thrust, including thrust bearings, dummy piston, and thrust-adjusting gear.

TURBINE THRUST

Even though the pressure drop across the moving blades of an impulse turbine is negligible, there is still always a small thrust, which tends to displace the shaft in an axial direction. This thrust must be counteracted to eliminate the chance of the moving and stationary parts of the turbine contacting each other.

Thrust in reaction turbines is much more severe. Since there is a considerable pressure drop across each row of moving blades, there is a cumulative end thrust on the turbine rotor, which attempts to push it towards the exhaust end.

One method of eliminating end thrust is the double flow turbine design in which steam is admitted midway along the turbine casing, from which it flows axially towards each end. Opposing rows of blading are mounted in each half of the turbine and the opposing thrusts created in them cancel each other. This is common in large low-pressure turbine sections.

Where this design is not possible, other methods are necessary to counteract thrust, including:

- thrust bearings,
- dummy pistons, and
- thrust adjusting gear.

Thrust Bearings

The main purposes of a thrust bearing are:

- to keep the rotor in an exact position in the casing, and
- to absorb any axial thrust on the rotor.

The thrust bearing must be strategically placed on the shaft of the turbine, to ensure that the shaft is free to expand in one direction. Since blade clearances are most critical at the steam inlet end of a turbine, this is the normal location of a thrust bearing. When tandem compound turbines are joined together by a solid, non-flexible coupling, only one thrust bearing can be used. When flexible couplings are installed to take up axial expansion, then each turbine shaft must have a thrust bearing.

In impulse turbines, where thrust is minimal, simple thrust bearings are used. These may be specially designed ball bearings or sleeve bearings with radial Babbitt faces, as shown in Figure 35. In this design, the axial thrust and radial load are handled by a single bearing. The horizontal bearing metal is extended radially at each end to form thrust surfaces, which ride against enlarged vertical faces on the shaft. These bearings are usually fitted with grooves to permit more efficient distribution of the lubricating oil, which separates the surfaces.

Figure 35 Ring Oiled Radial Bearings

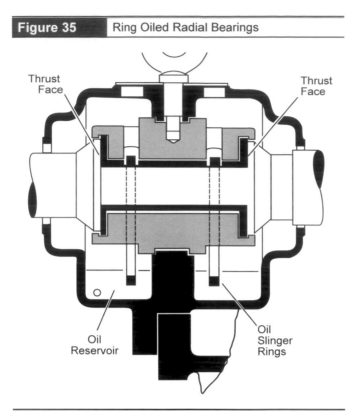

Figure 36 shows the most common thrust bearings for reaction turbines, which require more substantial designs considering their higher thrust loads.

The Kingsbury thrust bearing (often called Michell thrust bearing, after an almost identical invention) uses a number of tilting pads attached to a stationary plate, mounted in the casing. The pads face against a second, rotating thrust collar, machined into or mounted on the shaft. Oil is pumped through the bearing. As the shaft rotates the pads tilt and an oil wedge is created between the pads and the rotating collar. This oil wedge carries the thrust and distributes it evenly between the pads. The oil also carries away the heat generated by friction inside the bearing.

Figure 36 Kingsbury Thrust Bearing

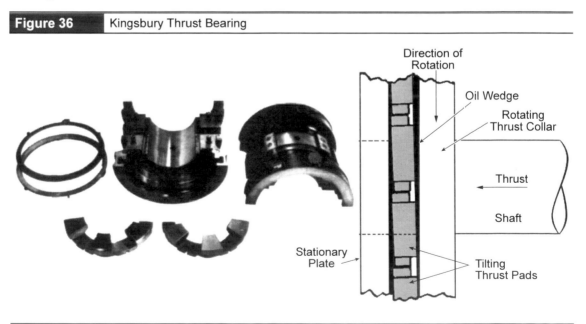

Dummy Pistons

A dummy piston, as shown in Figure 37, is an enlarged diameter section that is machined out of the rotor forging at the steam inlet end.

The piston surface is exposed to the steam pressure in the high-pressure end of the turbine. This pressure exerts a thrust force on the piston in the opposite direction to the normal thrust force. The piston diameter is calculated so that the force acting on it almost balances the thrust force. Preferably there should still be a slight thrust towards the exhaust end. To help maintain this condition at all turbine loads, a balance pipe is often connected between the low-pressure side of the dummy piston and an intermediate-pressure location along the turbine casing. Labyrinth seals are used to prevent steam leakage around the circumference of the piston.

Figure 37	Ring Oiled Radial Bearings

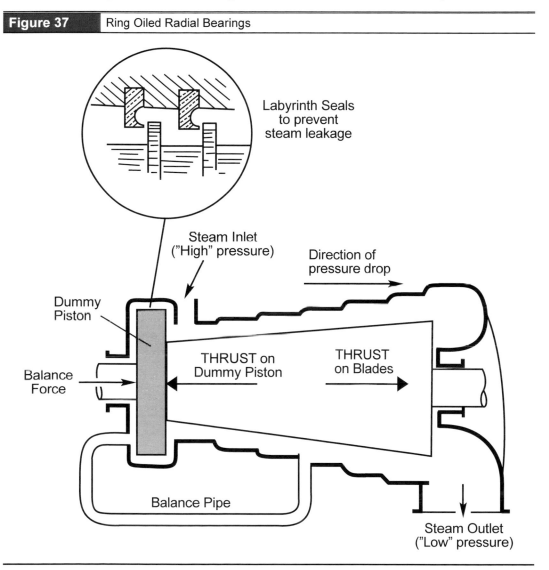

Thrust Adjusting Gear

Maximum efficiency of a reaction turbine is dependent upon maintaining the very close clearances between the stationary and moving blades. Therefore, the axial seals must be protected from damage or excessive wear, particularly during turbine startup. The relative position of stationary and rotating blades must also be maintained to ensure there is no contact.

Figure 38 shows thrust adjusting gear, which allows some manual control over shaft position. It includes an adjustable thrust bearing in a thrust block, which surrounds the turbine shaft and can be axially adjusted using an external gear arrangement.

- During startup, the thrust block is adjusted so it pushes against a stop in the direction of exhaust, thus maintaining maximum clearance between the stationary and moving blades. This avoids any danger of rubbing while the turbine temperatures increase (usually unevenly) and stabilize.

- When the turbine is loaded and the temperatures are stabilized, the thrust block can be adjusted for minimum clearance and, therefore, maximum blade efficiency.

Figure 38	Turbine Thrust Adjusting Gear

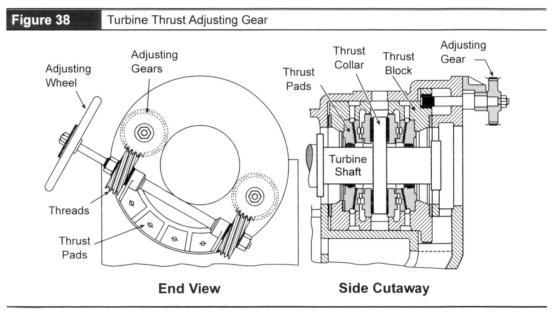

End View   **Side Cutaway**

OBJECTIVE 8

Identify typical designs and components for small and large industrial turbines. Explain typical size/capacity rating specifications and explain typical applications.

TYPICAL TURBINE DESIGNS

Figure 39 is an illustration of a General Electric Company mechanical drive turbine.

These turbines are built in ratings of 8 kW to 900 kW, running at speeds of 1000 rpm to 6500 rpm. They are used to drive pumps, compressors, fans, blowers, and similar equipment.

The turbine shown is a single stage, velocity compounded impulse type. There are two rows of moving blades with a row of stationary blades between them.

Figure 39	Single Stage Mechanical Drive Turbine

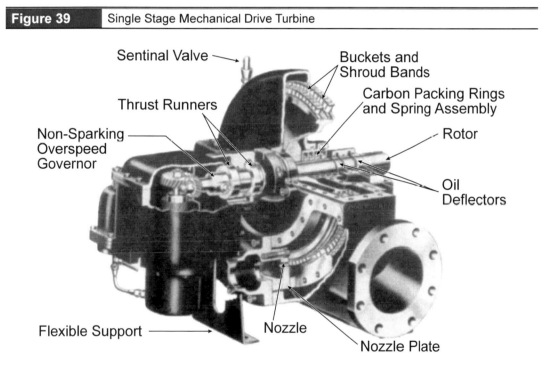

(Courtesy of General Electric)

Figure 40 shows an "open" view of a small industrial, mechanical drive turbine, manufactured by Skinner Engine Co., Dean Hill Turbine Division.

These turbines are built in ratings of 90 to 900 kW, consuming steam at 4200 kPa and 400°C and running at 1000 to 4000 rpm. The 90 kW turbine shown has a blade wheel diameter of 28 cm.

Figure 40	Mechanical Drive Turbine

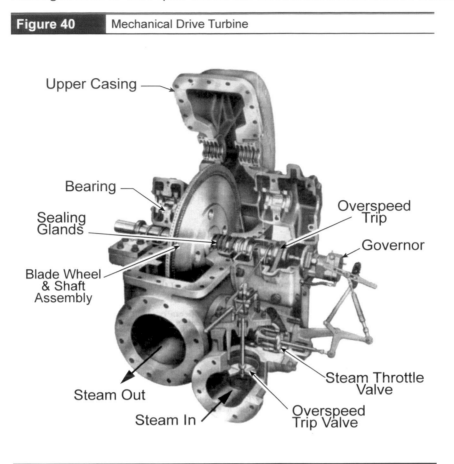

Figure 41 illustrates a mechanical drive turbine, widely used in industry. It is a single stage, impulse type turbine with a two-row velocity stage wheel and a row of stationary reversing blades between the rows of rotating blades.

Figure 41	Mechanical Drive Turbine

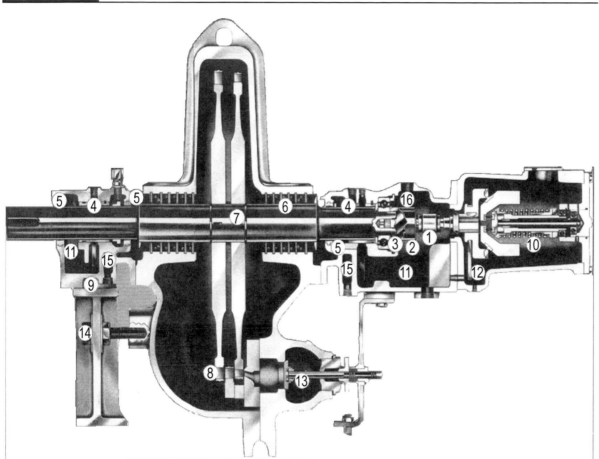

1.	Governor coupling	9.	Centerline support
2.	Bolt type overspeed trip	10.	Mechanical shaft governor
3.	Anti-friction thrust bearing	11.	Oil reservoirs
4.	Babbitt-lined journal bearings	12.	Governor lubrication
5.	Labyrinth-type bearing case seals	13.	Hand operated nozzle control
6.	Carbon ring packing	14.	Metric fasteners
7.	Rotor	15.	Water cooling jackets
8.	High efficiency blading	16.	Overspeed trip adjusting port

Figure 42 shows an Allis Chalmers turbine with two extraction points.

Two impulse wheels are used, one before the High-Pressure reaction staging and one before the Low-Pressure staging. Typical of the extraction type of turbine, it is rated at 3955 kW at 3600 r/min.

Figure 42	Double Extraction Turbine

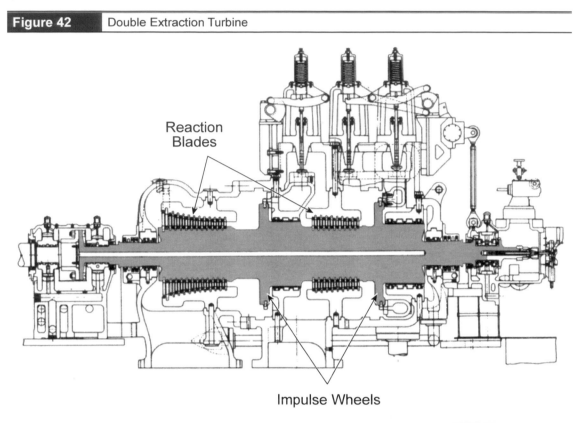

Reaction Blades

Impulse Wheels

Figure 43 illustrates a straight, non-condensing turbine, rated at 1100 kW.

This is an impulse turbine in which the first wheel is velocity-compounded and the remaining eight stages are pressure-compounded impulse stages. This design is very common where there is a large demand for lower pressure steam, which can be supplied by the turbine exhaust. The unit can be controlled so that its steam output varies directly with changes in the process steam demand. In this case, its governing system is sensitive only to the process steam pressure so that if the steam demand drops, the turbine will reduce output accordingly. If this results in turbine power that is insufficient for the electrical load demanded of the driven generator, the extra electrical load must be made up from another source.

Figure 43 Nine Stage Type GZF Turbine

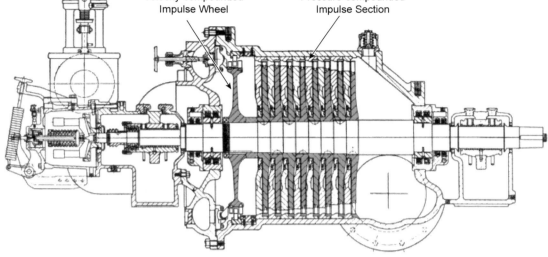

Velocity-compounded
Impulse Wheel

Pressure-compounded
Impulse Section

OBJECTIVE 9

Explain the use and design of reducing gears attached to steam turbines.

SPEED REDUCTION GEAR SETS

Steam turbines often operate at speeds higher than the required operating speed of the driven machine. Examples of this include turbine driven direct current generators, paper making machines, centrifugal pumps, blowers and fans.

In these situations a reduction gear set must be used to produce the speed required at the driven shaft. Reduction gear sets used on medium and large sized steam turbines are housed in a separate, oil tight casing. Small turbines may have the reduction gear within the same housing as the turbine.

Figure 44 shows a reducing gear attached to the end of a small turbine.

The reducing gear itself consists of two shafts, each with a gear. A smaller gear, called the pinion gear, is attached to the input shaft, which is coupled to the turbine shaft (or may be mounted directly to an extension of the turbine shaft) and turns at the same speed as the turbine. A larger gear meshes with the smaller gear and is attached to the output shaft of the reducer, which is then coupled to the driven equipment.

Since the smaller gear has fewer teeth than the larger gear, each revolution of the turbine shaft will produce less than one revolution of the driven shaft. The ratio of the rotational speeds will be inverse to the ratio of gear teeth. For example, if the turbine is rotating at 5600 rpm, the pinion has 30 teeth and the driven gear has 120 teeth, then the driven shaft will rotate at 30/120 x 5600 = 1400 rpm.

Figure 44	Turbine Driver with Gear Reducer

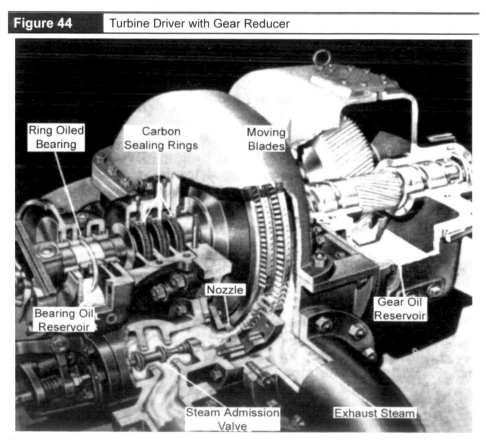

Figure 45 shows a speed reduction gearbox with the top portion of the cover removed. The driver is connected to the coupling of the small gear shaft. The driven machine is connected to the opposite end of the large gear shaft. A pipe from the oil pump supplies oil mist to the gears at their mesh point.

Note that the gears are set at an angle. These are called "Helical" gears. The purpose of the helical design is to reduce gear noise and vibration, since these gears mesh more easily and smoothly than straight-cut gears. Unfortunately, the design also creates some thrust on the gears and shafts. Where this is potentially excessive because of the size and the power transmitted, the gears are often cut in a "double helical" or "V" pattern (often called a "herringbone"), which eliminates thrust.

Figure 45	Gears in a Speed Reduction Gear Drive

Figures 44 and 45 show single-reduction gears with only two gears and two shafts. In both cases, there is only one speed reduction step, from the small diameter drive gear to the large diameter driven gear. In situations that require a very large speed reduction, a double-reduction gear may be used. In this design there are three gears and shafts. The drive gear (pinion) turns a larger, intermediate gear, which then turns the even larger driven gear. Another situation that will require three gears is when the driven shaft must rotate in the same direction as the turbine shaft.

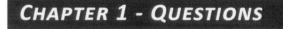

CHAPTER 1 - QUESTIONS

1. State briefly the difference between the operating principles of impulse turbine blades and reaction turbine blades.

2. a) What methods are used in impulse turbines to break down the steam pressure between the turbine inlet and turbine exhaust, and why is this done?

   b) It is common practice to use a velocity compounded impulse stage at the steam inlet or H-P end of a reaction turbine. Why?

3. Explain the operating principles of the following types of turbines:
   a) Condensing
   b) Back Pressure
   c) Compound
   d) Tandem compound
   e) Cross compound
   f) Topping
   g) Extraction

4. Describe four turbine rotor designs and state the type of turbine in which each would be used.

5. Explain common sealing methods for turbine casings (at the rotor shaft).

6. Sketch a "Dummy Piston" in a turbine. Why is it fitted and on what type of turbine?

7. Explain the purpose and location of a reducing gear.

8. What methods are used to minimize leakage across turbine blades?

ANSWERS: All answers are found within the content of the chapter.

Steam Turbine Auxiliaries & Operation

LEARNING OUTCOME

When you complete this chapter you should be able to:

Describe auxiliary support and control systems for steam turbines and explain start-up and shutdown procedures.

LEARNING OBJECTIVES

Here is what you should be able to do when you complete each objective:

1. *Describe typical lube oil systems for small and large steam turbines.*

2. *Explain the purpose and describe the design and operation of barring gear and jacking oil systems on a large turbine.*

3. *Describe a condensing turbine circuit and explain typical operating parameters.*

4. *Explain and state the applications, where applicable, of the following governor types: speed-sensitive, pressure-sensitive, nozzle, throttle, and bypass. Explain governor droop and isochronous control.*

5. *Explain the operation and the major components of the three main speed-sensitive governor systems: mechanical, mechanical-hydraulic, and electronic-hydraulic.*

6. *Explain the operation and describe the components of typical mechanical and electronic overspeed trip systems.*

7. *Explain the sequence followed for the cold start-up and the shutdown of a non-condensing steam turbine.*

8. *Explain the sequence followed for the cold start-up and the shutdown of a condensing and extracting steam turbine.*

OBJECTIVE 1

Describe typical lube oil systems for small and large steam turbines.

LUBE OIL SYSTEMS

Turbines must be provided with lubricating systems that will ensure a reliable supply of lubricating oil to all moving parts. The size of the turbine determines whether the lubrication system is simple or complex. Small turbines, of less than 150 kW, used to drive auxiliary equipment, are normally provided with ring-oiled bearings.

Medium-sized turbines, particularly if driving through a reduction gear, may have both ring-oiled bearings and a circulating oil system. These systems supply oil spray to the reducing gears and forced oil feed to the bearings of the reducing gear and the turbine.

Large turbines have oil-circulating systems, which supply lube oil to the turbine bearings, the bearings of the driven machine (eg. the generator), and the reducing gear plus provide hydraulic operating oil to the governor mechanisms and the steam throttle valves.

Figure 1 shows a typical lube oil system for a small turbine and generator set.

Oil is drawn from a reservoir and delivered at full pump discharge pressure (350 to 500 kPa) to a header, which supplies oil to the governing and control mechanisms. Oil from this header, after being reduced in pressure to between 55 to 103 kPa, flows through the oil cooler to another header, which supplies oil to all the bearings and other parts requiring lubrication. The oil, returning from the bearing and governor mechanism, drains back into the reservoir.

| Figure 1 | Lube Oil System on Small Turbine-Generator Set |

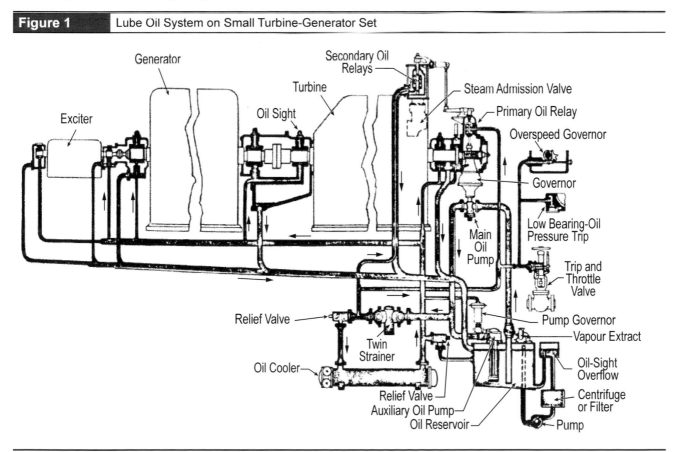

Figure 2 is a schematic of a typical lubricating oil system for a larger turbine-generator set.

Depending on unit size, the oil tank has a capacity of 5000 to 10 000 litres or more.

The main oil pump is directly driven by gears from the turbine shaft. When the turbine is running, this is the main source of lube oil. Two other pumps, driven by electric motors, act as standby pumps for use when the main pump is insufficient and during startup and shutdown, when the main pump is not yet available.

The oil pumps take suction from the oil tank through strainers and discharge the oil at high pressure, 552 to 827 kPa.

From the pumps, the oil flows in two different directions:

- to the power oil and governor relay oil systems and
- to the oil coolers and then to the turbine generator bearings.

Power oil, acting in servomotors, provides hydraulic pressure to open the emergency stop valves and governing valves. Governor relay oil acts as a regulating medium. The power oil and the governor relay oil must be at high pressure.

The oil used for lubrication is supplied from the main line, through a pressure-reducing valve, at a lower pressure, typically in the 69 to 138 kPa range.

If the turbine has been operating for some time, the oil from the oil tank will be quite warm. Therefore, the oil will need cooling, in the oil coolers, before it flows through the bearings. Typical outlet temperature, from the coolers, is in the 43° to 49°C range. Care must be taken to not cool the oil below this temperature, since the viscosity will increase and flow will be affected. Also, since warm temperature encourages evaporation of water from the oil, the oil is not cooled until it is downstream of the oil tank and pumps. This allows the oil in the tank to be warmer, thus improving evaporation. The water vapour is drawn off the oil tank by a small fan, called the vapour extractor (can see one in Fig. 1).

Inside the bearings, the oil acts as a lubricant between moving surfaces and also as a coolant for the bearings. Leaving the bearings, the oil drains by gravity into a return header, which leads back to the oil tank. A thermometer is located in the return oil line from each bearing to continuously indicate and allow continuous monitoring of bearing temperature.

A small stream (ie. slipstream) of oil is continuously drawn from the bottom of the oil tank, even when the turbine is not operating. This oil is pumped through a purifier filter (to remove any dirt or water) and is then returned to the tank. A variety of filter media is used. An alternative purification method uses centrifugal force in a machine, called a centrifuge, in which high speed rotation throws the heavier water out of the oil. The water is drained from the centrifuge.

Figure 2 Typical Lubricating Oil System on Large Turbine-Generator Set

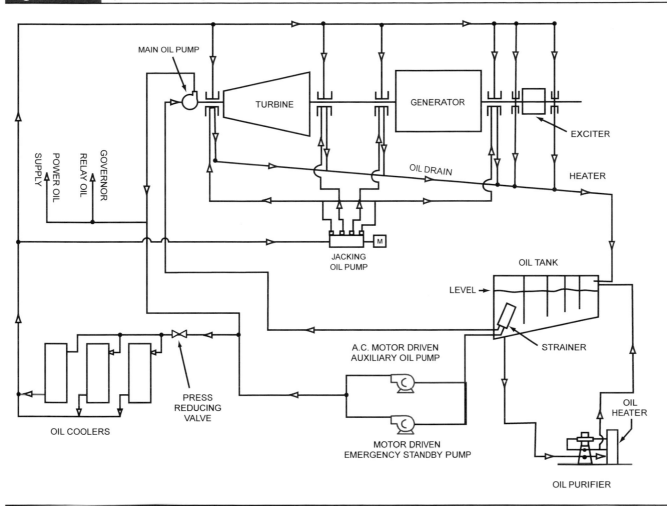

OBJECTIVE 2

Explain the purpose and describe the design and operation of barring gear and jacking oil systems on a large turbine.

BARRING GEAR (AKA TURNING GEAR)

When a turbine is left cold and at a standstill, the weight of the rotor will tend to cause the rotor to bend slightly downwards between the support bearings. This is called **sagging**. If left at a standstill while the turbine is still hot, the lower half of the rotor will cool faster than the upper half and the rotor will bend upwards, due to differential expansion. This is called **hogging**. In both cases, the turbine would be difficult, if not impossible, to start. To overcome this problem, many large turbines have a barring gear (also called turning gear), consisting of an electric motor, which, through reduction gears, turns the turbine shaft at low speed. The exact barring speed varies from unit to unit, but is generally around 1% of operating speed. In larger machines it can be as low as 1 rpm.

Before a cold turbine is started, it should be warmed up on the barring gear for a specified time to ensure even warming and avoid startup vibration. When a turbine is shut down, it should be barring for a specified time (often up to 24 hours) to ensure the rotor and casing cool evenly. If the turbine drives a hydrogen cooled generator, the turbine should be kept continuously on barring gear while shut down, to prevent excessive loss of hydrogen.

In the barring gear illustrated in Figure 3, a belt-drive and a worm and wheel reduce the motor speed. The disengaging gear wheel is carried on a yoke, which is slung from the worm shaft. An oil-operated piston is arranged to rotate the yoke about the worm shaft and so engage or disengage the turning gear from the turbine shaft.

Figure 3	Barring Gear

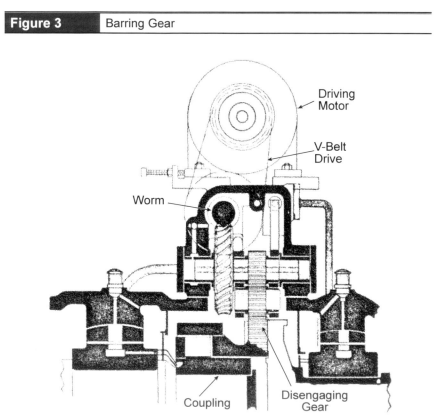

Figure 4 shows the location of the barring gear on a very large turbine.

The view is of a partly-assembled, tandem, double-flow turbine. Positioning the barring gear at the side of the bearing enables the gear to engage the shaft below the turbine center line.

The diagram also illustrates a side-mounted barring gear and vertical driving motor and their location in relation to the turbine shaft and control console.

Figure 4	Barring Gear on Large Turbine

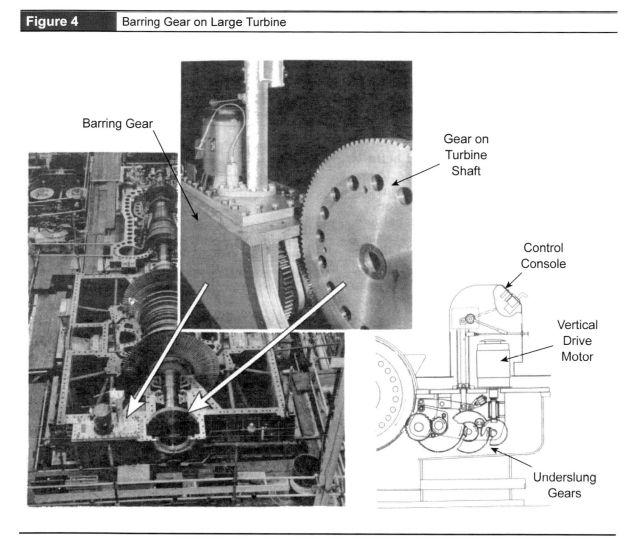

Figure 5 shows the installation of the barring or turning gear in a Low Pressure end of a turbine.

Figure 5	Barring Gear

JACKING OIL SYSTEMS

Large turbines with heavy rotors are usually equipped with a jacking oil pump, which supplies the lower part of the bearings with oil at approximately 10 000 kPa, thereby lifting the shaft and supplying lubricating oil.

The high oil pressure lifts (or jacks) the shaft just a fraction of a millimeter. This ensures there will be no metal-to-metal contact during the initial start-up of the barring gear and also reduces the starting load on the electric motor. The jacking oil is applied before start up of the barring gear and maintained while the turbine is at slow speed. Normally, the jacking oil pump is shut down when the barring gear disengages. The jacking oil is also used when the turbine is shutdown and is on barring gear for the cooldown period. In general, whenever the barring gear is engaged, the jacking oil pump is on.

OBJECTIVE 3

Describe a condensing turbine circuit and explain typical operating parameters.

CONDENSING TURBINE CIRCUITS

There are two general classes, based on the exhaust steam, into which all turbines fall:

- condensing units, which exhaust at pressures below atmosphere, and
- non-condensing units, which exhaust at or above atmospheric pressure

Figure 6 is a diagram of a simple, condensing steam plant.

- Heat energy, released in the boiler furnace, converts the boiler water to steam, which then goes to the turbine.
- Heat energy in the steam is converted to mechanical energy when the steam does work in the turbine and produces shaft rotation.
- The exhaust steam from the turbine enters the condenser, where heat exchange with cooling water causes the steam to condense. The amount of cooling also determines the exhaust pressure, which is below atmospheric pressure.
- The condensate collects in the bottom, hotwell section of the condenser and is pumped from there back to the boiler as feedwater, to complete the cycle.

Figure 6	Simple Steam Power Plant

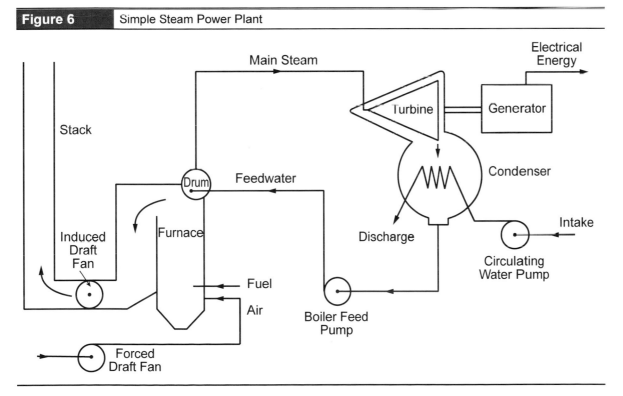

Figure 7 shows a similar cycle, but using a nuclear reactor as the heat source. A nuclear plant uses heat in a similar manner to do work in a prime mover, but in this case, the heat is produced from the reaction of a nuclear fuel. The heat produced is transferred to the heat exchanger by a circulating reactor coolant. The working fluid in the cycle is steam flowing through the turbine, in the same manner as in Figure 6.

Figure 7	Simple Steam Power Plant

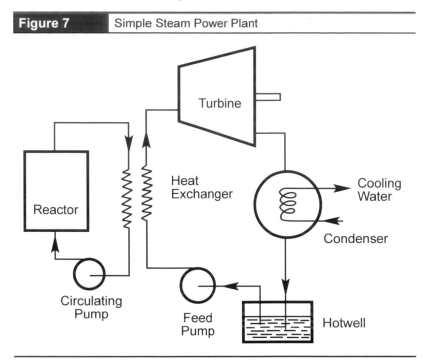

While the primary purpose of the steam in a power plant is to supply the turbine with heat energy to produce mechanical power, there are several auxiliary pieces of equipment, such as feedwater heaters, evaporators and deaerators, that depend upon the steam supply and are essential to efficient turbine operation.

Figure 8 is an example of a more detailed condensing steam turbine circuit.

- The main steam from the boiler expands in the high-pressure turbine, doing work and losing temperature and pressure.

- It is then sent back to the reheater section of the boiler, where it's temperature is increased.

- Leaving the reheater section, the steam then expands in the low-pressure turbine to near atmospheric pressure.

- The exhaust steam enters the surface condenser where heat exchange with the circulating cooling water removes the latent heat, causing the steam to condense.

- The condensate from the condenser hotwell is pumped through the low pressure feed heaters (where the exhaust or extraction steam from the LP turbine is used to preheat the feedwater going to the boiler) and to the deaerator.

- The boiler feed pump pumps the deaerated water to the high pressure feed heaters where the exhaust or extraction steam from the HP turbine further preheats the feedwater going to the boiler.

- From there the feedwater is heated even more by heat exchange with flue gases in the economizer before entering the boiler.

Figure 8   Condensing Turbine Circuit

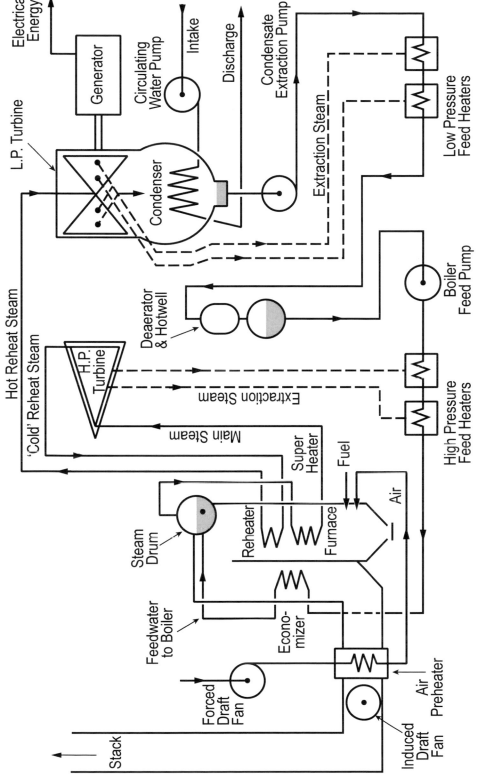

OBJECTIVE 4

Explain and state the applications, where applicable, of the following governor types: speed-sensitive, pressure-sensitive, nozzle, throttle, and bypass. Explain governor droop and isochronous control.

STEAM TURBINE GOVERNORS

Turbine governing systems control the steam flow to hold the speed of the turbine constant with varying loads, or to hold the pressure constant with varying demands for process steam.

The governor on a condensing turbine driving an alternator is required to control the turbine inlet steam flow so as to maintain constant speed with varying alternator load. In a backpressure turbine, supplying exhaust steam for process work, the supply of steam to the turbine may be controlled in such a way as to maintain a constant backpressure.

In an extraction turbine, the governor must control the steam flow so that both the turbine speed and the pressure of steam at the point of extraction remain reasonably constant. This involves regulating the total amount of steam admitted to the inlet stages of the turbine and the steam supplied to the turbine stages that follow the extraction point.

Therefore, turbine governors can be considered as falling into two classes:

- those responsive to speed changes and
- those responsive to pressure changes.

SPEED SENSITIVE GOVERNORS

Three methods of speed-sensitive governing are used in steam turbines:

- nozzle governing,
- throttle governing and
- bypass or overload governing.

Nozzle Governing

Nozzle governing is only used in impulse turbines. It maintains a set turbine speed by regulating the flow of steam to inlet nozzles, which then direct the steam to the turbine blades. Two common arrangements are the bar-lift and the cam-lift systems, shown respectively in Figures 9 and 10.

In Figure 9, the bar-lift design has a row of inlet nozzles above the first stage turbine blading and a set of nozzle valves, or plugs, that are held in a horizontal lifting beam. The lengths of the nozzle valve stems vary. Hydraulic oil controls a pilot valve, positioned by the flyweight of the governor, which moves the bar up and down to open and close the nozzles as required. The different lengths of the valve stems determines the sequence in which they open and close.

Figure 9   Bar Lift Nozzle Control Gear

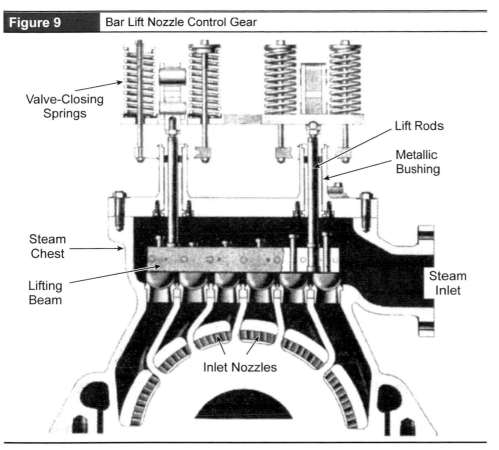

In Figure 10, the same principle is applied, but a cam-like device, which controls the sequence and opening of each nozzle, individually operates the nozzle valves.

Figure 10   Cam Lift Nozzle Control Gear

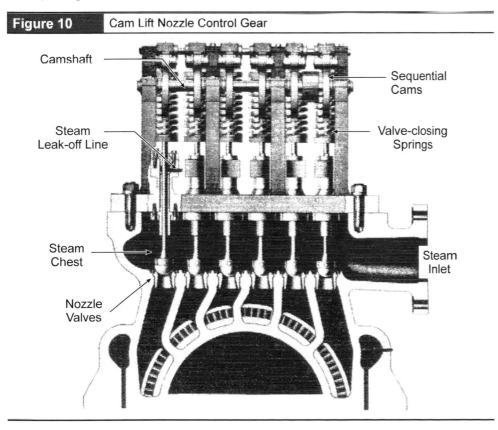

Throttle Governing

In throttle governing, a single valve at the inlet to the turbine throttles (adjusts) the steam flow into the turbine casing. From there it is directed to the nozzles equally by the internal design of the turbine. The inlet, throttle valve responds to the governor to increase the steam flow for more speed or reduce the steam flow for less speed. Larger turbines may have two throttle valves, arranged in parallel in the steam line.

This type of governing is always used with reaction turbines, since the pressure drop in the moving blades requires consistent steam admission to the full circumference of the blade wheels. With throttle governing, one or two control valves control the load from 0% to 100%.

Examples of throttle governing are shown in Figures 11 and 12.

In both cases, the position of flyweights is determined by the speed of the turbine shaft. If the speed increases, centrifugal force pushes the flyweights out further, which moves the governor rod and, through the linkage system adjusts the position of the throttling valve.

In Figure 12, a servo motor is added, which makes the action of the governor somewhat smoother and applies more force to the valve rod. The fulcrum linkage adjusts the position of pistons within the servo motor, which applies corresponding force and positioning of the steam valve.

Figure 12 also shows a speed changer (often called a "speeder gear"). This allows the governed speed to be adjusted within a certain range. Changing the tension on the spring increases or decreases the force on the flyweights.

Figure 11	Simple Throttle Governor

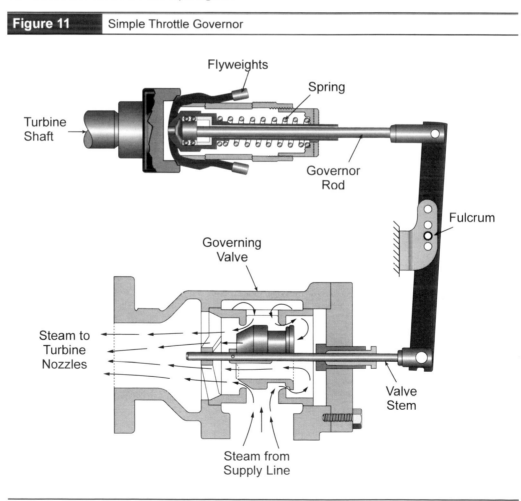

Figure 12 | Mechanical-Hydraulic Governor with Servo

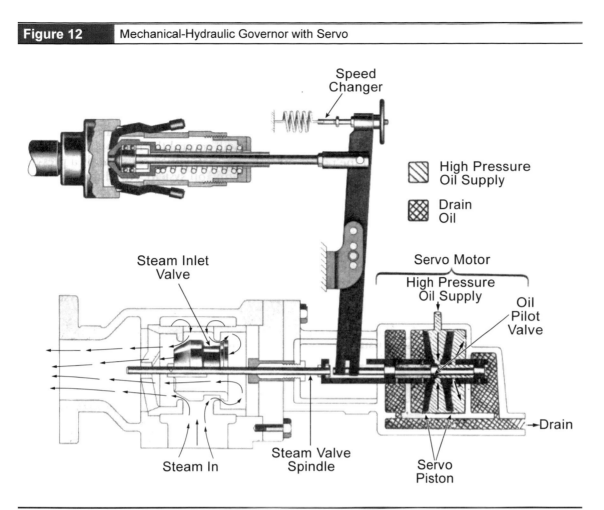

Note that with mechanical governors the linkage causes the movement between the flyweights and the valve to be directly proportional. This means that the valve can only open or close if the flyweights move in or out. In other words, if the load on the turbine increases, the turbine will slow down slightly and the flyweights will move inward, due to the reduced centrifugal force. Since the weights only move after a change in speed, this type of governor does not maintain a constant speed except between a maximum and minimum value, dependent on load. This is adequate for many applications, such as pumps and fans, but not for electrical generation where the speed must be constant.

Bypass or Overload Governing

This system is used on both impulse and reaction turbines. It consists of two throttling valves, one at the inlet of the first stage of the turbine and the other at an inlet located downstream of the first few stages. The purpose of the second inlet point is to allow the turbine to maintain speed while producing extra power, during high load or overload conditions.

Figure 13 shows a steam chest with a stop and trip valve (on the left), followed by the main steam throttle valve and the bypass throttle valve (on the right). This steam chest/valve arrangement is mounted on the turbine so as to direct steam to the appropriate nozzles, as shown in the turbine cross-section of Figure 14.

Figure 13	Steam Chest with Stop, Trip and Throttle Valves

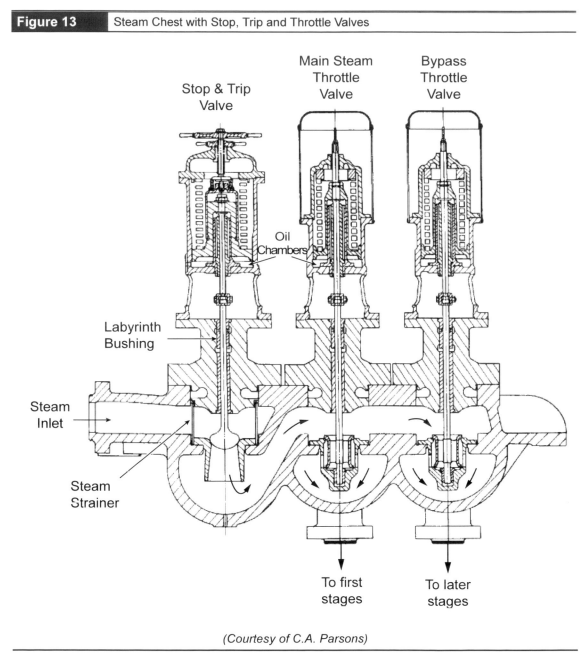

(Courtesy of C.A. Parsons)

Figure 14	Bypass-Governed Turbine

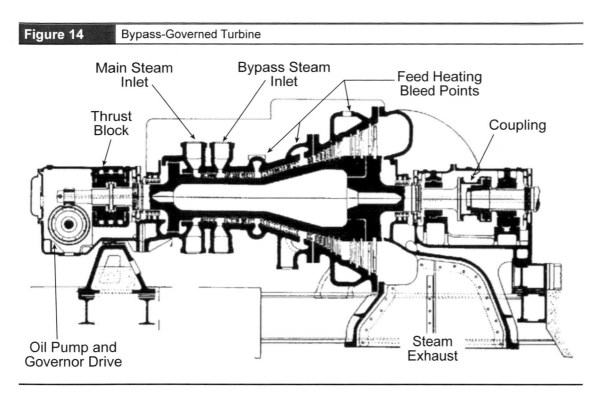

PRESSURE SENSITIVE GOVERNORS

Pressure sensitive governors either control a steady backpressure at the turbine exhaust (outlet) or they extract steam from part way through the turbine and discharge it from that point at a controlled pressure. There is usually a combination of speed and pressure control to assure relatively steady turbine operation.

Backpressure Governing

This system uses a pressure-sensing element on the exhaust steam line from the turbine. A setpoint is entered into the controller, which then adjusts the position of the inlet steam throttle valve. If pressure is low, the throttle valve will open further to admit more steam and raise the exhaust pressure. If pressure is high, the throttle valve will close further. This system is commonly used with condensing turbines, where the pressure to the condenser should be as steady as possible. It is also used in processes where the exhaust steam from the turbine is used for heating and where the pressure must be steady to ensure good heat control.

The efficiency of the backpressure turbine is very high because there are no exhaust steam losses. The disadvantage of this system is that the power output of the turbine is completely dependent on the demand for process steam.

Extraction Governing

Steam for use in a process can be extracted at controlled pressure from intermediate stages of a turbine, which is called an 'extraction turbine'. The control systems for extraction turbines are complicated, since they must allow changes in the turbine load without affecting the steam extraction. They also must allow changes in the quantity of steam extracted without affecting the turbine output.

A schematic of extraction governing is shown in Figure 15.

- When the extraction steam demand increases, the extraction pressure decreases and this forces the pressure regulator piston downwards. This moves point "G" down, and since point "D" is kept stationary by the speed governor, the linkage makes point "F" move the extraction valve down and point "E" move the steam inlet valve up. The result is that less steam can get through the extraction valve, so increased extraction steam flows at constant pressure.

- If the load on the turbine increases, the speed will decrease and the speed governor will force point "A" downwards. Since point "B" is fixed and point "G" is held stationary by the pressure regulator, points "C" and "D" will move upwards and points "E" and "F" will move their respective valves upwards. This results in more high-pressure steam being admitted. The extra steam goes via the more open extraction valve to the low pressure stages of the turbine, giving increased load with no change in the extraction flow and pressure.

Figure 15	Combined Speed and Pressure Governor

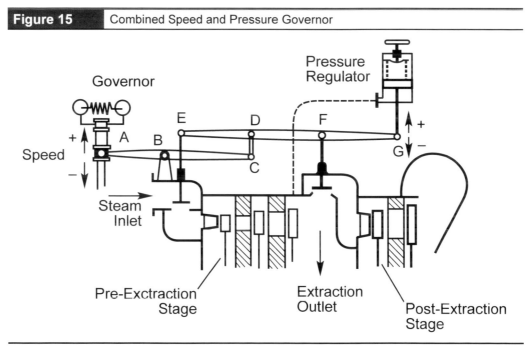

GOVERNOR DROOP

Speed droop is the change in speed that results from an increase in load. An ideal governor will have the ability to maintain a constant speed at any load. However, there are mechanical losses within most governors that prevent achievement of this speed control. If the load on a turbine changes from zero (no-load), to maximum (full-load), the turbine will slow down and the governor may not be capable of restoring it to set speed.

The difference between the no-load and full-load speed, expressed as a percentage of the set speed, is called the "droop" of the governor. That is, as the load increases, the speed will "droop" below the set speed.

For example, if the set speed of a turbine is 5000 rpm and it operates at this speed with no load, but the governor system can only achieve 4500 rpm when the turbine is fully loaded, the droop of the governor is (500/5000) x 100 = 10%.

Governors with low droop are more sensitive to load changes and generally have more accurate control than governors with high droop.

ISOCHRONOUS CONTROL

An isochronous governor regulates the turbine at a constant speed regardless of load. The speed regulation (ie. droop) is zero percent. Isochronous governing is used when prime movers are operating on their own. That is, they are not sharing the load with another turbine.

If turbines are sharing load, in a parallel operation, an action called "hunting" can occur in which each turbine attempts to adjust for changes in load. They begin "fighting" each other for control, which creates a cycling of the load and of the turbine speeds. The end result may be that one machine becomes fully loaded while the other machine may have no load.

OBJECTIVE 5

Explain the operation and the major components of the three main speed-sensitive governor systems: mechanical, mechanical-hydraulic, and electronic-hydraulic.

SPEED SENSITIVE GOVERNORS

The speed governor is a proportional-action controller, in that each change in load causes a change in the turbine speed. For example, increased load tends to cause the turbine to slow down. The governor controls the opening of the control valves as a function of this speed change. When driving an electric generator, due to the governor speed droop (loss in speed due to increased load) the frequency is not constant over the full range of load, unless there is an external adjustment.

The speed sensitive governor may be:

   a) mechanical,

   b) mechanical-hydraulic

   c) electronic-hydraulic

Mechanical Governors

Figure 16 shows the components and arrangement of a simple, mechanical governor.

Figure 16	Mechanical Governor

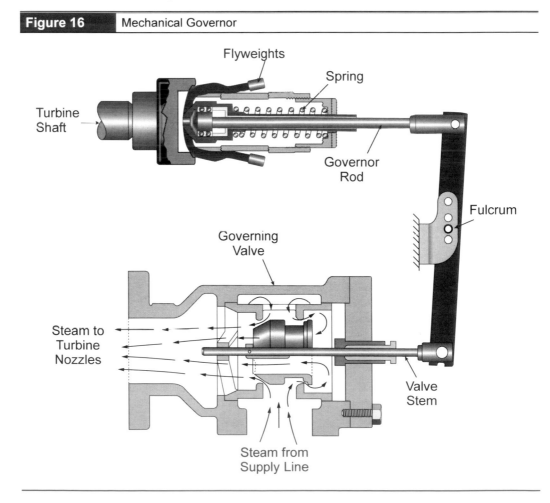

Attached to the end of the turbine shaft is a set of weights, called flyweights that pivot and have the ability to move in and out. The shaft ends of the flyweights contact the end of a governor, which is free to move to the left or right, but which is also acted upon by a counterspring. A governor valve, or steam inlet valve, is mounted at the inlet of the turbine and connected to the external steam supply line. The valve disc is double-seated and has a stem that extends out of the valve casing. Connecting the valve stem to the governor rod is a lever that is pinned to and free to pivot on a fixed fulcrum. This allows movement in the governor rod to be transmitted to the valve stem.

The governor functions, as follows. Rotation of the turbine shaft causes the flyweights to pivot outwards, due to centrifugal force. The greater the speed of rotation, the greater is the centrifugal force and the further outward the flyweights move. Movement of the flyweights causes movement of the governor rod, which, through the lever and fulcrum, causes movement of the governor valve.

For example, referring to Figure 17, if the load on the turbine increases, it slows down slightly. This causes the flyweights to move inwards (due to less centrifugal force) and the governor rod moves to the left, due to the force of the counterspring. The lever pivots at the fulcrum and the lower end moves to the right, thus opening the governor valve further. Now, as more steam enters the turbine, the speed begins to increase. The flyweights move outwards again until the system becomes balanced at the set speed, under the new load.

The disadvantage of simple mechanical governors is that they have a high-speed droop, usually around 10%. Therefore, they are not suitable for large machines or where control must be extremely accurate. Within limits, changing the pivot point at the fulcrum can reduce the effects of droop, so that the governor rod movement has more affect on the governor valve movement.

Figure 17	Mechanical Governor Flyweight Positions

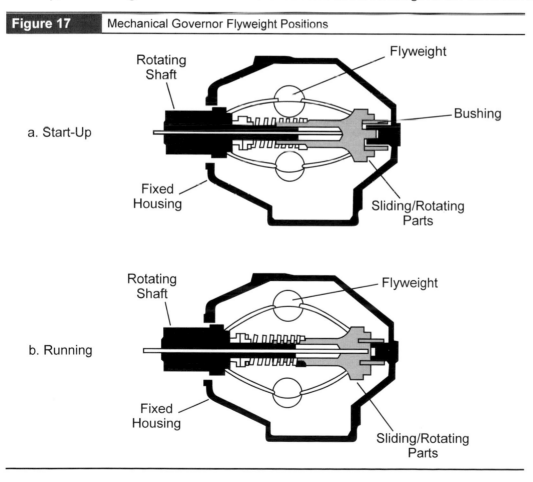

Mechanical-Hydraulic Governors

The mechanical-hydraulic governor has a pilot valve and a hydraulic amplifier. This arrangement removes the direct linkage of the flyweights to the governor valve. Instead, the flyweights position an oil pilot valve that admits high-pressure oil to a piston that moves the governor valve. The advantage of the design is that the mechanical losses of the governor are greatly reduced. The flyweights require less force to position the pilot valve. The pilot valve opens and closes ports to supply high pressure oil to one side of the power piston or the other, positioning the steam inlet valve. The droop of this governor can be reduced to almost zero.

Figure 18 is a simple diagram of a mechanical-hydraulic governor.

- Oil, at approximately 495 kPa, is continuously supplied to the center of the pilot valve, which, at governor control speed, covers the oil ports to the amplifier cylinder so that oil cannot enter or leave the cylinder.

- If the load drops and the turbine speed increases, the flyweights move outwards. This pulls the pilot valve upwards, admitting oil to the top of the cylinder while allowing oil to drain from the bottom of the cylinder. The piston moves downward, forcing the steam valve to close further.

- As the steam valve closes, the turbine speed decreases and the flyweights move inwards. At governor control speed, the pilot valve will have returned to the central, or neutral, position and the turbine will continue to operate at the set speed, under the new load. Conversely, if the turbine load increases and the turbine speed drops, the pilot valve will admit more oil below the piston and cause the governor valve to open further.

Figure 18	Mechanical-Hydraulic Governor

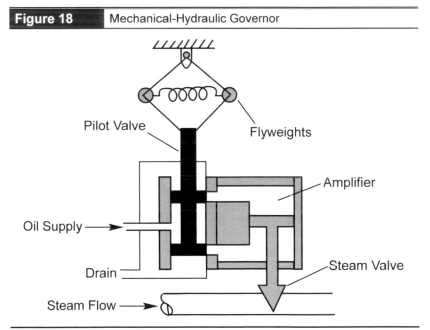

Figure 19 shows the same governor as Figure 16 with the addition of a hydraulic cylinder and piston. This hydraulic arrangement is often called a "servo" or "servo motor". Note that the lever positions the pilot valve, while the servo piston positions the steam valve. Also, notice the speed changer. Adjustment of this wheel creates a slight change in the positioning of the servo piston, which then alternates the internal hydraulics to cause a change in the operating speed of the turbine.

Therefore, the effort required by the governor, can be reduced to a relatively small force by the use of an oil relay, as illustrated in Figure 20. In this case, the governor arm operates only the pilot valve. When the pilot moves, it opens an oil port admitting oil, which forces the servo piston to move with it. The steam valve spindle movement shuts off the oil when the piston has caught up with the pilot. The pilot movement then admits high-pressure oil to one side of the servo piston and connects the other side to drain, producing a positive control.

Figure 19 | Mechanical-Hydraulic Governor with Servo

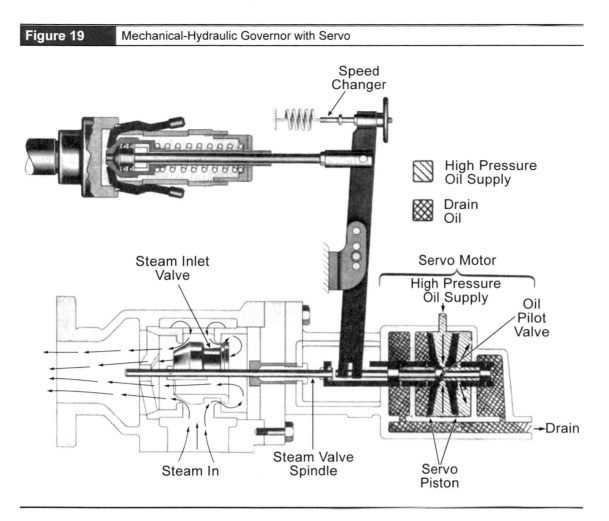

Mechanical-Hydraulic Governing System

The following diagram and description, Figure 20, demonstrates how components relate to each other to provide a complete governor system.

Referring to Figure 20:

- The turbine shaft drives a main, gear-type oil pump, which supplies the hydraulic oil pressure to the various governor components. An auxiliary oil pump, driven by an electric motor, provides oil pressure during start-up of the turbine, until the main oil pump can provide sufficient operating oil pressure.

- Before start-up, the overspeed trip assembly is manually re-latched so that the oil trip valve, "B", is open, allowing oil pressure and flow to the other governor components. This includes the turbine stop valve, which is held open by the pressure under the operating piston in cylinder "C".

- When the turbine is running steadily, the spinning flyweights take a position, balanced by their counterspring. Flyweight movement controls the position of a plunger sliding within sleeve "G", which is part of the servo, or speed adjuster. The relative position of the plunger and the sleeve determines the opening of the oil ports in the sleeve.

- Meanwhile, high pressure oil goes directly to the pilot valve, "K", in the control oil cylinder. The pilot valve regulates the oil pressure below the throttle valve cylinder, J, increasing pressure if the speed is high. The position of the throttle valve responds accordingly.

- However, the droop, proportionality and speed control of the governor is affected by the positioning of the moveable governor fulcrum, which is determined by the piston in cylinder, "H". Oil to this cylinder is taken from the main oil supply, through valve "F". The pressure in the line, and therefore the pressure below piston "H," is determined by the position of the oil ports at "G", in the servo. Adjusting the handwheel, "L", will change the servo port openings, causing more or less oil to be drained, thus affecting the pressure to cylinder "H" and causing the speed of the turbine to change. The movement of "L" may be done manually or it may be activated by a small electric motor, with remote control.

- In an overspeed situation, the overspeed trip will close the oil supply cylinder, "B", and open the drain. This will cause all oil pressure to be lost beneath the trip valve and the throttle valve. The turbine will stop, due to immediate loss of the steam supply.

Figure 20	Mechanical-Hydraulic Governor System

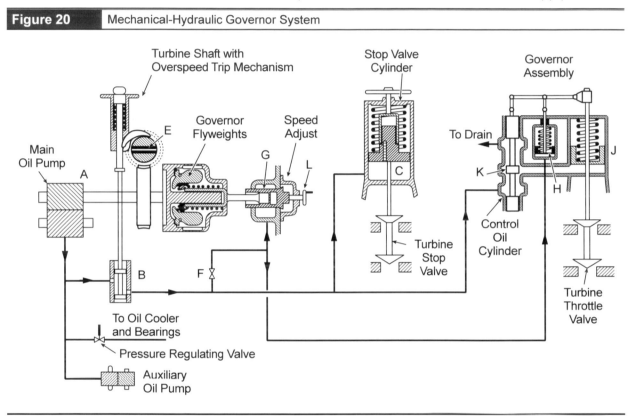

Electro-Hydraulic Governors

Electro-hydraulic governors use a combination of electronic and hydraulic controls. The turbine control console contains all the controls necessary for starting, accelerating, and loading the turbine, as well as for controlling the extraction steam flows and pressures if applicable.

Referring to Figure 21, the speed-measuring device, a permanent magnet generator, produces an electrical output signal that is amplified and compared to a reference signal by the computer in the control console. The difference is then amplified and applied to a servo-valve, which hydraulically positions the servo-rams, moving the steam valves and controlling the steam flow. The valve position is measured and fed back to the control console, providing more exact control. Provisions are made for on-line servicing of the computer circuit cards while the turbine is carrying load.

Electro-hydraulic governor systems use a separate fluid power unit to provide high-pressure hydraulic oil to operate the servo-rams, rather than using part of the lube oil system. The fluid power unit supplies hydraulic oil, at pressures in the range of 8275 to 11 030 kPa.

Figure 21 Electro-Hydraulic Governor System

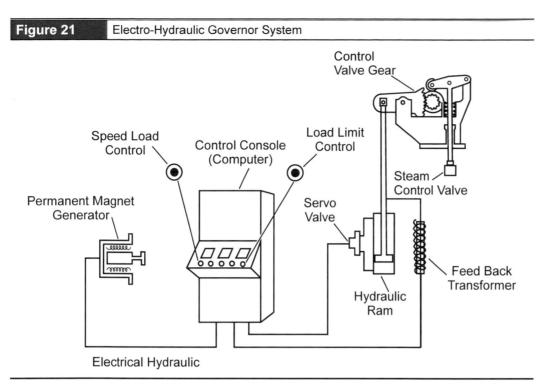

Figure 22 shows a typical example of a basic electronic governor system for a turbine generator. The actuator controls the pilot valve to readjust the position of the steam control valve and maintain the desired speed versus generator load changes. The force to move the throttle valve is usually hydraulic power acting through the servo piston.

Figure 22 Electro-Hydraulic Governor System

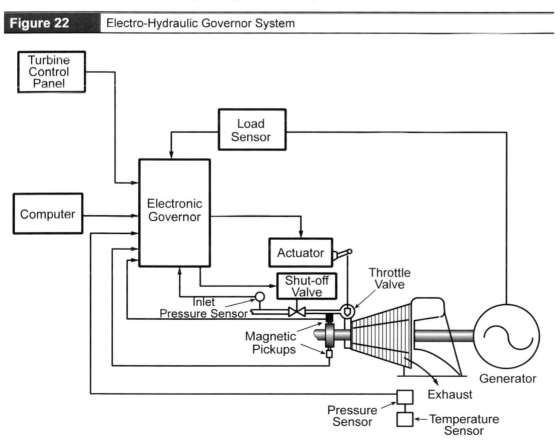

OBJECTIVE 6

Explain the operation and describe the components of typical mechanical and electronic overspeed trip systems.

MECHANICAL OVERSPEED TRIP SYSTEMS

The mechanical overspeed trip on a steam turbine is an integral part of the governing system in that it prevents steam from entering the turbine, if the speed becomes dangerously excessive. The mechanical overspeed trip gear is generally located at the front end of the high pressure turbine shaft and is designed to shut off the steam supply to the turbine. The trip speed is usually 10 to 12% above the normal operating speed.

A basic trip bolt is shown in Figure 23. It consists of a weighted bolt that is held inside a specially made hole in the shaft.

- A spring is held in compression to keep this trip bolt inside the shaft during normal operating conditions, as shown in Figure 23(a).

- If the turbine shaft reaches the overspeed setting, the spring compression is overcome and the bolt will be thrown out by centrifugal force, as shown in Figure 23(b).

Figure 23	Overspeed Trip Bolt Positions

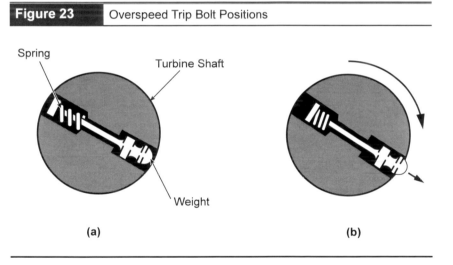

(a)   (b)

Figure 24 illustrates a mechanical overspeed trip system with a mechanical linkage to the steam inlet trip valve. It operates as follows.

- Figure 24(a): During normal operation, the trip valve is raised to the open position, using the trip valve arm, which pivots at one end and is connected to the casing by the trip valve spring. The free end of the arm rests on the machined, knife-edge surface of the trip latch and the tension in the spring holds the arm and latch tightly together.

- Figure 24(b): If the turbine speed reaches the setting of the overspeed trip, the weight in the shaft moves outward and pushes on the trip arm, causing it to pivot away from the trip arm. The tension in the spring immediately pulls the trip arm and causes the trip valve to close.

- The turbine can be manually tripped by the operator at any time by simply pulling the trip arm away from the latched position.

Figure 24	Mechanical Overspeed Trip System

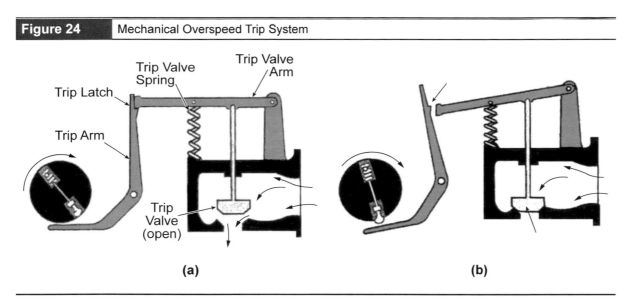

(a)   **(b)**

Figure 25 shows the operating principle of an overspeed trip for a turbine with a hydraulic governor systems in which the steam trip valve is held open by hydraulic oil pressure in a stop valve cylinder. Removing the oil pressure from the cylinder causes the trip valve to close.

The spring loaded trip bolt, located in the turbine shaft, has the center of gravity slightly off the center of the shaft in the direction of the bolt head. The nut at the end of the bolt provides a stop for the bolt in the tripped position and is used to set the trip speed. During normal operation, the main spring holds the relay rod against the trip lever. Piston "A" covers the oil drain opening and the high-pressure oil passes between pistons " A" and "B", to the stop valve (which is the position shown in Fig. 25).

Figure 25	Emergency Overspeed Trip

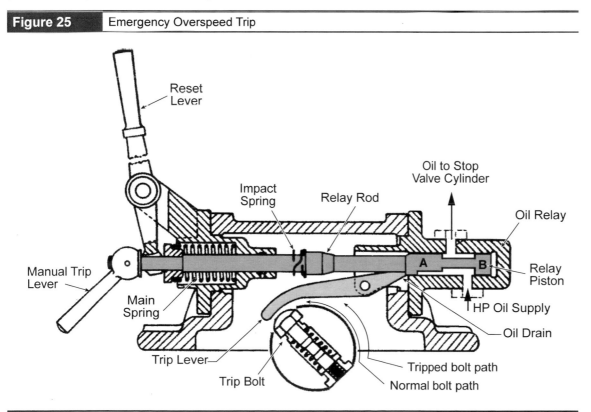

When the turbine speed increases to the trip setting, usually 110% of operating speed, the following occurs:

- centrifugal force overcomes the bolt spring tension,
- the bolt moves to the trip position and strikes the tripping lever,
- this unlatches the relay rod,
- the main spring moves the relay to the tripped position,
- piston "A" opens the stop valve oil-port to drain, and
- piston "B" closes off the high-pressure oil inlet port

Figure 26 shows another bolt-type overspeed trip, located at the end of the shaft of a high-pressure turbine. In normal operation, the trip relay piston is down. The supply oil passes through the inlet and outlet ports of the trip relay cylinder and goes to the steam valve actuator. At overspeed condition, the trip bolt trips the latch, allowing the trip relay spring to pull the piston upwards. The oil outlet port becomes open to the drain, thus depressuring the oil supply to the steam valve and causing it to go closed..

Figure 26	Overspeed Trip Gear

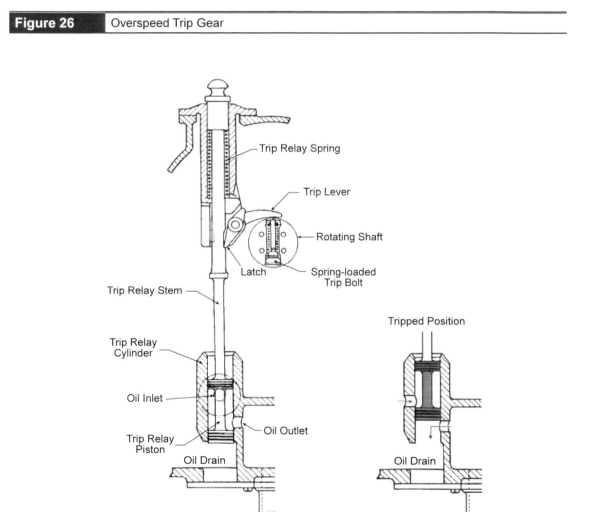

ELECTRONIC OVERSPEED TRIP SYSTEMS

In addition to a mechanical overspeed trip, some turbines also have an electronic overspeed trip system.

As shown in Figure 27, the turbine shaft contains a notched gear. Magnetic speed sensors are mounted to the turbine casing; as the gear teeth pass the sensors, magnetic induction generates an AC voltage that is read by an Electronic Control Module (ECM), which contains pulse counting sensors. The module converts the electronic pulse signals to revolutions per minute. If the speed reaches the overspeed set point, action is initiated to shut the emergency stop valve. To avoid nuisance trips, most electronic systems use three magnetic pickups and the trip does not activate unless at least two of the sensors agree that trip speed has been reached.

Figure 27	Magnetic Speed Pickup Sensor

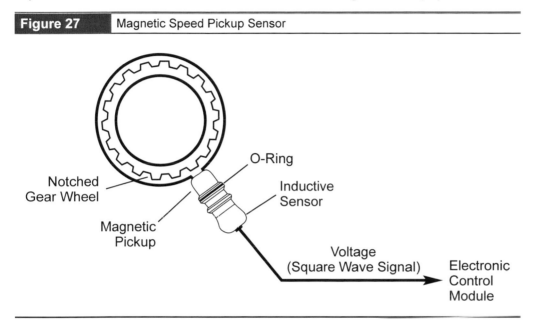

Figure 28 shows a schematic of the system. Electronic signals are sent from the ECM to the trip block, which shuts off the supply of hydraulic oil to the stop valve. A signal is also sent from the ECM to close the steam inlet control valve.

Figure 28	Electro-Hydraulic Control System

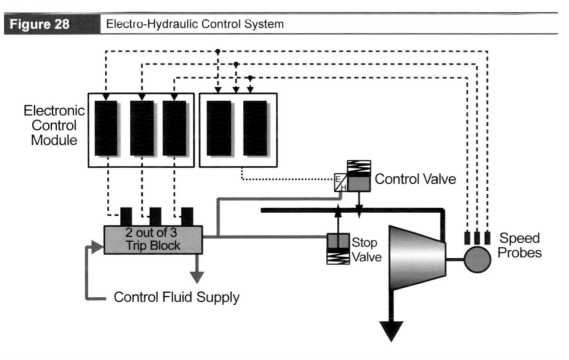

OBJECTIVE 7

Explain the sequence followed for the cold start-up and shutdown of a non-condensing steam turbine.

STARTING A NON-CONDENSING TURBINE

1. If the turbine is equipped with a pressure lubricating system operated by a separately driven oil pump, then start the pump. Verify that sufficient oil pressures and flows are established. On large turbines, the lube oil system should be started several hours before beginning to roll the turbine.

2. If the bearings use a ring oiler, check oil levels in the bearing sumps. If a pressure lubrication system is used, check the oil level in the main oil reservoir.

3. Make sure all condensate is drained from steam and exhaust lines. If these are drained by traps, open the bypass lines around the traps.

4. Open turbine casing drains.

5. Slowly open the shutoff valve between the turbine and the exhaust line.

6. Check that the governor linkages are well lubricated, and grease cups, if used, are filled.

7. If bearing oil sumps or oil reservoirs are water cooled, then turn on the cooling water system.

8. Commission the unit that the turbine is driving, as per the manufacturers recommended procedure.

9. Open the throttle valve part way to start the turbine rotor turning. Close the valve again to the point where the rotor turns slowly. Listen carefully for any noise indicating that the rotor is rubbing against the casing. If oiler rings are used, check to see that the rings are operating. If a pressurized oil system is used, check the oil flow at each bearing.

10. If no unusual noises or problems are detected, increase the turbine speed to 200-300 r/min. Maintain this speed for about half an hour to allow rotor and casing to approach operating temperature. For small turbines, warm-up time will be less, for large turbines, the time could be longer.

11. Increase turbine speed rapidly through critical speeds to next warm-up or soaking speed (per manufacturer's recommendations). When warm-up is complete, open the manual throttle valve until the governor takes control, as indicated by the movement of the governor linkage. Then open the stop valve completely.

12. Slowly adjust the governor to increase the speed until the turbine trips on overspeed, and then adjust the governor back to minimum speed.

13. When the turbine speed has decreased to about 20% below normal operating speed, reset the stop valve and the trip gear.

14. Slowly open the stop valve until the governor takes over, open the stop valve completely and adjust the governor to operating speed.

15. If a main oil pump driven by the turbine is installed, the separately driven auxiliary oil pump may now be shut down. Check oil pressures and flows again.

16. Close steam line drains, trap bypasses and casing drains.

17. Gradually increase the load on the turbine.

18. Enter in the logbook the date, time, and trip rev/min of the turbine.

STOPPING A NON-CONDENSING TURBINE

1. Reduce the turbine load to zero.

2. If a separately driven auxiliary oil pump is used, start it.

3. Shut off the steam supply to the turbine by manually closing the throttle valve.

4. When the turbine has come to a rest, close the exhaust line valve.

5. Keep oil pumps running until bearings have cooled according to the manufacturer's instructions. When oil temperature begins to drop, reduce or shut off the cooling water to the oil coolers.

OBJECTIVE 8

Explain the sequence followed for the cold start-up and the shutdown of a condensing and extracting steam turbine.

STARTING A CONDENSING & EXTRACTION TURBINE

1. Make sure the main oil tank contains sufficient high quality turbine lubricating oil.

2. Commission the external heating system for the lubricating oil supply tank, if so equipped. The lube oil should be at the minimum temperature recommended by the turbine manufacturer, usually in the 35°C to 40°C range.

3. Start the lubricating oil pump two to three hours before steam is admitted to the turbine. The pump supplies lubricating oil to the bearings in the range of 140 to 150 kPa. Check the lube oil return sight glasses to make sure that each bearing is receiving a good supply of oil.

4. Warm up the main supply and extraction steam lines to the turbine by opening drain valves. If slugs of water are admitted into the turbine at high velocity, they can cause severe damage to the rotor.

5. Establish a level in the surface condenser by adding demineralized water. Commission the surface condenser level control system. Continue adding demineralized water until the turbine is operating and producing steam condensate or adequate steam condensate is provided through the gland steam system.

6. Start the cooling water pump and establish cooling water flow through the surface condenser, gland steam condenser and the air ejector condenser (although the ejector condenser is normally cooled with condensate from the extraction pumps).

7. Start the extraction (condensate) pump and circulate condensate through the surface and gland steam condensers.

8. Start the jacking oil pump which supplies lubricating oil, at 8000 to 10 000 kPa, to the bottom of the bearings to float and lift the turbine shaft.

9. Commission the turning or barring gear.

10. Commission the unit that the turbine is driving.

11. Admit sealing steam to the turbine glands.

12. Put the air ejector into operation and draw a partial vacuum 50 kPa absolute of mercury on the condenser or start the mechanical vacuum pump.

13. Verify that all the turbine trips have been satisfied and then reset the governor. Watch to make sure that the extraction valves go wide open, which will allow full steam flow to the condensing section of the turbine.

14. Unblock the extraction steam block valve.

15. Open the throttle or steam admission valve just enough to start the turbine rotating. The barring gear will now disengage and automatically shut down. It is essential to ensure the turning gear is disengaged and LOCKED OUT.

16. Increase the turbine speed to 200 to 300 r/min. Maintain this speed while checking around the turbine, listening and looking, for any unusual noises or vibrations. Follow the manufacturer's recommended startup procedure. If condensing - ensure maximum vacuum.

Note: You must follow the warm through timing prescribed by the manufacturer. Also observe sliding FT movement and rotor expansion rate to stator clearance!

17. Gradually admit more steam to the turbine to slowly increase the speed. If any unexpected vibrations do occur, then decrease the speed and continue warming up the turbine until it runs smoothly, when the speed is increased again. Monitor the turbine vibration panel, if so equipped.

18. Shut off the supply of demineralized water, once a normal level is established in the surface condenser.

19. When the governor takes over, open the throttle valve completely. Adjust gland steam, if used.

20. When the oil has reached normal operating temperature, admit cooling water to the oil coolers to maintain the desired oil temperature. Shut off the external heating system for the lubricating oil supply tank, if so equipped.

21. All drain valves may now be closed.

22. Adjust the extraction valve to give the desired extraction and condensing flows.

STOPPING A CONDENSING & EXTRACTION TURBINE

1. Gradually reduce the turbine load to zero.

2. Shut off the supply of steam to the turbine by manually closing the main inlet and the extraction block valves.

3. Shut off the air ejectors and break the condenser vacuum.

4. Shut off the gland condenser steam.

5. Open the demineralized water supply and verify that a normal level is being maintained in the surface condenser.

6. Open the steam drain valves.

7. Start the jacking oil pump.

8. Start the turning (barring) gear.

9. When the machine has cooled sufficiently, stop the cooling water pump.

10. After the required barring time, shut down the barring gear. It should disengage automatically, but check for proper disengagement.

11. When the shaft has fully stopped rotating, shut down the jacking oil pump

12. Shut off the lubricating oil pump.

CHAPTER 2 - QUESTIONS

1. Sketch and describe a typical lubricating oil system for a turbo-generator.

2. Give a brief explanation for the use of a barring gear on a large turbine shaft.

3. Sketch and describe a condensing turbine circuit. Include in your description how this type of system improves the overall efficiency of the system.

4. Describe three methods of turbine speed governing.

5. Make a simple sketch of an electronic turbine overspeed trip system and explain its operation.

6. Describe the procedure you would follow to start up a large condensing/extraction turbine.

7. Define the following terms applied to steam turbines governors.
   a) Isochronous
   b) Hunting
   c) Droop
   d) Mechanical-hydraulic governor system

8. Explain the principle of operation of speed-sensitive and pressure-sensitive governors.

9. Explain the meaning of throttle and nozzle governing.

ANSWERS: All answers are found within the content of the chapter.

Turbine Condenser Systems

LEARNING OUTCOME

When you complete this chapter you should be able to:

Explain typical designs, components and operating principles of steam turbine condensers.

LEARNING OBJECTIVES

Here is what you should be able to do when you complete each objective:

1. *Explain the purposes of a turbine condenser in a steam plant cycle and describe a typical condensing circuit, with operating temperatures and pressures.*

2. *Explain the design, operation and applications of the jet condenser, including the ejector type.*

3. *Explain the design, operation and applications of the surface condenser, including air cooled and water-cooled, down flow and central flow.*

4. *Describe construction details for surface condensers, including shells, tube attachment, supports, and allowances for expansion.*

5. *Explain the effects of air in a condenser and describe the design and operation of single and two-stage air ejectors. Explain the detection of condenser air leaks. Explain vacuum pumps.*

6. *Explain the devices and operating considerations used to protect a condenser against high backpressure, high condensate level, and cooling water contamination. Describe a cooling water leak test.*

7. *Describe the operating conditions and corresponding design considerations for condensate extraction pumps and cooling water pumps.*

8. *Describe a feed water heater system in conjunction with a steam condenser and explain the designs of low-pressure and high-pressure feed water heaters.*

OBJECTIVE 1

Explain the purposes of a condenser in a steam plant cycle and describe a typical condensing circuit, with operating temperatures and pressures.

PURPOSE OF THE CONDENSER

The primary purpose of a condenser in a steam plant is to improve the overall thermal efficiency of the plant by producing and maintaining a vacuum at the turbine exhaust, thus allowing the steam to expand to a lower pressure. This allows the turbine to recover more of the heat energy from the steam and, therefore, do more work per kg of steam.

A secondary purpose is to reduce thermal losses by condensing the exhaust steam to produce condensate that can be returned to the boiler as feedwater. This reduces the demand on the feedwater treatment processes.

A third "purpose: (although it's more of a side benefit of the condenser operation) is to remove air and other non-condensible gases from the steam/condensate, thus reducing their presence in the systems downstream of the turbine and condenser. In effect, the condenser acts like a deaerator.

SIMPLE CONDENSING STEAM CYCLE

A large percentage of the electricity generated in the world is produced in power stations using generators driven by condensing steam turbines. Figure 1 is a simple diagram of the steam cycle in such a plant. The boiler burns fuel to generate steam and the turbine converts the energy in the steam into mechanical work.

Figure 1	Simple Steam Plant Cycle

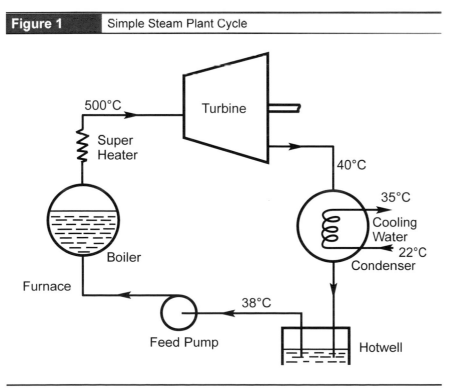

The largest heat exchanger in the steam plant is the condenser. It condenses the turbine exhaust steam back to water, which returns to the boiler as feedwater.

Condensing the steam is the largest single heat loss in the steam cycle. This is because the latent heat of the steam entering the condenser is transferred to the cooling water and then dissipated (and lost) to the atmosphere via a cooling tower.

Condensing the steam must occur at the lowest practical pressure. This enables the turbine to extract the maximum amount of work from the steam. To achieve this, the condenser must be capable of maintaining a vacuum in the region of 710 mm mercury or 6.9 kPa abs, while handling a full load of exhaust steam from the turbine. The condenser will do this most efficiently if latent heat only is removed from the steam, which means the condensate temperature should be as close as possible to the steam temperature.

Further, the cooling water circulated through the condenser will be most efficiently utilized when the difference between its exit temperature and the steam inlet temperature is a minimum.

The efficiency of a turbine may be increased by 50% by adding a condenser. If the exhaust steam can be used for heating or process work, the overall plant efficiency is even higher. Typical thermal efficiencies are 20% when exhausting to atmosphere, 30% when condensing, and 80% or better when the exhaust steam is used for heating or process work.

OBJECTIVE 2

Explain the design, operation and applications of the jet condenser, including the ejector type.

CONDENSER TYPES

Condensers can be divided into two main groups, "Contact" and "Surface". Contact condensers, also called "Jet" condensers, operate by bringing exhaust steam and cooling water into direct contact with each other. The steam mingles with the cooling water, condenses, and the condensate leaves the condenser with the cooling water.

Surface condensers are the more common type. They interpose a surface between the exhaust steam and the cooling water so they never contact each other. The cooling water is circulated through small diameter tubes. The exhaust steam flows over and around these tubes and the condensate is collected from the bottom of the condenser shell. Both of these condenser types can be subdivided, with each type having a specific application.

CONTACT (JET) CONDENSERS

Figure 2 is a simple illustration of jet condenser operation.

Figure 2	Jet Condenser

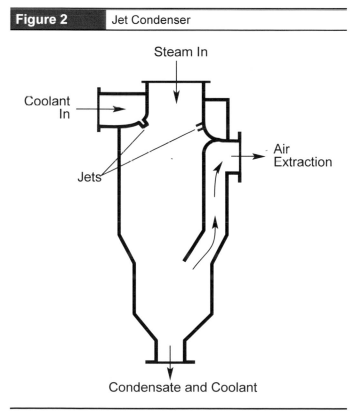

Condensate and Coolant

As stated, jet condensers use the principle of spraying cooling water into direct contact with the incoming exhaust steam in order to condense it. The combined cooling water (coolant) and condensed steam (condensate) drain to the hotwell.

The boiler feedwater pump takes suction from the hotwell and sends the quantity of feed required by the boiler. Any excess condensate usually overflows (or is pumped) into the cooling pond where it is cooled and returned to the condenser as cooling water.

Figure 3 shows two different applications of jet condensers.

- Figure 3(a) is referred to as a "low-level jet condenser", due to its lower elevation and its requirement for a pump to remove the water from the condenser. The air is also pumped from the condenser. Cooling water flow to the condenser does not require a pump; the condenser vacuum (ie. less than atmospheric pressure) induces cooling water to flow from the cooling pond, which is at atmospheric pressure.

- In Figure 3(b) the condenser is located about 10.5 m above the hotwell. No pump is required to remove the condensate, since the pressure head of the water in the condenser outlet pipe is sufficient to overcome the vacuum in the condenser and allow flow into the hotwell. Due to head pressure, the cooling water must be pumped into the condenser.

Direct contact condensers have the definite disadvantage of requiring the cooling water to be chemically treated to avoid contamination of the condensate and thus maintain acceptable feedwater purity. For this reason, there are relatively few direct contact condensers in service.

Figure 3	Jet Condenser Applications

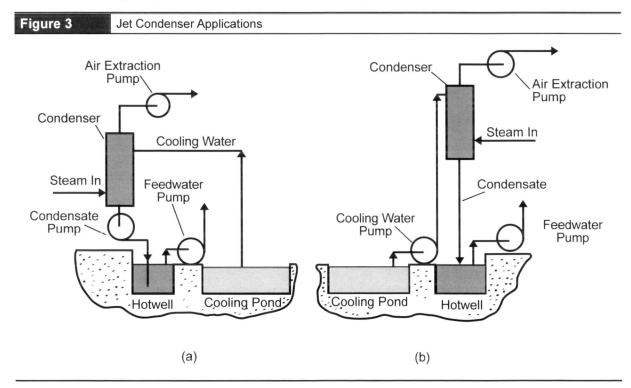

(a)   (b)

Barometric Jet Condensers

The condenser shown in Fig. 3(b), where the condenser elevation above the hotwell is sufficient to allow the water to flow out by gravity, is commonly called a "barometric condenser".

Figure 4 illustrates this design in more detail.

The pipe that carries the condensate down to the hotwell is called the tailpipe or the barometric leg. The required (design) length of this tailpipe will depend upon atmospheric conditions (ie. the average barometric pressure) and the required vacuum in the condenser. Normally the length is about 10.5 m.

The steam from the turbine exhaust enters the bottom, side of the condenser and rises up through trays, where it is met and contacted by falling cooling water. The steam condenses and falls to the bottom and into the tailpipe with the cooling water. Air and other non-condensable gases are drawn from the top of the condensing space, either by a vacuum pump or by a steam ejector system.

Figure 4	Barometric Condenser

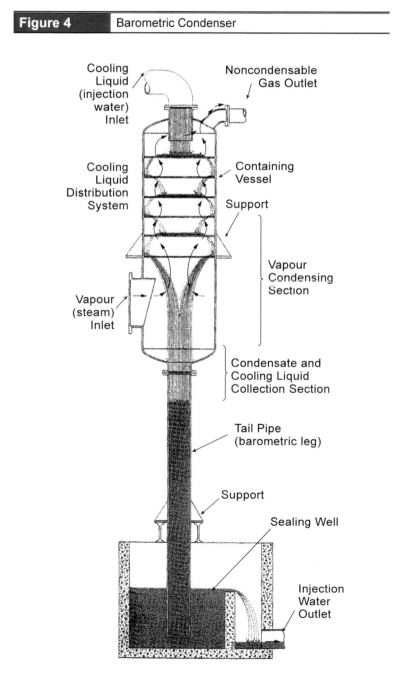

Ejector Condenser

Figure 5 illustrates a special design of jet condenser, called the ejector condenser.

In this design, the cooling water flows downward in the condenser and passes through a series of convergent nozzles. The nozzles increase the velocity and create corresponding areas of low pressure (ie. vacuum). This creates a lower pressure inside the condenser than in the turbine exhaust and this pressure differential causes exhaust steam to flow into the condenser. The steam meets the cooling water and condenses. The ejector condenser is suitable for moderate vacuum only.

Figure 5   Ejector Condenser

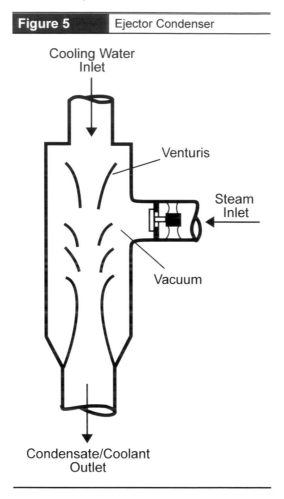

OBJECTIVE 3

Explain the design, operation and applications of the surface condenser, including air-cooled and water-cooled, downflow and central flow.

SURFACE CONDENSERS

Surface condensers operate by placing a heat transfer surface between the steam and the cooling medium. The steam and cooling medium never contact each other. Heat is transferred from the steam, through the separating surface to the cooling medium. The cooling medium may be water or air.

In a water cooled condenser the transfer surface is a bank or sections of tubes within the condenser shell. The cooling medium (water) flows through the tubes, while the steam occupies the shell and surrounds the outside surface of the tubes. The cooling water may be supplied from a river, in which case the water need not be cooled for reuse, but simply discharged back into the river at a point downstream of the water intake.

Figure 6 shows a surface condenser that uses river water for cooling.

Figure 6	River Water Cooled Condenser

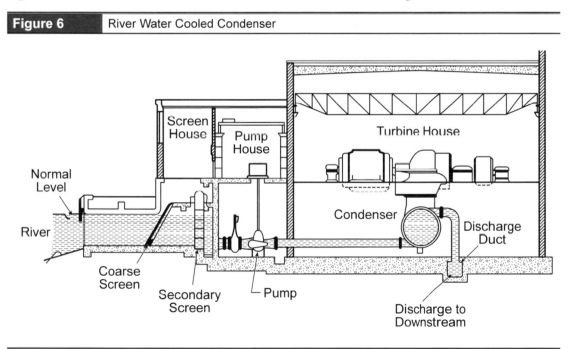

When a reusable supply of cooling water is used, the water must be cooled down after absorbing heat in the condenser. Figure 7 shows a system that incorporates a cooling tower for this purpose. The "hot" cooling water outlet from the condenser passes through the cooling tower, which uses water spray and evaporation to remove heat from the cooling water. The cooled water drops into a pond and from there is pumped again through the condenser. Smaller systems may use a smaller design of cooling tower or may use overhead aerial, fan-type coolers.

Figure 7	Condenser using Cooling Water from Cooling Tower

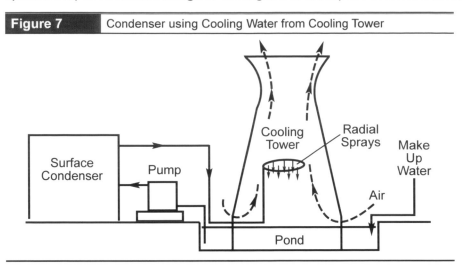

Figure 8 shows an **air-cooled condenser**. This is a common design in power plants and waste energy plants and is suitable for a wide range of plant sizes. The condenser consists of several bundles of finned tubes through which the exhaust steam flows. Usually the bundles are arranged in inverted "V" sections, with steam headers supplying the exhaust steam at the apex of each section. Each section may have a single row of tubes or multiple rows. Cooling (condensing) air is supplied upwards from large horizontal fans located below the tube bundles.

Figure 8	Air Cooled Condenser

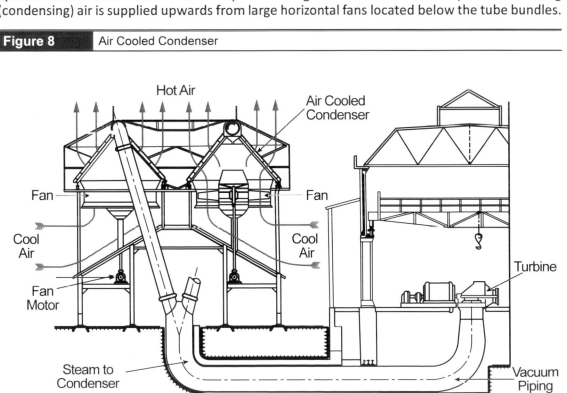

Figure 9 shows part of a tube bundle. In this case the tubes have an oval cross-section, but in many cases they are circular. The external fins increase the surface area available for heat transfer.

Figure 9	Nest of Finned Air Cooled Tubes

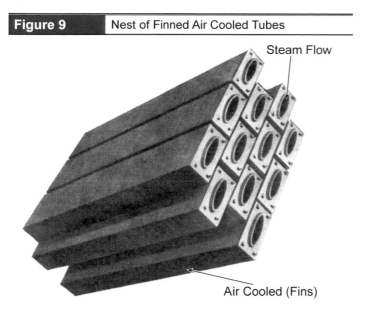

Steam Flow

Air Cooled (Fins)

Downflow Condensers

Shell-and-tube surface condensers are often described according to the direction of the steam and condensate in the shell. The term "Downflow" refers to a condenser in which the steam enters at the top of the shell and the condensate exits at the bottom.

Figure 10 shows one downflow pattern. In this case the steam enters at one end and the condensate exits at the bottom center, into the hotwell section. Non-condensable gases accumulate and leave at the opposite end from the steam inlet. The cooling water enters at the top of the water box and makes four passes through the U-tubes before exiting at the bottom.

Figure 10	Surface Condenser (Downflow Design)

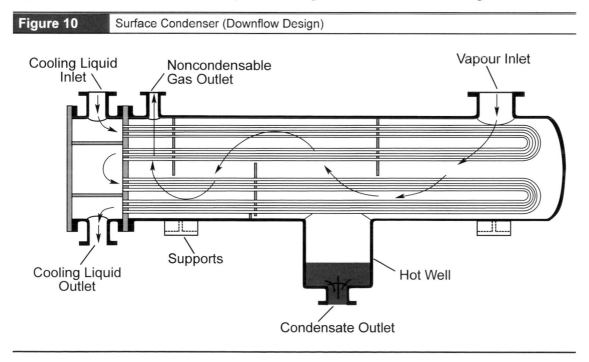

Cooling Liquid Inlet

Noncondensable Gas Outlet

Vapour Inlet

Cooling Liquid Outlet

Supports

Hot Well

Condensate Outlet

Figure 11 also shows a downflow condenser, but in this design the steam enters at the top center of the shell. Vertical steam lanes (ie. strategically placed vertical spaces between tubes) allow some of the inlet steam to flow down to the hotwell to heat and deaerate the condensate cascading into the hotwell.

Figure 11	Downflow Condenser with Center Inlet

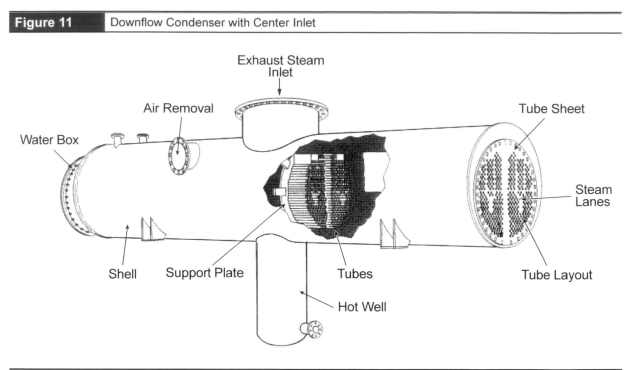

In downflow condensers, the descending steam is usually directed into the center by air extraction baffles, while the rising air (and other gases) are directed under the baffles. The heavy concentration of tubes under the air removal baffles prevents the steam from entering the air removal equipment (ejectors or mechanical pumps). This can cause poor vacuum when starting the turbine.

Figure 12 shows the cross-section of another downflow condenser design.

- This horizontal, shell-and-tube exchanger has the exhaust steam entering at the top.
- Cooling water flows through the tubes and extracts heat from the steam and the condensate formed falls to the hotwell.
- A controlled water level is maintained in the hotwell. The cross-section shows the steam lanes, including the large central lane, which allow steam to the hotwell to maintain the condensate temperature near the saturation temperature.
- Air is extracted from beneath side baffles in the bottom section of the shell.

Note: In a surface condenser the flow of steam is created by condensation of the steam, which creates a low pressure zone, and by the location of the air extraction points. The steam will tend to flow towards the extraction points, which are located in lower pressure areas.

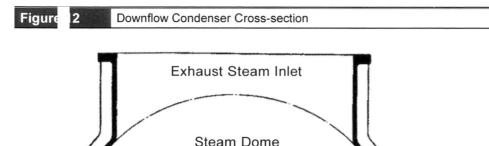

Figure 12   Downflow Condenser Cross-section

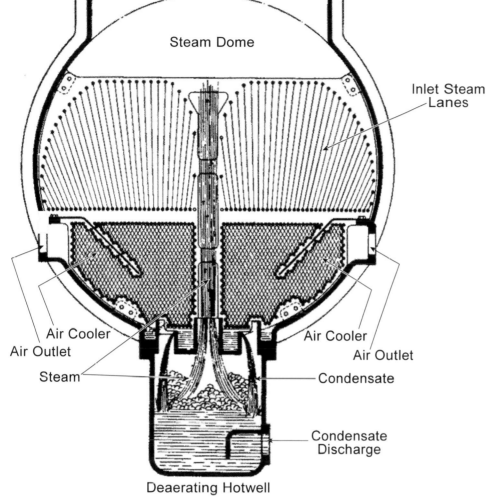

Central Flow Condensers

A central flow condenser is one in which the flow of steam is radial, from the outside toward the center of the condenser. They are often referred to as "radial flow" condensers. Air extraction is from the center, which encourages the radial steam flow. Condensate flow is downwards and is removed from the bottom hotwell.

Figure 13 shows one design of a central flow condenser.

- The steam enters at the top and occupies the volute-shaped shell.
- The cooling water flows first through the central pass, below the inverted "V" baffle, creating a low-pressure area (due to condensing steam), which encourages steam to flow toward the center.
- Air extraction is from the center of the tube nest, which also encourages the steam to flow radially inward.

Figure 13   Central (Radial) Flow Condenser

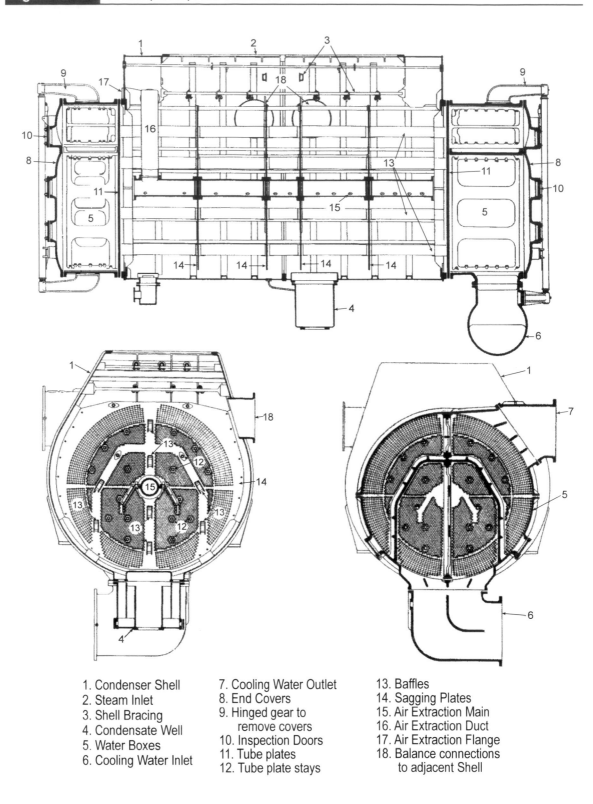

1. Condenser Shell
2. Steam Inlet
3. Shell Bracing
4. Condensate Well
5. Water Boxes
6. Cooling Water Inlet
7. Cooling Water Outlet
8. End Covers
9. Hinged gear to remove covers
10. Inspection Doors
11. Tube plates
12. Tube plate stays
13. Baffles
14. Sagging Plates
15. Air Extraction Main
16. Air Extraction Duct
17. Air Extraction Flange
18. Balance connections to adjacent Shell

OBJECTIVE 4

Describe construction details for surface condensers, including shells, tube attachment, supports, and allowances for expansion.

CONDENSER CONSTRUCTION

Figure 14 shows the main components of a surface condenser.

This is a downflow design with steam entering at the top. The hotwell is at the bottom, with two condensate pump connections. Each side of the condenser has an air ejector connection. The cooling water enters at the bottom of the water box and exits the same end at the top.

Figure 14	Surface Condenser

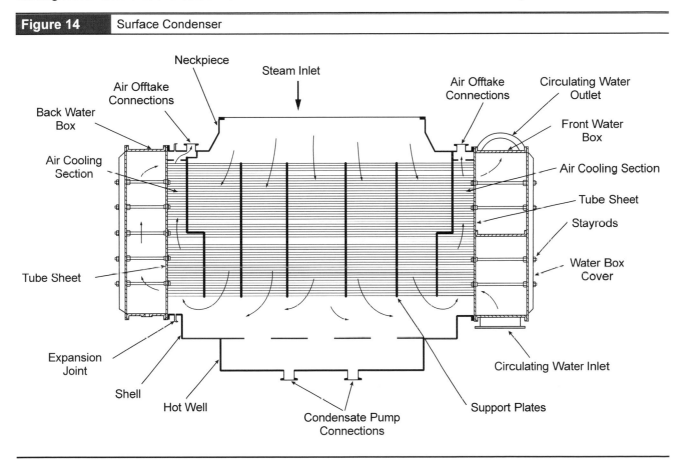

Condenser Shell

The cross-section of the condenser shell may be cylindrical, oval, or rectangular (for large shells). The shell, exhaust neck and hotwell are welded steel, reinforced with external ribs. The exhaust neck and hotwell are welded to the shell. The support plates, welded to the shell, support the shell and the tubes, plus dampen tube vibrations.

Provision must be made for relative movement between the exhaust flange and the machine foundations. In smaller designs this is done by bolting the condenser feet rigidly to the foundations and fitting an expansion joint, such as a corrugated bellows, between the exhaust flange and the condenser inlet flange. Larger designs bolt the condenser directly to the machine exhaust but support the condenser feet on springs.

The condenser shell in Figure 15(a) sits on a solid foundation and has an expansion joint between the shell and the turbine.

The condenser in Figure 15(b) is mounted on spring support feet.

Figure 15	Condenser Expansion Joint and Spring Supports

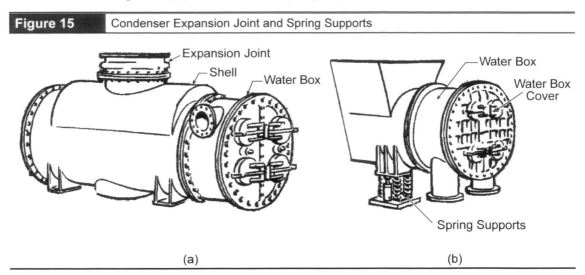

(a)   (b)

The shell may also be fitted with an expansion joint to allow longitudinal movement. This is done when the design requires the tubes to be expanded into their tube sheets at both ends. Differential expansion between the tubes and the shell will cause excessive stress and possible leaks, unless an expansion joint is installed.

Figure 16 shows a tube that is expanded into both tubesheets plus an expansion joint in the shell, which eliminates stresses on the tubes.

Figure 16	Expanded Condenser Tube and Condenser Shell Expansion Joint

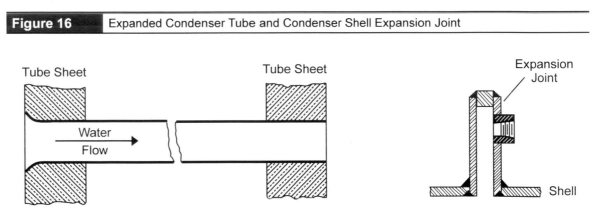

Condenser Tube Plates

Condenser tube plates (aka tubesheets) are usually made of Admiralty brass (about 69% copper, 30% zinc, 1% tin) or Muntz metal (about 60% copper, 40% zinc, plus a trace of iron), 1 to 2 inches thick. They are bolted to the shell flanges with collar bolts, as shown in Fig. 17. Rubber gaskets are installed between the shell and tube plate and between the tube plate and water box. Collar bolts are used to fasten the tube plate to the shell and after the tubes have all been installed, the water box is placed over the collar bolts and fastened. The collar bolts allow the water box to be opened, without disturbing the shell-to-tube plate joint.

Figure 17   Collar Bolt and Tubesheet

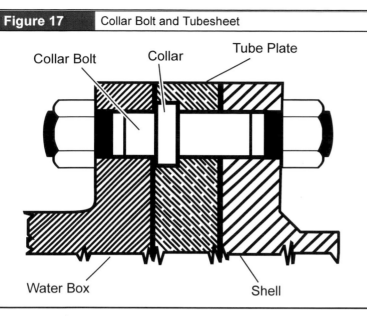

Tube plates made of brass or Muntz metal, for large condensers, are very expensive and may not be available in the required sizes. An alternative is to use welded, steel plates with stainless steel cladding.

Figure 18 shows a welded water box with the tube plate welded in position and the protective cladding on the waterside.

Figure 18   Water Box Welded Construction

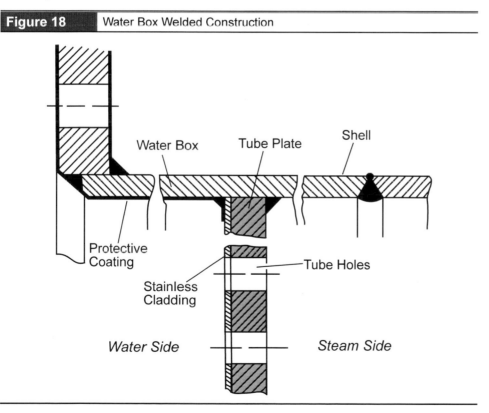

Condenser Tubes

A larger heating surface is most easily obtained by using small diameter tubes. These also give the best heat transfer, since the required wall thickness is less. The tubes may be of Stainless Steel, Admiralty brass, aluminum brass, or cupro-nickel. Typical tube sizes 6, 19, 22 and 25 mm diameter.

The tubes may be installed with ferrules, metallic and fiber packings, by expanding, or with combinations of these, such as inlet end expanded and belled and the outlet end packed or ferruled. Figures 19 and 20 show these methods. In some condensers, when plates and tubes are made of the same material, the tubes are welded into the tube plate.

Since allowance must be made for differential expansion of tubes and shell, one advantage of packed tube ends is they allow the tube to move axially in the packing. Expanded or welded tubes may require the shell to have an expansion joint as explained earlier.

Figure 19	Tube End Fastening Methods

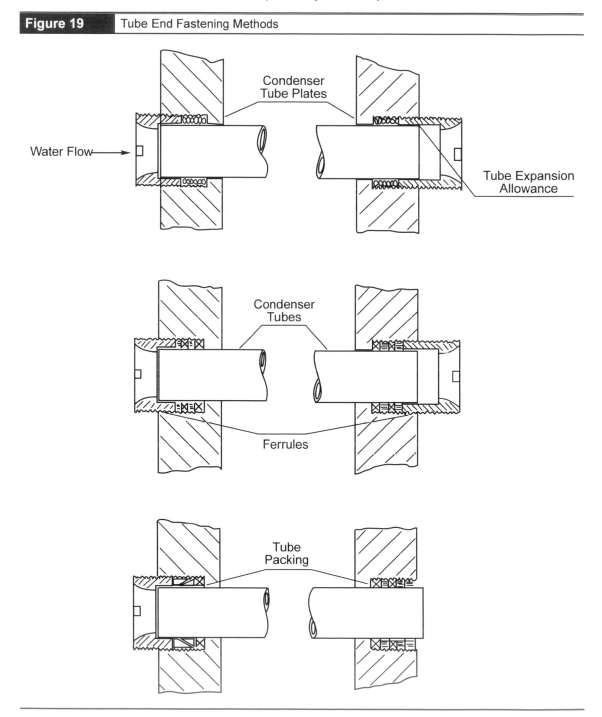

Figure 20 Tube End Fastening Methods

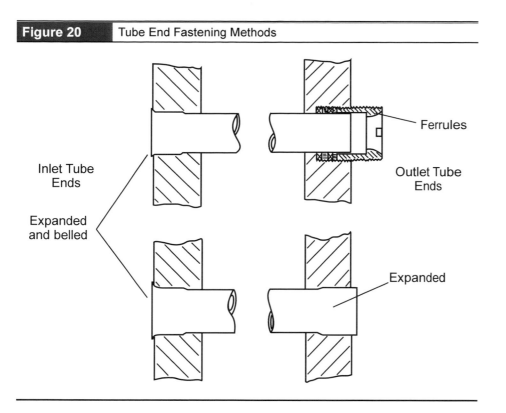

Ferrules

Inlet Tube
Ends

Outlet Tube
Ends

Expanded
and belled

Expanded

Water Boxes

The classic material for water boxes is cast iron. Water boxes are usually bolted to the shell with the tube plate collar bolts (as seen in Fig. 17). Hinges on end covers allow them to be easily opened for access to the tube plate and tubes for maintenance. Large water boxes have small access doors for inspection, tube cleaning and tube plugging.

For economical and practical reasons, the water boxes of large condensers are made of steel and are either welded to the shell or are an extension of the shell, as shown in Figure 15. When a corrosive coolant is used, such as seawater, the water box has a coating of rubber or glass-fiber reinforced epoxy resin to prevent corrosion.

The main purpose of the stay bolts, or stay rods in the water boxes (see Fig. 14) is to support the tube sheet against the condenser vacuum.

OBJECTIVE 5

Explain the effects of air in a condenser and describe the design and operation of single and two-stage air ejectors. Explain the detection of condenser air leaks. Explain vacuum pumps.

AIR EJECTORS

Since the pressure inside a condenser shell is well below that of the surrounding atmosphere, there is opportunity for atmospheric air leakage through glands, joints, and flanges. Other non-condensable gases may be carried in with the steam from the boilers.

Air must be removed continuously. If allowed to accumulate in the steam space of the condenser, the air will reduce the vacuum (ie. the pressure will increase). The air may also blanket part of the cooling surface, thus reducing heat transfer. The usual method of extracting air is with an air ejector. In some cases a reciprocating or rotary air pump may be used. The condenser in Figure 21 shows air extraction points from a downflow condenser. They are located below baffle plates that are designed to trap the air.

Figure 21	Downflow Condenser - Air Extraction Locations

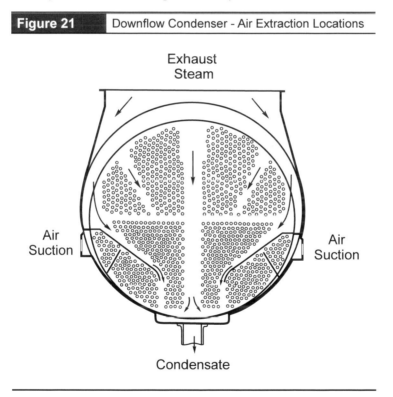

One of the most common devices to continuously remove air is the steam-jet ejector. Figure 22 shows an external view, and Figure 23 a cross-sectional view of a single-stage ejector.

In the air ejector, high-pressure steam is allowed to expand through a nozzle, thus converting its pressure energy into kinetic energy and producing a high velocity jet at the nozzle discharge. From the nozzle, the steam enters a venturi tube, which increases the velocity and creates a lower pressure at the entrance to the ejector. This draws air in from the condenser, entrains it and carries it out with the steam. Most condensers have baffle plates to guide the air/steam mixture to special coolers at the air extraction points. The coolers condense the steam and recover it as condensate, leaving the air to escape to atmosphere.

Figure 22	Single-Stage Steam-Jet Ejector	Figure 23	Sectional View of Ejector

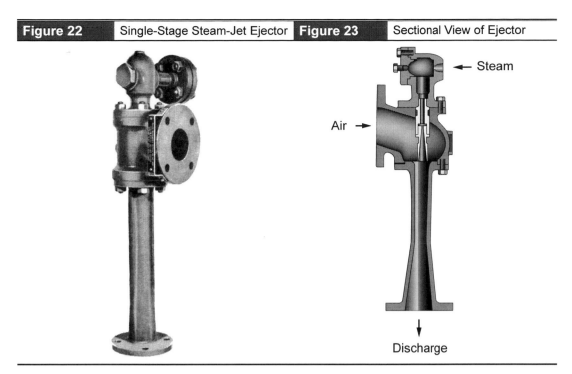

Figure 24 shows a more efficient, two-stage steam-jet air ejector, with two ejectors in series. Each ejector has a nozzle and venturi and the air discharging from the first stage becomes the inlet for the second stage. Second stage pressure is higher than the first stage. Each stage has a vertical two-pass shell-and-tube cooler, which surrounds the central venturi. The purpose of the cooler is to condense the steam from the mixture and collect it at the cooler outlet.

Figure 24	Two-Stage Steam Ejector

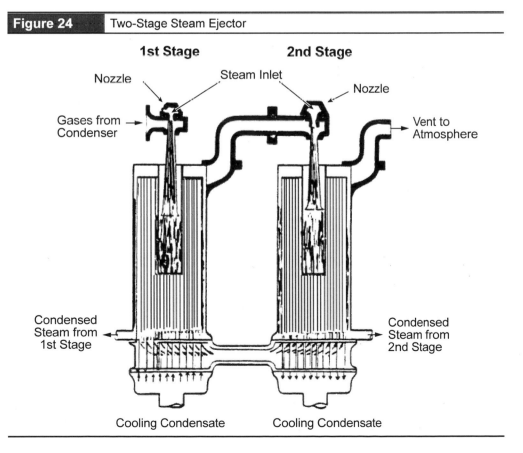

Figure 25 shows the operation in more detail.

- High-pressure steam enters at A and passes through nozzle B.
- The nozzle and venturi effect at section E draws the non-condensable gases from the condenser into the ejector through D.
- The steam and gases are directed over the cooler tubes, F, several times by the baffles, K. The steam is condensed by the cooling water and the gases leave the first stage and enter the second stage through G.
- This process is repeated in the second stage, with the gases being finally vented to atmosphere through L.
- The cooling water enters at I_1, and flows up through the inner tubes, H, to the top of the cooler.
- The closed top directs the water back down through the outer tubes, F, to the first chamber, J_1, and then to the second chamber (J_2).
- The water flows through the second stage in the same pattern, before leaving I_2.

Figure 25	Two-Stage Steam-Jet Air Ejector

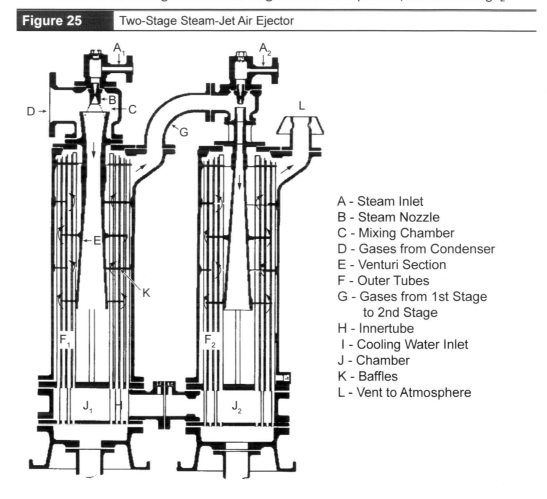

A - Steam Inlet
B - Steam Nozzle
C - Mixing Chamber
D - Gases from Condenser
E - Venturi Section
F - Outer Tubes
G - Gases from 1st Stage
      to 2nd Stage
H - Innertube
 I - Cooling Water Inlet
J - Chamber
K - Baffles
L - Vent to Atmosphere

The water used for cooling may be dedicated cooling water, boiler feedwater or condensate. The cooling water for the ejector cooler in Figure 25 is condensate from the extraction pump. When feedwater or condensate are used, the heat from the ejector steam is absorbed into the water, which makes the ejector, in effect, another feedwater heater. This makes efficient use of the ejector steam.

The orifice in the ejector nozzle is small and care must be taken to see that it does not become choked with foreign matter from the steam supply pipes. For this reason, a fine mesh steam strainer is usually fitted upstream of the nozzles.

Figure 26 shows a three-stage ejector, used for even higher vacuums.

Each stage may have its own independent cooler or the three coolers may be arranged, as shown, as a single, three-pass exchanger. In this figure, the cooling water used is condensate, which enters at the bottom and exits at the top. Separate drains remove steam condensate from the three stages to the hotwell of the main condenser. To prevent air being sucked into the hotwell, the third stage drain line has a steam trap and the drains from the first and second stages have U-bends, which act as air seals.

Figure 26	Three-Stage Steam-Jet Ejector

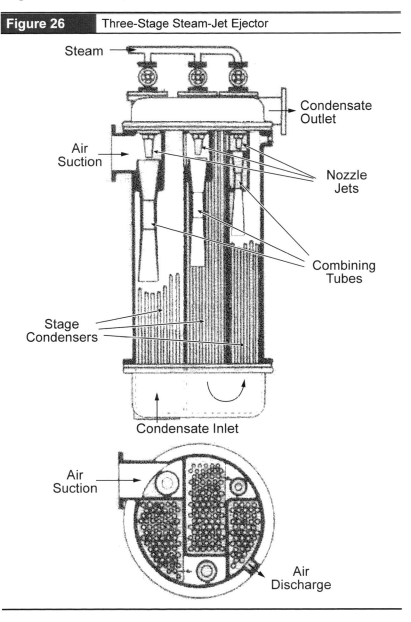

Figure 27 is a very simplified flow diagram, showing one arrangement of the various components of a condenser system, including the extraction pump and air ejector. In this example, condensate from the extraction pump is used to cool the air ejectors. Steam is supplied to the ejector from the turbine supply line. In reality, the steam pressure to the ejectors is usually regulated down to 350 to 1000 kPa.

Figure 27	Flow Diagram

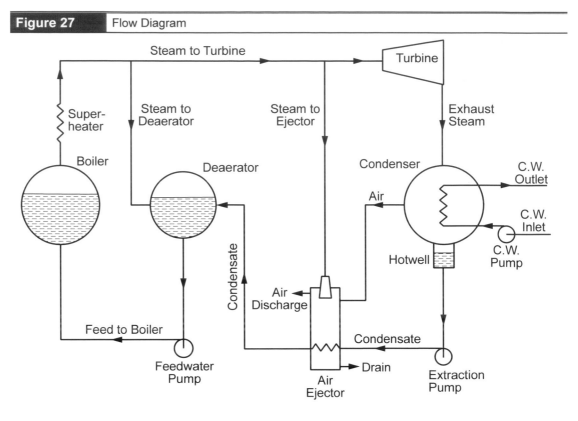

AIR LEAKS

Air leaks will adversely affect condenser performance by increasing condenser pressure with little or no increase in condensate temperature. The air accumulates in the steam space of the condenser and decreases the plant efficiency.

Air leaks may be quite large, up to 5 mm in diameter, before they interfere with the vacuum, since the air ejectors can usually handle smaller leaks. Air leaks can best be located by shutting down both the turbine and the condenser, then filling the condenser, including the steam space, with water.

Common locations for air leaks are:

- flanges that have vacuum on one side and atmospheric pressure on the other
- valves under vacuum; their flanges or packing glands may leak
- shaft packing or seals on the suction side of extraction pumps
- turbine shafts at the vacuum end, due to low sealing steam pressure

Methods used to identify air leaks while the equipment is running, include:

- taping all suspect flanges
- tightening all valve packing
- using smoke to detect leakage points (the smoke will be drawn in at a leak)
- using ultrasonic listening devices

OBJECTIVE 6

Explain the devices and operating considerations used to protect a condenser against high backpressure, high condensate level, and cooling water contamination. Describe a cooling water leak test.

CONDENSER SAFETY DEVICES

A condenser must have certain safety devices, which are designed to protect both the condenser and the turbine exhausting into it. The main dangers to be guarded against include an increase in backpressure, a rise in condensate level, and contamination of the condensate.

Atmospheric Relief Devices

Since the condenser is a closed vessel, it would be quite possible for the backpressure (on the steam turbine and, therefore, inside the condenser) to rise until it was above atmospheric pressure. This would occur, for example, if the cooling water flow stopped while the condenser was in service. Since a condenser shell is not designed to withstand significant positive pressure from the inside, it would soon fail.

The atmospheric relief valve is designed to open and allow steam to escape from the shell if the pressure in the condenser rises above atmospheric. The atmospheric relief must vent the full flow of exhaust steam to atmosphere, so it is very large. Under normal operation this valve is held closed by the difference in pressure between the outside atmosphere and the vacuum in the shell. To ensure that atmospheric air does not leak past the valve into the condenser, the line is usually fitted with a water seal. The relief valve has a test lever, allowing it to be tested at frequent intervals when the machine is off load, ensuring the valve is operating freely.

In very large condensers, where an atmospheric relief valve would not be practical because of size, other devices are used, such as explosion diaphragms or rupture discs on the low-pressure turbine exhaust lines. Other devices include vacuum relays. The vacuum relay is incorporated in the turbine governor system and is usually set to operate between 10 and 40 kPa absolute pressure. The turbine begins to unload at 10 kPa absolute and is fully unloaded at 40 kPa absolute. Another vacuum relay is set to trip the turbine at about 50 kPa absolute.

Condenser Gauge Glass

The gauge glass gives a clear indication of the level of the condensate in the condenser hotwell. The top and bottom of the glass are connected above and below the water level and the whole of the fitting operates under condenser vacuum.

Care must be taken to see that there are no air-leaks in the fitting, particularly through the cocks or valves.

High Water-Level Alarm

The gauge glass is often supplemented by a float operated, high water-level alarm.

A steadily rising condensate level would seal off the air outlet, fill the vacuum space with noncondensable gases, increase the back pressure of the exhaust steam, and decrease turbine output by activating the vacuum unloader relay.

DETECTION OF COOLING WATER LEAKS

If a condenser tube is damaged or a ferrule begins to leak, cooling water may leak into the steam space and contaminate the condensate. Leaks must be quickly detected and corrected. Several methods can be used to detect leaks, with the electrical purity method (conductivity) being the most common.

Very pure water, like condensate, is a nonconductor of electricity, while impure water, like cooling water, is a good conductor. A conductivity meter can detect changes in the conductivity of the condensate and so detect leaks.

Sodium chloride in water can be detected by the silver nitrate test. The addition of a few drops of silver nitrate to salt water immediately creates a milky-white silver chloride precipitate. This is a simple and sensitive test for leakage of salt water into a condenser and is used when the cooling water is salty.

Very small leaks can be tolerated, if the condensate is cleaned up with condensate polishers. When the leak is larger than the polishers can handle, the leak must be repaired.

REPAIR OF COOLING WATER LEAKS

Single-flow type condensers must be taken out of service for repairs. When the turbine is shut down, the water boxes can be drained and the inspection doors opened.

The steam space is filled with clean water, after the supporting or jackscrews are applied to carry the weight of the condenser. When the steam space is full of water, the water will leak out of the leaky tube. Since leaks detected by the conductivity meter may be very small, fluorescein dye (about 10 ppm) can be added to aid detection. The dye glows a fluorescent green in the light of an ultraviolet lamp.

Large condensers are usually double flow, with tubes expanded at both ends. They can be repaired at half load or less. Usually one side is drained and a conductivity measurement indicates if the leaking side is the side still in service or not.

OBJECTIVE 7

Describe the operating conditions and corresponding design considerations for condensate extraction pumps and cooling water pumps.

EXTRACTION OR CONDENSATE PUMPS

The extraction or condensate pump continuously pumps condensate from the condenser hotwell, through the air ejector coolers and low-pressure heaters, into the deaerator.

Extraction pumps are usually centrifugal pumps with two or three stages. Figure 28 is a two-impeller, horizontal, extraction pump with opposed impellers. The opposed impellers work in parallel. Extraction pump suction side seals are usually supplied with pump discharge water to seal the shaft.

Extraction pumps must operate under severe conditions; they must maintain a constant level in the hot well, while pumping nearly boiling water at near zero absolute suction pressure. They must also handle a large range of capacities due to the varying loads of the turbine that is exhausting to the condenser.

Figure 28	Horizontal Extraction Pump

Staggered volutes...hold pump rotar in radial balance

Small diameter casing... heavy section, close bolting assures tight joint

Ample vent... on suction of 1st stage

Stuffing box

Belt thrust bearing double row, angular contact water cooled, oil lubricated

Special water-cooled stuffing box arrangement

Stage arrangement... subjects this stuffing box to first stage pressure only

Ball bearings... oil lubricated

Worthington elastic seal rings... on casing rings and on stage piece

Pump feet ...under bearings near centerline, add strength and eliminate expansion stresses

Wear rings, renewable... tongue and groove joint in lower casing

Opposed impellers.. hold pump in axial hydraulic balance

Horizontally-split casing.. suction and discharge openings in lower half

The extraction pump must pump water that is close to boiling, a condition that requires a very low NPSH (net positive suction head), and exposes the pump to possible cavitation. To reduce cavitation the vertical, well type extraction pump (Fig. 29) is often used. The flange of the well is level with the floor to increase the suction head. The well is airtight with an air-release line to the condenser. These pumps have better performance and experience less cavitation than horizontal pumps.

Figure 29	Vertical Multistage Extraction Pump

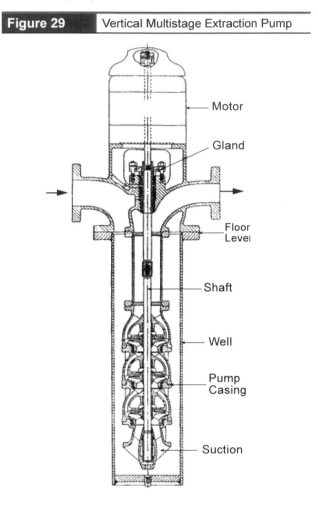

Motor

Gland

Floor Level

Shaft

Well

Pump Casing

Suction

COOLING WATER FLOW

The cooling water circulated through the condenser may come from a river or a lake. In these cases, the cooling water makes one pass through the cooling water system and then is discharged back into the river or lake. This is the most economical cooling system to build and operate, provided the water source is sufficient to supply the required cooling water flows.

If the source of cooling water is limited, the water is circulated through a closed system that includes some means of cooling the water after it leaves the condenser. The methods used to cool the water are cooling ponds or cooling towers. The only water required from a nearby river or lake is makeup water, which compensates for losses due to evaporation, leaks in the system, or blowdown losses.

If a cooling pond is used, the water is pumped from the cooling pond through the condenser and back out to the pond. If the pond is not large enough to adequately cool the water, water sprays are installed in the pond or in the canal leading to the pond. If a cooling tower is used, the water is pumped from the basin of the cooling tower through the condenser and back to the cooling tower.

COOLING WATER PUMPS

The purpose of the cooling water pumps is to circulate the cooling water through the cooling water system and the condenser. After leaving the condenser tubes, the heated cooling water is returned to the river (after first passing through a cooler), cooling pond or a cooling tower.

The most common type of cooling pump is the vertical mixed flow pump, which is illustrated in Figure 30. It is called "mixed flow" because it obtains its pumping action from a mixture of centrifugal force and the lifting effect (due to axial flow) of the impeller vanes. The vertical design removes the need for pump priming since the impeller is submerged in the cooling water. These pumps operate at a low speed, usually 320 to 450 rev/min.

In some applications, horizontal rather than vertical pumps are used. They are centrifugal pumps, usually of the single-stage volute type.

Figure 30	Vertical Mixed Flow Circulating Water Pump

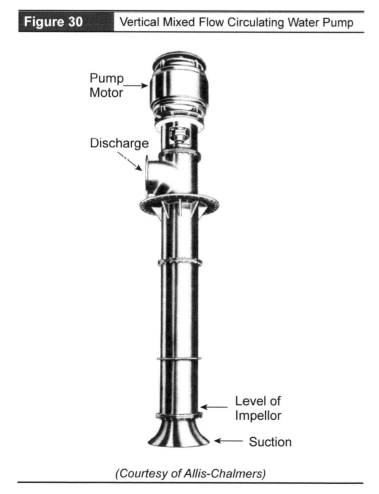

Pump Motor

Discharge

Level of Impellor

Suction

(Courtesy of Allis-Chalmers)

OBJECTIVE 8

Describe a feedwater heater system in conjunction with a steam condenser and explain the designs of low-pressure and high-pressure feedwater heaters.

FEEDWATER HEATERS

The latent heat of the turbine exhaust steam is lost to the condenser cooling water. The application of feedwater heaters, where the latent heat of bleed steam from the turbine is used to heat feedwater, reduces the quantity of steam exhausted to the condenser and thereby increases the overall efficiency of the system. Feedwater heaters are classed as either low-pressure or high-pressure. Low-pressure heaters have the waterside exposed to the discharge pressure of the extraction pump, while the high-pressure heaters have the water side exposed to boiler feedpump pressure.

Figure 31 is an example of a vertical, low-pressure heater.

Low-pressure heaters are usually of the straight-tube design. Tubes and tube-sheets are constructed of brass, the shell of mild steel, and the waterboxes of steel or cast iron. The shell may have an expansion bellows or the tube bank a floating head (as in Fig. 31), which allows for unequal expansion and contraction between the shell and the tubes.

Figure 31	Low Pressure Feedwater Heater

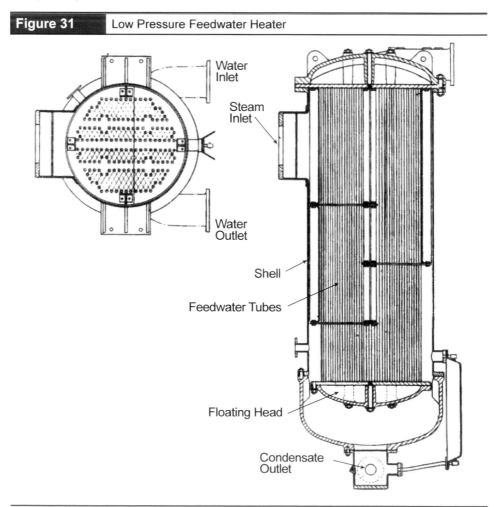

Water Inlet

Steam Inlet

Water Outlet

Shell

Feedwater Tubes

Floating Head

Condensate Outlet

Figure 32 shows one design of a high-pressure heater.

In this design, the boiler feed pump forces the feedwater through the U-tubes, which are made of carbon steel. Steam enters on the shell side of the heater and condensate exits from the bottom. The "U" tube design allows the tubes and shell to expand at different rates without causing stress. The tubes may be expanded or welded to the tube sheet.

Figure 32	High Pressure Feedwater Heater

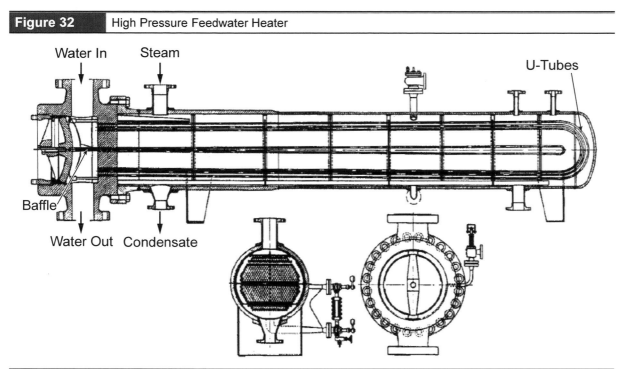

Figure 33 illustrates a horizontal, two-pass heat exchanger with an internal floating head. The floating head, connected to the tube bundle by a tubesheet, fits snugly against the outer exchanger shell, but is free to slide horizontally. The tubes can expand at a different rate than the shell.

Figure 33	Horizontal Feed Heater with Floating Head

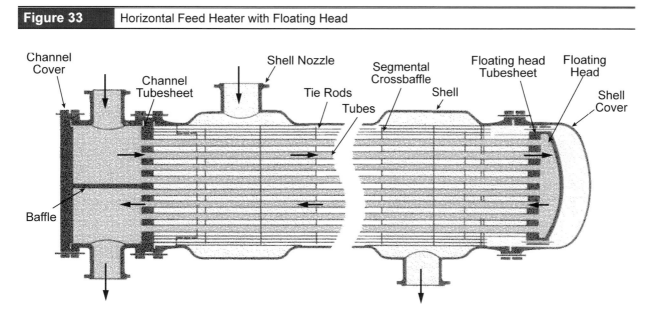

Figure 34 shows the feedwater heater system associated with a large steam turbine and condenser. The condensate from the condenser passes through the air-ejector coolers, drain-cooler, and low-pressure heaters before going to the deaerator. The boiler feed pump then pumps the deaerated water from the deaerator through a series of three high-pressure heaters to the boiler. The high-pressure and low-pressure heaters are all supplied with heating steam that is bled from various stages of the turbine.

Figure 34 Feedwater Heater System

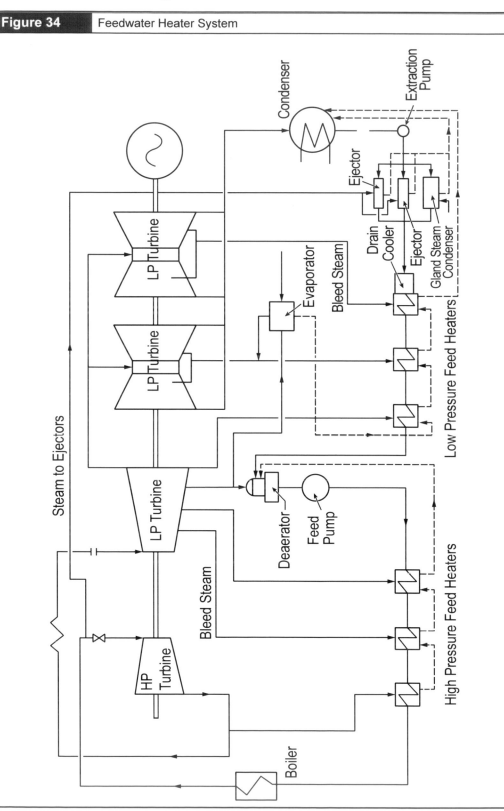

Figure 35 shows the condensate flowing through a six-stage feedwater heating system, from the condenser to the boiler. The temperature of the condensate is shown throughout the system. The bleed steam supplying the heaters is not shown. The dotted lines indicate flashed condensate (ie. steam) from one heater to the next lower pressure heater. The deaerating heater is the 3rd stage of feedwater heating. Overall, the water temperature is raised from 38°C at the condenser hotwell to 255°C entering the economizer of the steam generator.

Notice that there are two levels of high-pressure heater in this system. The 4th and 5th heaters are fed by a condensate booster pump at an intermediate pressure. The 6th heater is supplied by the main boiler feed pump at full feed pressure.

Figure 35	Six Stage Feedwater Heating System with Temperatures

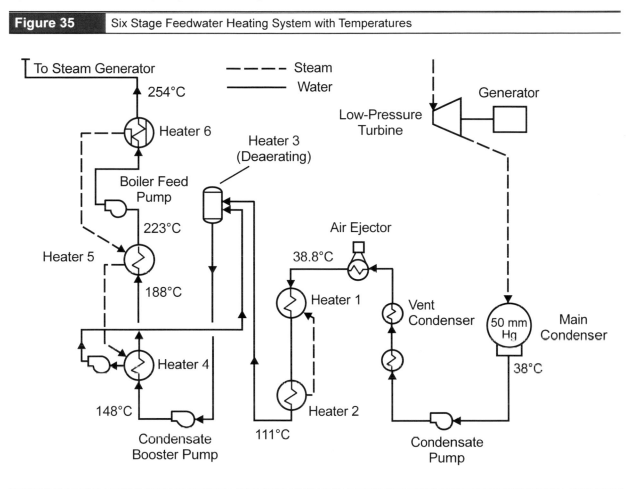

CHAPTER 3 - QUESTIONS

1. What are the two main groups of condensers called? Name seven different condenser types.

2. What advantages can a jet condenser claim over a surface condenser?

3. List three purposes of a surface condenser and explain how each purpose is achieved.

4. Describe the principle of operation of a direct contact condenser and give a disadvantage of this type.

5. A condenser you are operating has an air leak. How would you find this air leak without shutting down the turbine and condenser?

6. How are cooling water leaks into the steam condensate detected? How are they repaired?

ANSWERS: All answers are found within the content of the chapter.

Gas Turbine Principles & Designs

LEARNING OUTCOME

When you complete this chapter you should be able to:

Explain common designs, major components, operating principles, and arrangements for industrial gas turbines.

LEARNING OBJECTIVES

Here is what you should be able to do when you complete each objective:

1. Explain gas turbine advantages and disadvantages, background and industrial applications. Identify the types of gas turbines, their major components and describe the operating principles of a simple gas turbine.

2. Explain single and dual shaft arrangements for gas turbines. Describe open cycle and closed cycle operation.

3. Describe a typical open cycle gas turbine installation, including buildings or enclosures, intake and exhaust systems, auxiliary systems, and reducing gear.

4. Explain the efficiency and rating of gas turbines and describe the purpose and applications of gas turbine cycle improvements, including intercooling, regenerating, reheating and combined cycle.

5. Describe various aspects of compressor design and centrifugal and axial types of compressors.

6. Describe the types, operation, components and arrangements of combustors.

7. Describe turbine section design and operation especially with respect to blading and materials.

8. Explain the types and functions of the control systems and instrumentation needed for gas turbine operation.

9. Explain the typical operating parameters of a gas turbine; describe the effects of compressor inlet temperature, compressor discharge pressure, and turbine inlet temperature on gas turbine performance.

OBJECTIVE 1

Explain gas turbine advantages and disadvantages, background and industrial applications. Identify the types of gas turbines, their major components and describe the operating principles of a simple gas turbine.

INTRODUCTION

Gas turbines are a major source of driving power for a variety of industrial applications. They are designed in a wide range of sizes and configurations. Their capabilities, efficiency and power output are continually being improved through design changes.

GAS TURBINE ADVANTAGES

Modern gas turbines have several significant advantages over other types of internal combustion engines, including:

- Ability to produce large amounts of power (currently up to 400 MW)
- High power to weight ratio, making them especially suitable for applications (such as offshore) where weight must be minimized
- Ability to use a wide range of liquid and gaseous fuels
- Ability to start rapidly, which is important for backup power generation
- High availability and reliability and ability to minimize outage time by quick replacement of the gas turbine in case of major failure
- Remote operation capability with minimal operational manpower requirements

GAS TURBINE DISADVANTAGES

The gas turbine engine has a few disadvantages (compared to other internal combustion engines), including:

- Gas turbines have high manufacturing costs, due to their complicated design.
- A gas turbine changes speed more slowly (compared to other engines); it is slower to respond to changes in load demand.
- A gas turbine is less suitable for low-power applications, since the efficiency of the gas turbine decreases at lower loads.
- To reach maximum efficiency, a gas turbine requires intercoolers, regenerators and/or reheaters; this adds significant cost and complexity.

TYPES OF INDUSTRIAL GAS TURBINES

The two basic types of industrial gas turbines are the aero-derivative gas turbines and the heavy duty gas turbine. Each type has advantages and disadvantages that make them more or less suitable for certain applications. However, there is considerable overlap in their usage and there are no hard and fast application rules.

Aero-derivative gas turbines, such as the 55 MW General Electric LM 5000 in Figure 1, are engines adapted (ie. derived) from aircraft (jet) engines. The engines are modified somewhat, particularly by removing the thrust producing components and replacing them with a power turbine. The combustion gases are expanded through the power turbine to drive a generator or other mechanical load. Where the original aero engines are relatively short (for obvious space reasons), the derivative engines are longer, with the additional compressor stages and the power turbine.

Figure 1	Aero Derivative Gas Turbine

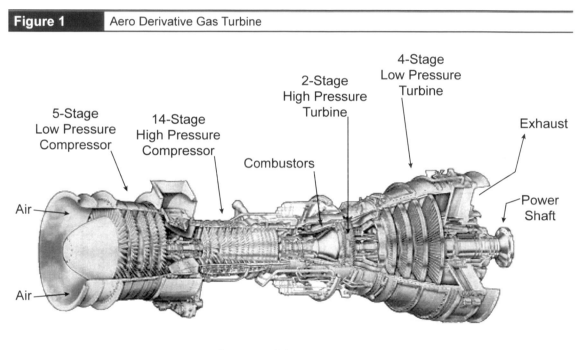

(Courtesy of General Electric)

In general, aero-derivative gas turbines are:

- Low weight, which makes them suitable for locations such as offshore platforms, ships, trains and vehicles where weight is a consideration.
- Easily maintained, removed and replaced, which maximizes availability
- Fast starting, which is crucial for backup power generation and pipeline applications
- Usually less durable, with a shorter life than heavy-duty gas turbines
- Potentially more efficient than reciprocating engines with the same power rating (depending on the way they are integrated into the plant power system)
- Able to use either natural gas or good quality liquid fuels and often designed to allow switching between fuels.

Heavy-duty gas turbines are specifically designed and constructed for relatively heavy industrial applications. Size and weight are not issues (as they are with aero-derivative machines) so their design and layout is more flexible and more rugged.

In general, heavy-duty gas turbines are:

- Larger and heavier than their aero-derivative machines
- Very durable, with long intervals between overhauls; this makes them especially suitable for base load applications
- More efficient than aero-derivative engines of the same capacity
- Able to use all fuels including distillates, residuals and crude oil
- Able to accommodate a flexible layout between compressor, combustors and turbine to allow for inter-cooling, regeneration, steam injection, combined cycle, closed cycle and reheat

Figure 2 is one example of a heavy duty industrial turbine.

One visible difference between this gas turbine and the aeroderivative (in Fig. 1) is the external combustors, which significantly increase the overall size of the machine. The turning gear attached to the end of the shaft also suggests it is a relatively large, heavy-duty machine.

Figure 2	Heavy-Duty Gas Turbine

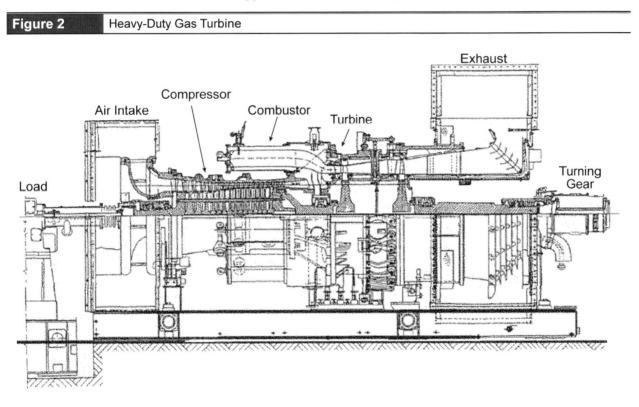

INDUSTRIAL & COMMERCIAL GAS TURBINES

Gas turbines are used in a wide range of industrial applications, such as driving electric power generators, gas compressors and large pumps.

They are used to drive generators that produce a relatively constant "base load" or generators that operate intermittently to provide emergency (back-up) power or "peak power". Base loading means that the unit produces electricity on a continuous basis, within a fairly steady load range. Emergency power is power that must be supplied very quickly and for a short period of time, such as when the main generator(s) fail. Peak power refers to the production of power only during those periods of the day when the overall electrical distribution network for a community (town, city, province, state or larger region) is close to being overloaded. Large electrical distributors create incentives for industrial companies to provide some of their own power during those periods. These incentives more than compensate for the cost of the gas turbine unit.

Many commercial institutions use small gas turbines to produce power and heat, usually in a cogeneration arrangement. Even smaller systems, involving micro-turbines, are being used in smaller buildings.

Figure 3 shows a small, 28 kW micro-turbine producing base load power. The hot exhaust gases from the gas turbine pass to the once through boiler where steam is generated at a pressure of 800 kPa and is used for heating purposes.

Figure 3	Micro Gas Turbine

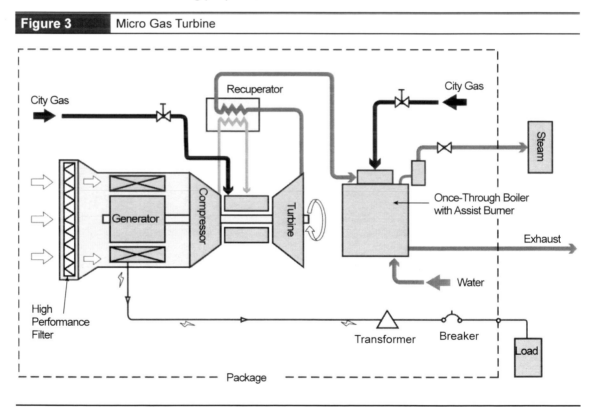

SIMPLE GAS TURBINE OPERATING PRINCIPLES

Gas turbines, regardless of design, size or application, have three major components.

- **Compressor section**: to supply high-pressure air for combustion and mass flow
- **Combustion section:** to burn a fuel and produce hot combustion gases
- **Power turbine section**: to convert the energy created by the hot, high-pressure gases into rotational power

Figure 4 illustrates the main gas flow through a simple gas turbine. The principle of operation is as follows:

Note: The pressures and temperatures quoted are only approximations, since actual parameters vary with machine design and size.

- The compressor draws in ambient air and compresses it to 1100 to 3000 kPa. The temperature also increases, due to compression, to as high as 650°C.

- The air then goes to the combustion chamber (combustor) where a fuel (natural gas or oil) is continuously burned to heat the air and produce hot combustion gases. Some of the air is used for combustion, some provides cooling around the outside of the inner combustion chamber, and the rest provides dilution air into the inner combustion chamber. The combustion flame itself may be as high as 2100°C (+/-), but the dilution and cooling results in a lower temperature mixture (1000 to 1500°C +/-) leaving the combustion section.

- The hot combustion gases and air then enter the power turbine, with maximum pressure and thermal energy. Since the turbine exhausts to atmosphere, the large pressured drop causes the gases to expand through the turbine blades, creating reaction forces that cause rotation. The pressure and thermal energy of the gases is thus converted into mechanical, rotational energy and power. The gases exit the turbine at about 500 to 640°C.

- The rotational power developed in the power turbine is used to drive the compressor through their common shaft. The additional power produced drives the external load, such as an electrical generator.

Figure 4	Simple Gas Turbine

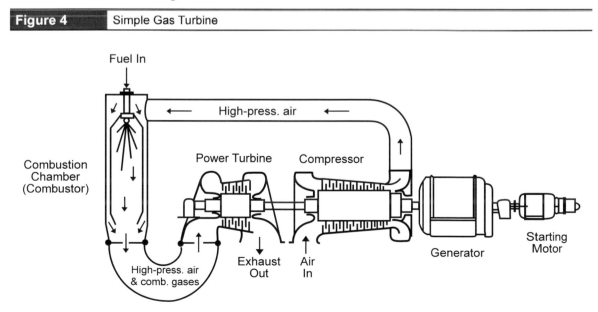

OBJECTIVE 2

Explain single and dual shaft arrangements for gas turbines. Describe open cycle and closed cycle operation.

SINGLE SHAFT

In the single shaft arrangements, shown in Figure 5, the compressor and power turbine are mounted on the same shaft. The load is usually also connected to the same shaft (through a coupling and/or a reducing gear). The usual arrangement is to have the load connected at the power turbine end (Fig. 5a), but it can also be connected at the compressor end (Fig. 5b).

Figure 5	Single Shaft Layouts

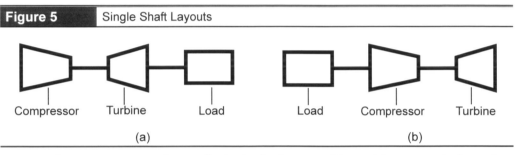

Compressor   Turbine   Load   Load   Compressor   Turbine

(a)   (b)

Figure 6 shows a cutaway of a small, single shaft gas turbine, with two vertical combustors. The power output shaft is at the power turbine end.

Figure 6	Single Shaft Gas Turbine

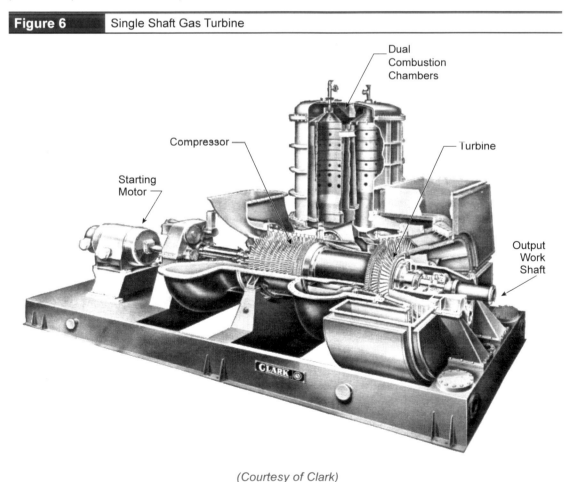

(Courtesy of Clark)

DUAL SHAFT

Figure 7 shows a dual shaft arrangement.

In this design, the compressor is driven by a high pressure turbine, which is on the same shaft as the compressor. The load (a generator in this case) is driven on a second shaft by the low-pressure power turbine. There is no shaft connection between the high-pressure and low-pressure turbines. The primary purpose of the HP turbine is to drive the compressor, while the purpose of the LP turbine is to drive the generator.

Figure 7	Dual Shaft Arrangement

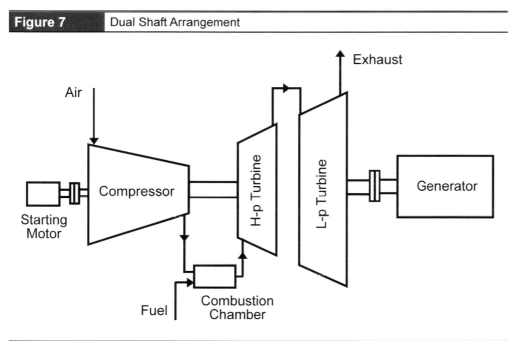

A single-shaft arrangement is used for power generation, where a constant speed is required. It is mechanically simpler than a two-shaft arrangement, but requires a large starting motor. This is because the starting motor must turn the total mass of the compressor, power turbine and load. In the dual-shaft arrangement, the starting motor only turns the compressor and the HP power turbine, so the starting motor can be smaller.

The advantage of the dual-shaft design is greater operating flexibility. The load may be operated at varying speeds while the compressor speed remains constant. Conversely, the load speed may remain constant (as in a generator) while the compressor speed varies.

OPEN CYCLE

An open cycle gas turbine system is shown in Figure 8.

The system is termed "open cycle" because the working fluid (air) is drawn from the atmosphere at the beginning of the cycle and returned back to atmosphere at the end of the cycle. The term "simple open cycle" means the gas turbine has no additional components, such as heat exchangers, reheaters, or intercoolers. Air is drawn into the compressor from the atmosphere, compressed and supplied to the turbine after heating in the combustion chamber. The air and hot gases expand through the power turbine and exhaust to atmosphere.

The advantage of the open cycle is its simplicity. However, the efficiency is very low, since all excess heat from the turbine is lost to atmosphere.

Figure 8	Simple Open Cycle Gas Turbine System

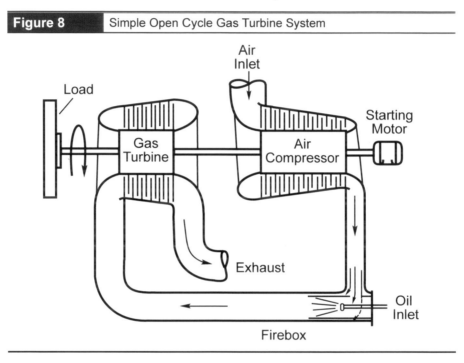

CLOSED CYCLE

An improvement on the open cycle is the closed cycle, in which the working fluid is contained and re-circulated within a completely closed system. Atmospheric air is only used in the combustor and heat exchanger to heat the re-circulating working fluid. The purpose of closed cycle systems is to increase the net power output and thermal efficiency of the plant.

Figure 9 shows one example of a closed cycle gas turbine system.

The working fluid is pressurized in the compressor, then pre-heated in a regenerator by heat exchange with the hot exhaust gases from the power turbine. From there the working fluid goes to the air heater and is further heated by an external source of hot combustion gases. The fluid then expands through the power turbine, doing work. The hot turbine exhaust gases must now be cooled before compression. This is done by two stages of heat exchange, first in the regenerator and then in the cooler.

Figure 9	Closed Cycle Gas Turbine System

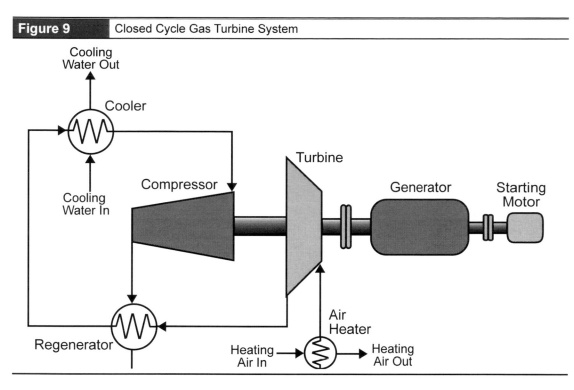

Advantages of Closed Cycle Systems

- Higher pressures can be used throughout the cycle and therefore higher densities of the working fluid are possible. This increases the output of the machine for the same physical dimensions.

- The working fluid is clean and does not cause corrosion or erosion of the turbine.

- The working fluid need not support combustion and may be chosen for its superior thermodynamic properties.

- A cheaper fuel may be used in the air heater than would be required in an internal combustor.

Disadvantages of Closed Cycle Systems

- A supply of cooling water is required.

- The complexity, size, and cost of the system are much increased.

OBJECTIVE 3

Describe a typical open cycle gas turbine installation, including buildings or enclosures, intake and exhaust systems, auxiliary systems and reducing gear.

GAS TURBINE INSTALLATION

A complete gas turbine installation includes, besides the turbine itself, several additional components, support systems and equipment, which vary widely with the type of gas turbine and its location, environmental conditions and application.

Figure 10 gives a comprehensive picture of most systems needed to support a gas turbine.

Buildings & Enclosures

Gas turbines are usually contained inside an enclosure that protects it from the environment, reduces noise in the surroundings, and provides protection for personnel in case of turbine failure. Particularly in colder climates, the unit may be located in a separate building, complete with extra, lay-down space for maintenance. The buildings or enclosures may incorporate fire and gas detectors, ventilation systems and fire suppression systems (such as CO_2 or Halon).

Intake & Exhaust

A gas turbine always has an air intake that filters the air to remove contaminants and prevent damage from foreign objects. The intake plenum ensures smooth flow into the gas turbine compressor section. Since cooler air is denser than warm air, some air intakes incorporate special cooling systems to decrease the air inlet temperature. This increases the air density, which means more mass can flow through the turbine and more power can be developed.

The exhaust system provides a safe exit for the hot exhaust gases and may include a silencer to reduce sound to acceptable limits. The exhaust may also flow to a waste heat recovery heat exchanger to supply heat to some other process at the overall facility. To minimize losses in power and efficiency, both the intake and exhaust must operate with the lowest possible pressure drop (ie. the least restriction to flow).

Auxiliary Systems

Several auxiliary systems are either mandatory or optional to support the operation of the gas turbine, including:

- A fuel gas system to ensure that fuel is provided to the combustion section at the proper temperature, pressure and flow
- An alternate fuel system, if designed for dual fuel (eg. light oil plus gas)
- Fuel treatment systems to clean and treat fuels, if required
- A lube oil system for the lubrication of bearings
- A hydraulic oil system for the operation of the fuel valves
- A steam injection system to reduce emissions (ie. NO_x control) and/or increase output (injected steam increases mass flow)
- Anti-icing systems, which provide heat to the air intake to eliminate the buildup of ice in very cold climates
- Water wash system for cleaning compressor blades

Reducing Gears

For many applications, the speed of the power turbine shaft is too high for the driven load. In these cases, a reducing gear must be installed between the turbine shaft and the load shaft. The output shaft of the reducing gear will turn at the same speed as the load. An example is gas turbines that drive generators, which must run at a constant speed (usually 1800/3600 r/min for 60 Hz generators and 1500/3000 r/min for 50 Hz) to ensure the correct frequency is maintained.

Figure 10	Overview of Systems for a Gas Turbine

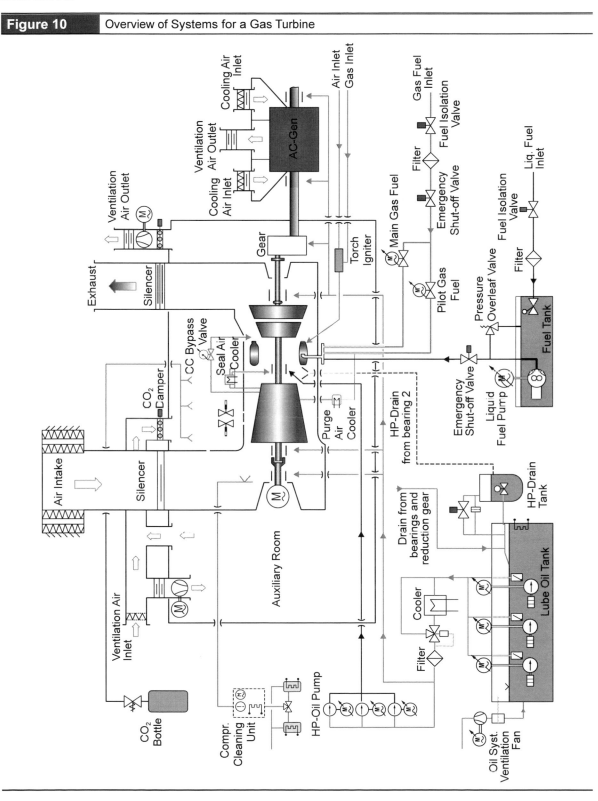

OBJECTIVE 4

Explain the efficiency and rating of gas turbines and describe the purpose and applications of gas turbine cycle improvements, including intercooling, regenerating, reheating and combined cycle.

EFFICIENCY & RATING OF GAS TURBINES

Gas turbines are normally rated in terms of the power produced at the output shaft where it connects to the load. The power rating specified by the manufacturer will be in kilowatts, at a standard of 15°C and at sea level, using natural gas as a fuel, air with 60% humidity and with no intake or exhaust losses.

Thermal efficiency is the ratio (in %) of the rated power and the fuel energy rate. The fuel energy rate is calculated by multiplying the fuel flow rate by the lower heating value of the fuel. Modern gas turbines are able to reach efficiencies of 35% to 40% in simple cycle mode without the cycle improvements or combined cycle described below.

CYCLE IMPROVEMENTS

In order to improve the efficiency of the basic gas turbine cycle, three methods, or a combination of them, can be implemented. As simple cycle gas turbines are improving in efficiency, these cycle improvements are becoming less necessary as combined cycle (ie. utilizing the turbine exhaust heat for other purposes) is becoming more prevalent.

The three possibilities for improving the gas turbine cycle, regeneration, intercooling and reheat, are shown together in Figure 11.

Regeneration

The most common cycle improvement is regeneration where exhaust heat is used to increase the temperature of compressed air before combustion. This is accomplished by installing a heat exchanger in the exhaust to preheat the air between the compressor and the combustors.

This approach, which is becoming less common, allows the efficiency of the gas turbine to be improved by 15 to 20%. Disadvantages are the increased capital cost and the fact that there are increased pressure losses with the newer high-pressure ratio compressors. Instead, many installations now use the exhaust heat for combined cycle or cogeneration.

Intercooling

In some gas turbine arrangements, the inlet air is compressed in two stages and cooled between these stages in a heat exchanger (intercooler). This makes more of the turbine power available to the output load, since isothermal compression (compression without an increase in temperature) takes less work than adiabatic compression (compression where no heat is removed so that the air temperature increases). Another advantage of intercooling is that the specific volume of the air is reduced, permitting a smaller physical size for the machine.

The benefits of intercooling decrease as pressure ratio increases. A high-pressure ratio also means that losses through the intercooler become more significant. The use of an intercooler is more beneficial if it is combined with regeneration since more exhaust heat will be recovered and this will improve the overall cycle efficiency.

The intercooler is a shell and tube heat exchanger similar in construction to the regenerator. Cooling water passes through the tubes while the air passes over the outside of the tubes. In some cases, the air may pass through tubes, with cooling water in the shell.

Reheat

The gas turbine plant may be arranged to expand the hot gases in two stages, with the gases being reheated between the stages. The gases are expanded first in a high-pressure turbine and then reheated before entering a low-pressure turbine. The location of the reheater is shown in Figure 11.

The effect of this reheating is to increase the energy content of the gases and thus improve the thermal efficiency of the cycle. As a result, less air must be compressed to do the same amount of work. The reheating is done by burning fuel in a second combustion chamber using the excess oxygen content of the gases from the high-pressure turbine for combustion.

Figure 11	Intercooling, Reheat and Regeneration

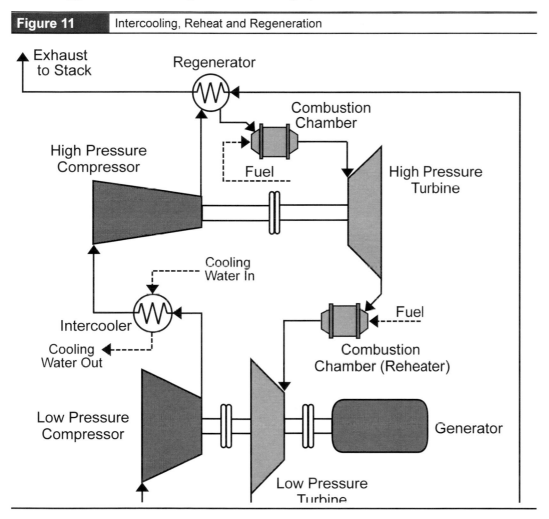

Combined Cycle

Gas turbines can be integrated into a wide variety of combined cycle or cogeneration systems. Many of these are in use today, and their utilization is increasing. These systems usually extract the exhaust heat from the gas turbine by means of a heat exchanger, usually a type of boiler. Steam is produced, which can be used to drive a steam turbine, or to provide steam for process plant purposes or other heating applications. The steam turbine can be connected to the same generator as the gas turbine, another generator, a compressor or some other mechanical drive.

An example is shown in Figure 12.

| **Figure 12** | A Typical Combined Cycle |

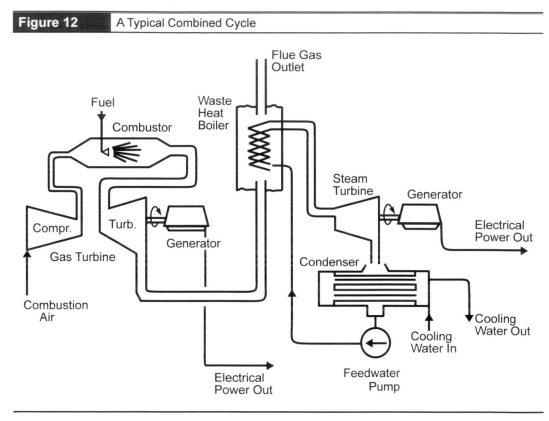

OBJECTIVE 5

Describe the various aspects of compressor design and centrifugal and axial types of compressors.

COMPRESSOR DESIGNS

A highly efficient compressor is critical for the efficient operation of a gas turbine. Two types of compressors are used:

- Centrifugal (aka radial)
- Axial

In small gas turbines, centrifugal compressors are often used, in combination with several axial stages. The majority of large gas turbines use a multi-stage axial compressor. Since the compressor uses up to 2/3 of the energy provided by the fuel, it must be structurally sound, as well as efficient.

Centrifugal (Radial) Compressors

These compressors take air in at the centre or "eye" of the rotor. Due to the high rotational speeds of the rotor, the air is accelerated to high velocity by the blades and forced radially by centrifugal force to the edge of the rotor. There, the air is received by the diffuser, which converts the velocity energy to pressure energy.

Advantages of the centrifugal compressor are:

- simplicity,
- strength and
- short overall length.

Figure 13 shows the impeller and diffuser arrangement.

Figure 13	Centrifugal Compressor

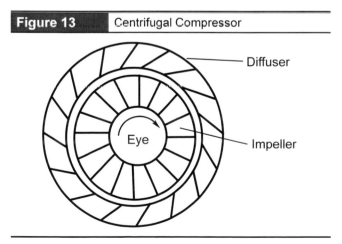

Figure 14 shows a multi-stage centrifugal rotor with four impellers.

Figure 14	Multistage Centrifugal Compressor Rotor

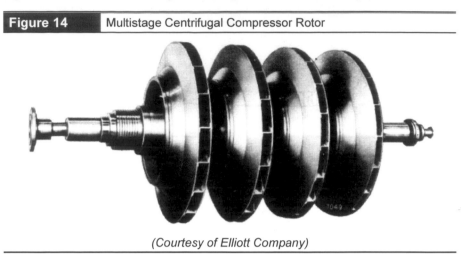

(Courtesy of Elliott Company)

Axial Compressors

Axial compressors move the air axially along the shaft. Several rows of rotating blades draw the air through the compressor. The casing gets gradually smaller (in diameter), which causes the air velocity to increase. Fixed blades, between each row of moving blades, tend to slow the air down and raise the pressure.

The air will be compressed when passing through the moving blades also. If the pressure rise in each is equal, the compressor is symmetrically staged and is similar to a reaction turbine (in reverse).

An axial compressor rotor is shown in Figure 15.

Figure 15	Multi-Stage Axial Compressor Rotor

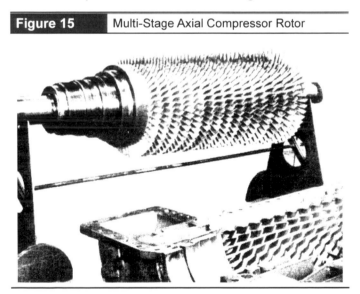

OBJECTIVE 6

Describe the types, operation, components and arrangements of combustors.

COMBUSTORS

The combustion chamber (combustor) in a gas turbine is used to heat the compressed air after it leaves the compressor and before it enters the power turbine. It must do this with minimum pressure drop (ie. minimum restriction to flow) and produce minimal combustion impurities, since these impurities will be carried with the air into the turbine blading.

In general, about 20% of the air entering the combustor is mixed with the fuel in the flame tube as combustion air; the remaining 80% flows along the outside of the flame tube and serves as cooling air. Some of this air re-enters the flame tube as dilution air. The combustion flame itself may be as high as 2100°C (+/-), but the dilution and cooling results in a lower temperature mixture (1000 to 1500°C +/-) leaving the combustion section. The cooling ensures a temperature that can be withstood by the power turbine blades.

TYPES OF COMBUSTORS

There are three basic types (designs) of combustors. These are called:

- Annular
- Can
- Can-Annular

Annular Combustor

An annular combustor is shown in Figure 16.

It consists of a single concentric flame 'tube', located in the space between an inner and outer casing. Several fuel nozzles, located around the flame tube, spray or inject the fuel into the flame tube. Compressed air fills the space between the inner and outer casings and enters the flame tube through holes in the tube wall.

This design is the most efficient use of the space available to the airflow. Advantages of the annular combustion chamber include:

- relatively light weight,
- less restriction to air flow, and
- compactness, which makes it most desirable for aircraft engines
- the single combustion chamber provides even distribution of combustion around the annular area.

| Figure 16 | Annular Combustor Cutaway View |

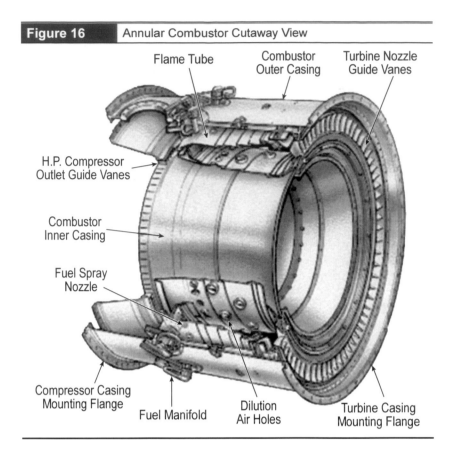

Flame Tube — Combustor Outer Casing — Turbine Nozzle Guide Vanes — H.P. Compressor Outlet Guide Vanes — Combustor Inner Casing — Fuel Spray Nozzle — Compressor Casing Mounting Flange — Fuel Manifold — Dilution Air Holes — Turbine Casing Mounting Flange

Can Combustors

The term "can", in the context of gas turbines, refers to a cylindrical chamber in which combustion occurs. A can combustor has an inner casing (aka, flame tube) and an outer casing. Combustion occurs inside the inner casing, with combustion and dilution air being supplied, through holes, from the outer casing.

Figure 17 shows a single can combustor.

- In this design, the air from the compressor flows upwards in the outer casing (jacket). Some of the air enters the inner casing through holes and acts as dilution air to cool the combustion gases.

- Combustion air from the top of the can enters the inner casing, along with the injected fuel. A swirl plate mixes the air and fuel.

- Combustion gases flow downward, mix with the dilution air, and flow out the bottom and into the power turbine.

This often referred to as a reverse flow design, since the air flows to the end (top) of the combustor and then back toward the outlet. The air in the external casing provides cooling for the inner flame tube, plus it absorbs heat, which improves combustion.

Smaller turbines may have a single can (or two) mounted vertically between the compressor and the power turbine. Refer back to Figure 6 to see a gas turbine with two vertical, can combustors. Note the burner cutaways, which show the double casing and the air holes in the inner casing.

Figure 17   Gas Turbine Vertical Can Combustor

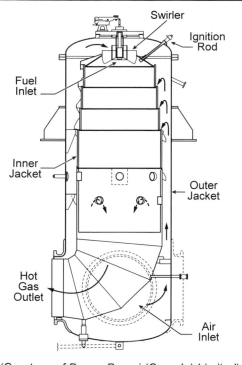

(Courtesy of Brown Boveri (Canada) Limited)

Figure 18 shows a common arrangement of can combustors in heavy duty industrial machines. In this design there are several individual cans, arranged horizontally (parallel to the turbine shaft) in a circle around the casing (see the, cross-sectional view in Fig. 18, showing the arrangement of 6 combustors). The cans may be internal or external to the main gas turbine casing.

In Figure 18, the air flow from the compressor enters each combustor through a separate inlet tube. Fuel is injected into the end of the combustor, while air enters at the fuel end through dilution holes in the inner casing. Air crossover tubes between the cans help them operate at the same pressure and ensure equal operating conditions. This combustor is referred to as "straight-through", since the air and combustion gases exit at the opposite end from the inlet.

Figure 18   Straight-through Can Combustor Cutaway

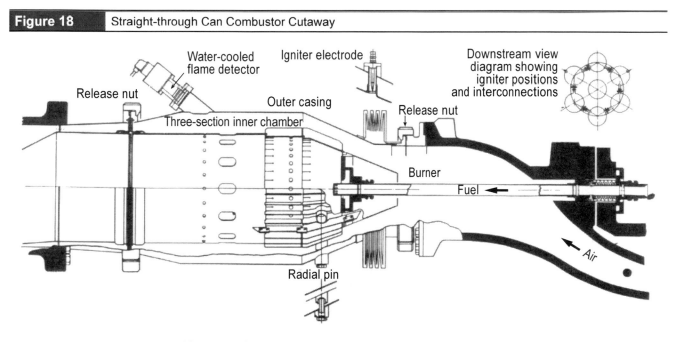

(Courtesy of Associated Electrical Industries (Canada) Ltd.)

Figure 19 shows a more complete external view of this arrangement, with 8 separate, internal combustors.

| **Figure 19** | Straight Through Can Combustors |

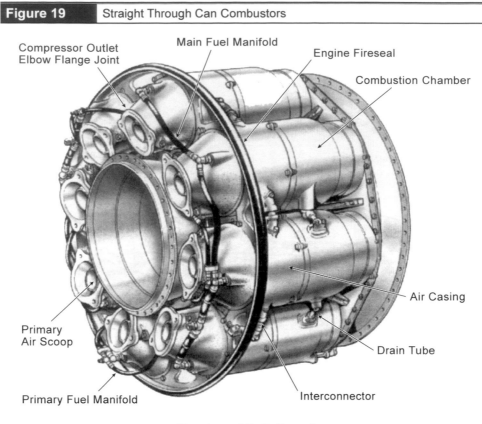

(Courtesy of Rolls-Royce)

Figure 20 shows an external, reverse flow can, which would be one of several mounted around the outside of the turbine casing. Here the air flows into the combustor, then back toward the power turbine. In some units, these external combustors are mounted on an angle, rather than being perfectly horizontal. This design allows greater strength, easier access for maintenance and allows the main turbine to be shorter where floor space is an issue. It is very common in large, heavy duty gas turbines.

| **Figure 20** | External Reverse Flow Can Combustor |

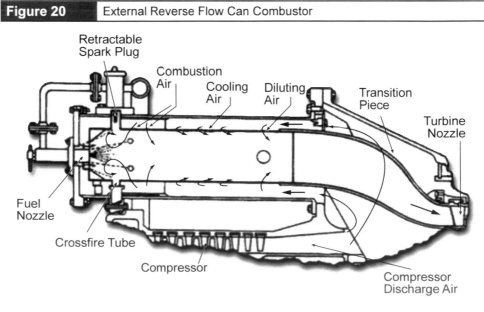

(Courtesy of GE Power Systems)

The advantage of the can design is that problems associated with aerodynamics and combustion, such as non-uniform outlet temperatures, are minimized. The disadvantages are that multiple igniters and fuel lines are required and the cans are not the most efficient use of the space in an annular volume. Flow resistance is higher than in the annular design, although operation at higher pressures is possible.

Can-Annular

Can-annular combustors are very similar to can combustors. However, they combine the annular and can designs and obtain the benefits of both. They are compact and strong. The main difference is in how the air is distributed to the combustor cans. Again, combustion takes place in multiple combustor cans, placed around the center line of the gas turbine. Each can has its own ignition nozzle and fuel nozzle. The combustors are located in a common annular space between inner and outer air casings. The air is supplied to the combustors from this common space, through scoops (for primary combustion air) and holes in the combustors (for cooling and dilution air).

Figure 21 shows a typical can-annular arrangement.

Each combustor is made up of an inner chamber, which is carried on radial pins to allow relative expansion, and an outer casing. Interconnecting pipes are provided between the combustors to give uniform combustion conditions and to carry the flame from one to the other during the starting sequence; only two of the combustors have igniter elements.

Figure 21	External Reverse flow Can-Annular Combustor

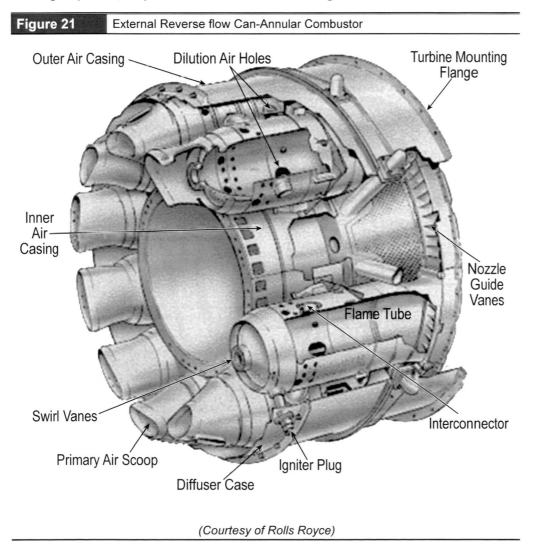

(Courtesy of Rolls Royce)

OBJECTIVE 7

Describe power turbine section design and operation especially with respect to blading and materials.

POWER TURBINE DESIGN

The power turbine extracts power from the hot gases supplied from the combustion section by expanding the gases and decreasing pressure and temperature. About 50% of the power is used to drive the compressor and the remainder provides mechanical power for the generator, compressor or other load. As discussed earlier, the turbine may be split into two or three separate sections and shafts. Like compressors, power turbines may be axial-flow or radial-inflow, with axial-flow being the most common. Power turbines operate at very high temperatures, with high blade loads and large rotational stresses.

Axial-Flow Turbines

Fewer stages are needed in the power turbine than in the compressor. In the axial-flow turbine, a stage consists of a row of stationary blades, usually called nozzle guide vanes or nozzles, and a row of rotating blades, often called buckets. The nozzles increase the velocity of the hot gases (with a partial pressure drop) and the moving blades extract power with a further drop in pressure and temperature.

In impulse turbines, the nozzles decrease in cross-sectional area, converting pressure energy into velocity energy. In reaction turbines, the nozzles have constant cross-sectional area and serve only to redirect the flow at the correct angle for the turbine blades, which have divergent passages to reduce pressure and increase velocity. All gas turbines utilize power turbines of the impulse-reaction type, which is a combination of impulse and reaction.

BLADE COOLING

Many gas turbines use air-cooled (and sometimes water-cooled) blades to reduce metal temperature and increase life. Air is supplied from the compressor section, circulated through the blade and then extracted through holes in the leading edge, trailing edge and surface of each blade. The incorporation of complicated cooling passages in turbine nozzles and blades is also a major manufacturing challenge that has resulted in many special techniques and methods.

TURBINE MATERIALS

The greatest challenges in gas turbine materials are in the turbine nozzles and blades, particularly the first stage. Conventional nozzles are cast with special nickel-based super alloys, such as Inconel, Udimet, Waspalloy and Hastelloy. Gas turbine blading is made of heat resisting steel, forged and machined to shape. Steps are taken in some designs to cool the blading, using hollow blading with some coolant such as compressed air flowing through. Figures 22(a) and (b) show a turbine moving blade and a turbine fixed blading half diaphragm.

Figure 22 | Gas Turbine Blades

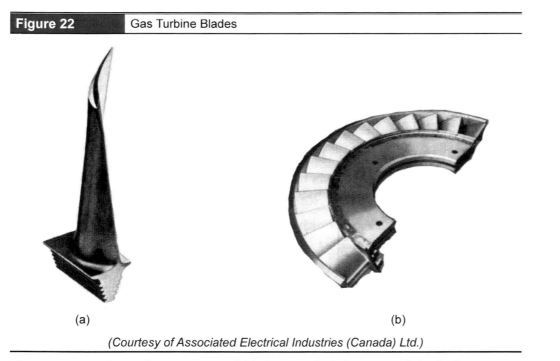

(a)   (b)

(Courtesy of Associated Electrical Industries (Canada) Ltd.)

The stresses in the turbine rotors and blading are high because of the high gas temperatures and rotational speeds. To withstand the stress, the rotors are made from heat resisting steel and, owing to the difficulty of making large forgings of this material, they are generally made of discs that are bolted or welded together.

Figures 23 shows a Westinghouse Gas turbine rotor of bolted construction.

Figure 23 | Gas Turbine Rotor of Bolted Construction

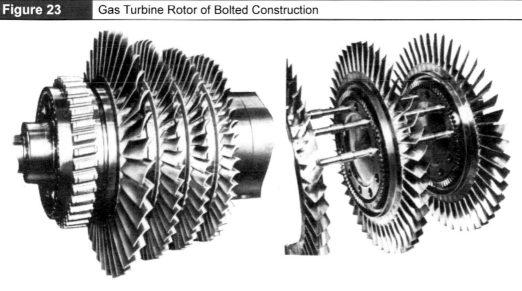

(Courtesy of Canadian Westinghouse Company Limited)

At very high temperatures and stresses, metals incur a phenomenon called creep. Over time, the metal stretches and voids open, which severely weakens the metal. If this occurs in turbine blades, together with the high rotational speeds, there could be catastrophic failure of the blades. To avoid this, the turbine blades are usually replaced at fixed intervals, typically between 75 000 and 100 000 hours of operation.

Special casting techniques are allowing blades to be manufactured with superior strength and temperature resistance. Ceramic components are also allowing a significant increase in firing temperatures.

OBJECTIVE 8

Explain the types and functions of the control systems and instrumentation needed for gas turbine operation.

CONTROL SYSTEMS

Control of a gas turbine is affected by varying the fuel flow to the combustors according to load demand and operating conditions. The actual control system configuration varies according to the turbine's application and the type of fuel used.

Figure 24 shows a block diagram of a dual-shaft gas turbine with some of the basic control units common to both liquid and gaseous fuel systems.

The supply of pressurized fuel may come from a liquid fuel reservoir and engine-driven gear pumps incorporating a bypass system. If gas fired, the gas is supplied directly from a gas supply line through a pressure regulator.

The "all speed governing" of the power turbine controls the speed and power output of the unit. A reset mechanism in the governor determines the position of the fuel metering valve and hence, controls the engine fuel flow. Initially, the operator sets the desired engine speed at the loading station. This establishes a speed reference setting in the reset mechanism. If engine speed is above or below the setting, a proportional error signal is transmitted to the metering valve positioner. The valve is repositioned until the error is eliminated and the power turbine is at the desired output.

Various override trims, such as over temperature and overspeed protection for the gas producer, are applied on the governor reset mechanism through the loading station to produce an artificial error signal until the adverse condition is overcome.

To avoid compressor surge during acceleration, a separate signal, applied directly to the metering valve positioner, overrides the governor error signal. The acceleration fuel flow schedule is based on the rise in compressor outlet pressure.

An automatic emergency trip system closes the main fuel shutoff valve if:

- The lubricating oil pressure drops to an unsafe value
- The exhaust temperature exceeds the allowable limit
- Either of the rotor speeds becomes excessive

Manual shutdown is also affected through this circuit by means of a manual hydraulic valve.

Figure 24   Gas Turbine Control System

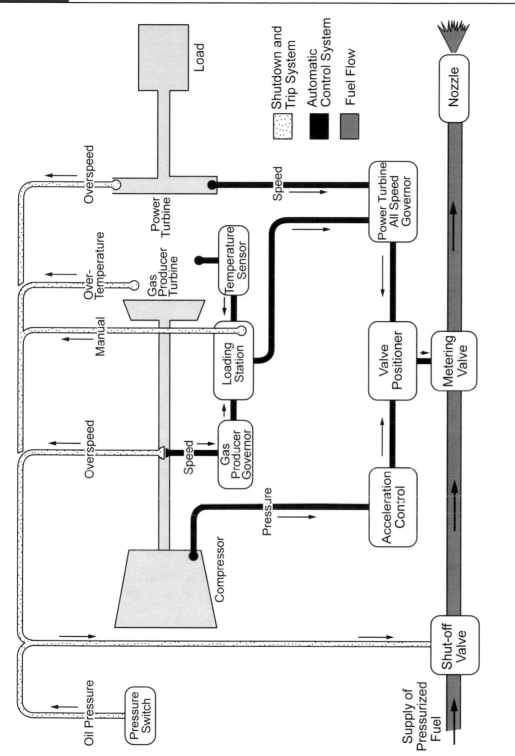

INSTRUMENTATION

Instrumentation is normally provided to continuously monitor and control the following parameters of a gas turbine:

- Rotor speed for each shaft, in r/min
- Air inlet temperature in °C, preferably after the intake filter but often ambient air temperature.
- Differential pressure across the intake filters
- Compressor discharge pressure measured at the exit of the compressor and before combustion, in kPa
- Exhaust gas temperatures in °C, usually measured at multiple circumferential points and as an average after the first or second turbine stage or in between the engine turbine and power turbine
- Vibration, using accelerometers mounted on the engine case if anti-friction bearings are used (applies to most aero-derivatives)
- Vibration using eddy-current displacement probes if journal or tilt-pad bearings are used (applies to most heavy-duty gas turbines)
- Bearing temperatures in °C if journal or tilt-pad bearings are used (applies to most heavy-duty gas turbines)
- Fuel gas flow, pressure and temperature
- Oil system pressures and temperatures
- Generator output, in kW, or compressor shaft power

Operator Interface

With every control system, there is an operator interface (sometimes called an MMI – Man Machine Interface or HMI – Human Machine Interface). It allows an operator to:

- Startup or shutdown the gas turbine
- Control the turbines speed
- Modify the control system logic, with special access only
- Monitor measured parameters

Startup & Shutdown Sequencing

The startup and shutdown of a gas turbine may occur automatically if predetermined conditions occur. For example, a backup power generation unit may start if there is an increase in demand and a compressor may start if the pressure drops in a process. Often, operators monitoring the overall process will initiate a manual start. Once the start or shutdown is initiated, the sequencing is almost always automatic.

Protection

A number of protective devices will first alarm and then shutdown the engine if certain levels are exceeded. They normally protect against:

- Power turbine overspeed
- Exhaust gas temperatures higher than the maximum limit
- Excessive vibration
- Excessive oil and bearing temperatures
- Fuel gas pressure too low or too high
- Excessive air intake filter differential pressure

OBJECTIVE 9

Explain the typical operating parameters of a gas turbine; describe the effects of compressor inlet temperature, compressor discharge pressure, and turbine inlet temperature on gas turbine performance.

OPERATING PARAMETERS

The operation of a gas turbine is defined by a number of operating parameters that consist mainly of flows, pressures and temperatures along the gas path of the engine. It is possible to produce a map of these parameters, such as the one shown in Figure 25, which shows the interrelationship between these parameters over a range of operating conditions up to some predetermined maximum limit. Producers of gas turbines provide electrical production performance data in terms of the heat rate input. Heat rate is the amount of joules required to produce one kWh of electrical energy (MJ/kWh).

Figure 25	Performance Graph for a Gas Turbine

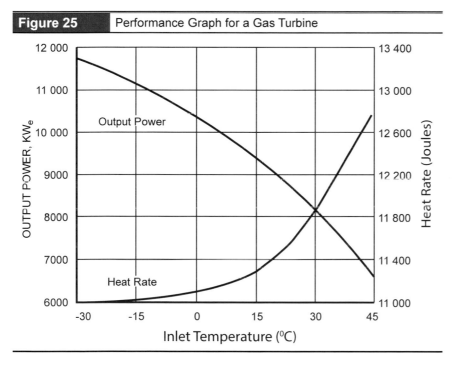

Effect of Inlet Air Temperature

The temperature of the air entering the gas turbine has a great impact on its operation and performance. As the air temperature decreases, its density increases and the mass airflow through the engine increases, accordingly. The power that is produced by the gas turbine is proportional to the mass flow.

Therefore, a gas turbine will produce more power at lower ambient temperatures. This is the basis for using heat exchangers that increase power by cooling the inlet air.

From Figure 25, it can be seen that the rated power at standard conditions of 15°C is 9500 kW. At 45°C, the power output drops to approximately 6600 kW. At an ambient air temperature of -30°C, the power output is almost 12 000 kW.

Effect of Compressor Discharge Pressure & Turbine Inlet Temperature

The two major factors in determining efficiency and power are compression ratio across the compressor and turbine inlet temperature:

- The greater the compressor ratio, the higher is the cycle efficiency and the greater the power output.
- An increase in the turbine inlet temperature has the same effect because more work is done by the same amount of air.

Although factors, such as compressor and turbine efficiency and pressure losses, are important, the largest efforts in gas turbine design have been to increase the compression ratio and to improve combustion and turbine materials so that the turbine inlet temperature can be increased. With these improvements, simple cycle efficiency has now reached 40%. With combined cycle applications, the total efficiency of the gas turbine plant can exceed 60%.

Maximum Power

The maximum power that can be achieved is also a function of the life expected of the hot gas path components. Vendors usually specify a maximum power that will permit the engine to achieve a reasonable life. They also specify a maximum peak power limit that can be applied if a user is willing to incur higher maintenance costs. This tradeoff is often used for peak power generation where gas turbines operate for only short periods of time to satisfy peak electrical load conditions. For base load operation, maximum power is not desirable because of the increased maintenance costs and the risk of failure.

CHAPTER 4 - QUESTIONS

1. Describe the advantages of a gas turbine and its applications.

2. Identify the major components of a simple cycle gas turbine and their basic functions.

3. Explain the different types of shaft arrangements for gas turbines.

4. Describe the difference between simple and closed cycles.

5. What are the respective purposes of intercooling, regeneration and reheat?

6. Describe the important considerations for compressor design and the types of compressors.

7. Describe the types of combustors and how they operate.

8. Explain how the turbine section works.

9. List the functions of a gas turbine control system.

10. Describe the effects of compressor inlet temperature, compressor discharge pressure, and turbine inlet temperature on gas turbine performance.

   ANSWERS: All answers are found within the content of the chapter.

Gas Turbine Auxiliaries & Operation

LEARNING OUTCOME

When you complete this chapter you should be able to:

Describe the support auxiliaries for a gas turbine and explain common operational, control and maintenance procedures.

LEARNING OBJECTIVES

Here is what you should be able to do when you complete each objective:

1. Describe the types of bearings used in a gas turbine and explain the components, operation, protective devices and routine maintenance of a typical lube oil system.

2. Describe and explain the operation and routine maintenance of a typical fuel gas supply system for a gas turbine.

3. Describe and explain the operation and routine maintenance of a typical fuel oil supply system for a gas turbine.

4. Explain the control of NOx from a gas turbine and describe the purpose and operation of water/steam injection and dry low NOx systems.

5. Explain the purpose, location and operation of the gas turbine starting motor and turning gear.

6. Describe the compressor intake and the turbine exhaust components.

7. Describe the preparation and complete start-up sequence for a gas turbine.

8. Describe the shutdown sequence and procedure for a gas turbine.

9. Explain the purpose and describe typical on-line and off-line waterwash procedures for gas turbine blades.

OBJECTIVE 1

Describe the types of bearings used in a gas turbine and explain the components, operation, protective devices and routine maintenance of a typical lube oil system.

GAS TURBINE BEARINGS

Gas turbines use two different types of bearings:

- Antifriction (roller and/or ball) bearings, which are common in aero-derivative gas turbines with relatively lightweight rotors
- Radial (journal or tilt-pad) bearings for heavy-duty, industrial gas turbines, which have heavier rotors

Figure 1 illustrates an antifriction (roller) bearing. It features a special upper squeeze film to dampen the bearing and increase its life. An engine with this bearing would usually also have thrust bearings of the ball design.

Figure 1	Antifriction Bearing

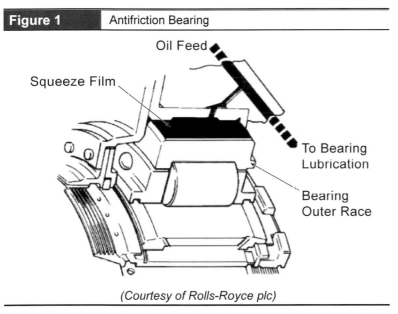

(Courtesy of Rolls-Royce plc)

Heavy-duty gas turbines require bearings that can take higher loads. Although standard journal bearings have been used, the most common type of radial bearing is the tilt-pad bearing.

Figure 2 shows a bearing with five tilting pads on individual pivot pins.

Figure 3 shows a tilt-pad thrust bearing.

On a typical dual-shaft heavy-duty gas turbine, bearings will be located at both ends of the compressor and at both ends of the power turbine. Thrust bearings will be positioned at the inlet end of the compressor and next to the power turbine bearings (one for each shaft).

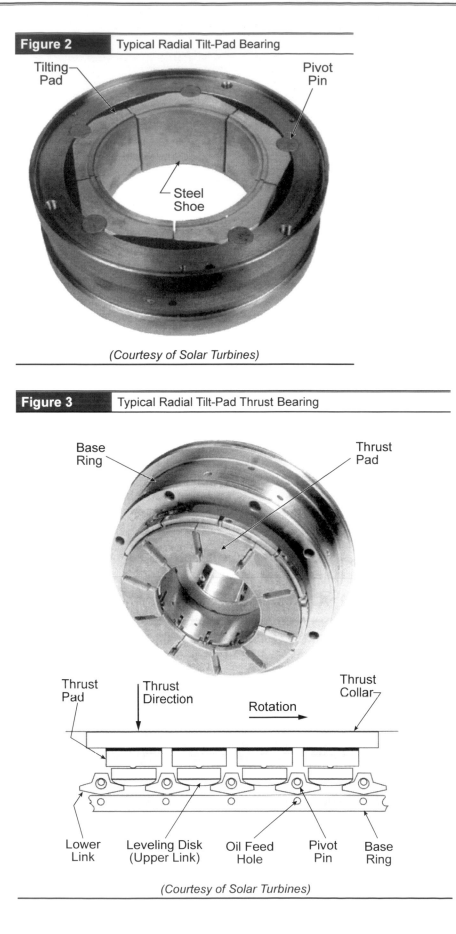

Figure 2   Typical Radial Tilt-Pad Bearing

Tilting Pad

Pivot Pin

Steel Shoe

(Courtesy of Solar Turbines)

Figure 3   Typical Radial Tilt-Pad Thrust Bearing

Base Ring

Thrust Pad

Thrust Pad

Thrust Direction

Rotation

Thrust Collar

Lower Link

Leveling Disk (Upper Link)

Oil Feed Hole

Pivot Pin

Base Ring

(Courtesy of Solar Turbines)

LUBE OIL SYSTEMS

Almost all gas turbines have a lube oil system that lubricates the bearings that support the rotor or rotors. Aero-derivative gas turbines normally use antifriction bearings which require only a small lube oil system. Heavy-duty gas turbines use radial bearings that necessitate a larger lube oil system. Microturbines are an exception and, because of their small size, are able to operate with air bearings that do not require a lube oil system.

Gas turbine installations may have more than one lube oil system. These are the major configurations:

- Some heavy-duty gas turbines have a single integrated lube oil system that serves the gas turbine, power turbine, gearbox and driven equipment (compressor or generator)
- Other heavy-duty gas turbines have a lube oil system dedicated to the gas turbine and power turbine but a separate lube oil system for the load machine
- Most aero-derivatives require separate lube oil systems for the engine and for the power turbine and load

All lube oil systems provide two basic functions:

- Lubricate sliding surfaces in the bearings
- Cool the bearings; especially those located close to the combustion and turbine sections of the gas turbine

All oil systems consist of these basic components:

- An oil reservoir to ensure an adequate supply of oil
- Filters to ensure the oil is clean
- Pumps to provide pressure
- Coolers to ensure oil temperatures are kept within operating limits
- Protective, monitoring and control devices

Aero-Derivative Gas Turbine Lube Oil System

Figure 4 shows a typical lube oil system for an aero-derivative gas turbine used for power generation. It lubricates the bearings of both the compressor turbine and the power turbine. Lubrication of the driven machine is handled by a separate system.

The oil system is divided into two sections: a supply system and a scavenge system. The scavenge system returns the oil from the bearings to the supply and treating equipment. All piping, fittings and reservoir are Type 304 Stainless Steel to prevent corrosion. The system uses synthetic oil suitable for high temperatures.

The oil reservoir contains approximately 500 litres in a 568 litre tank. Protection devices are fitted for low oil level and low oil temperature. A thermostatically controlled heater ensures a minimum temperature is maintained when the unit is not operating, to ensure easy starting.

A positive displacement pump, driven by an auxiliary gearbox on the engine, provides the required pressure to the bearings. After the pump, the oil is filtered by a duplex, full-flow filter that allows the filter elements to be changed while running. The oil supplied equipment is protected by high oil temperature, low oil pressure and high filter differential pressure switches.

The oil flows through the bearings and accumulates in the bearing sumps. The oil temperature is measured at each scavenge line.

Scavenge pumps, driven by the auxiliary gearbox of the turbine, provide the pressure for the oil to flow through another set of filters and then through duplex, water-cooled coolers that are thermostatically controlled. The oil then flows back to the reservoir.

| Figure 4 | Typical Aeroderivative Lube Oil System |

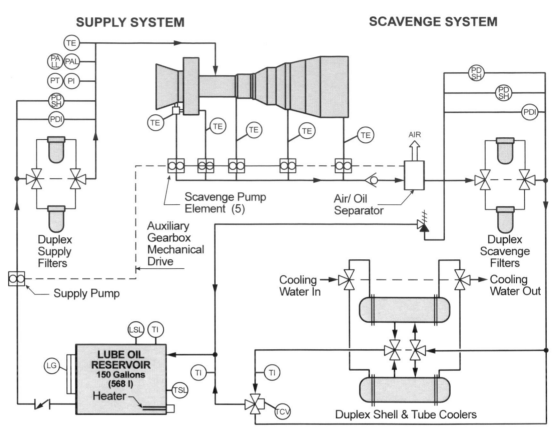

(Courtesy of General Electric)

Chip detectors are often located in the sumps to detect any metal particles that originate from damaged bearings. A chip detector uses a magnet to attract metallic particles and alarms when they accumulate on the magnet. The detector is removed and inspected to diagnose the type and extent of bearing damage.

Heavy-Duty Gas Turbine Lube Oil System

The lube oil system shown in Figure 5 is typical for a heavy-duty gas turbine, with a single, integrated oil system that supplies the gas turbine, gearbox and driven equipment.

The oil reservoir is much larger than for aero-derivative gas turbines. It normally contains mineral oil, which does not have as high a temperature capability as synthetic oil, but is more economical. Generally, oil temperatures are not as high in heavy-duty gas turbines since the oil flow is greater. Oil heating may be supplied if required.

Oil pressure is supplied during normal operation by a main lube oil pump driven from the accessory drive mounted on the front of the compressor shaft. Prior to startup and on shutdown, oil pressure is supplied by a motor driven pre/post lube oil pump. This pump runs for a period of time after shutdown to cool and lubricate the bearings and prevent damage. A third pump using another source of energy (for example a direct current motor supplied by batteries) is available as backup in case of power loss or pre/post lube oil pump failure.

The oil is cleaned with duplex filters that allow filter replacement during operation. There is a differential pressure alarm and pressure gauge. The oil is then cooled prior to entering the bearings by either an air or water cooler. At the lube oil header, there is protection against high oil temperature and low oil pressure.

The oil drains back into the oil reservoir using gravity. The oil temperature is also normally measured in the drains to monitor bearing health.

Figure 5	Lube Oil System for a Typical Heavy Duty Gas Turbine

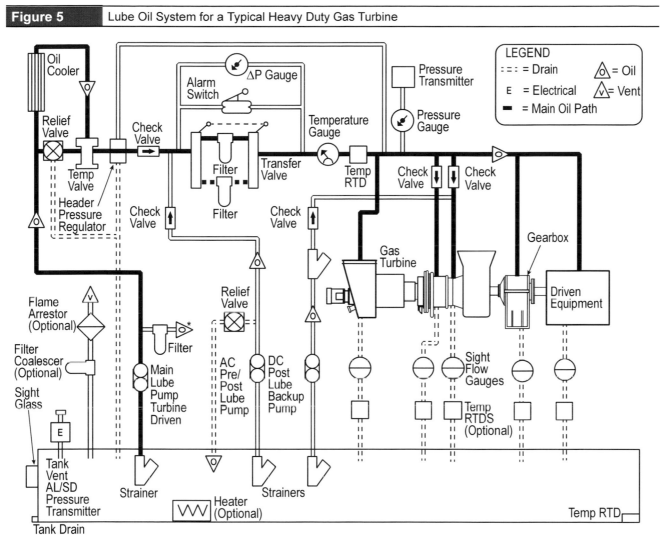

*To guide vane, bleed valve and fuel actuators

Hydraulic System

A hydraulic pump is sometimes provided downstream of the main lube oil pump to supply high pressure oil for the actuation of the main turbine instrumentation for controlling speed and load. The location of the connection for this point is shown in Figure 5 by an asterisk (*), located just after a filter branching off of the main lube oil line, immediately downstream of the main lube pump. The hydraulic system is typically the medium through which the turbine speed sensor sends its signal to the speed control valve that modulates the fuel flow to the turbine, as well as to the variable inlet and stator vanes, and bleed valves.

Oil System Maintenance

Oil systems are relatively maintenance free and automatic protection is usually provided against common problems. Maintenance consists of:

- Checking for oil leaks (usually daily)
- Monitoring oil pressures and temperatures (usually daily)
- Checking chip detectors when they alarm
- Topping up the oil reservoir or secondary lube oil tank. Often the reservoir is kept filled by a second supply tank with an automatic slow fill valve and level control.
- Changing oil filters when the differential pressure alarms
- Cleaning the cooler externally
- Taking oil samples regularly for analysis and replacing oil when required
- Calibrating instrumentation and testing protective devices

System temperatures and pressures, and the status of pumps, filters and coolers, are usually monitored and displayed on computer screens. This type of interface may also be used to start or stop the lubrication and hydraulic system pumps.

OBJECTIVE 2

Describe and explain the operation and routine maintenance of a typical fuel gas supply system for a gas turbine.

NATURAL GAS FUEL

Natural gas is the best fuel for gas turbines since it promotes the most efficient combustion and produces the lowest environmental emissions. Engine life is also the longest with clean natural gas. It has to be within a specified range of heating values and be free of liquid contaminants. Natural gas is often heated to ensure no liquids are present. If fuel with a low energy value is used, special fuel nozzles and combustors have to be installed and the fuel gas system has to be adapted because of the corresponding requirement for higher flow rates.

FUEL GAS SYSTEM

The fuel gas system shown in Figure 6 is typical for most gas turbines.

Figure 6	Typical Fuel Gas System

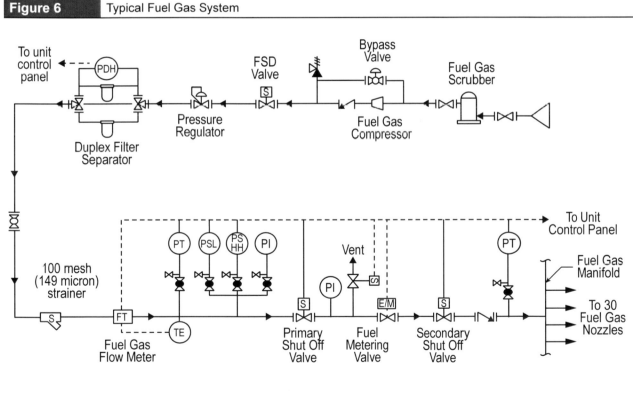

(Courtesy of General Electric)

A fuel gas compressor is shown in case extra compression is required to boost a low pressure fuel source. The pressure of the fuel gas has to be higher than the compressed air delivered to the combustion section. A pressure regulator and relief valve are also installed to ensure steady fuel pressures at the combustor. Low and high pressure switches protect against over or under pressure conditions.

A fuel filter is then installed to ensure contaminants do not enter the fuel system. Some systems also have a heat exchanger to remove liquids and increase fuel temperature to required levels.

A fuel gas flow meter is installed to enable the determination of fuel consumption but is otherwise not needed for fuel control.

The fuel flow rate is measured and controlled by the fuel metering valve which is the most important component of the fuel gas system. It ensures that the right amount of fuel is provided for the operating conditions. It is precisely controlled to ensure that the maximum turbine temperature is not exceeded. It is an essential component of the startup and shutdown sequence. The rate at which the fuel valve is opened or closed is also limited to prevent temperature increases that might damage the turbine. Additional shutoff valves are provided for emergency purposes.

Figure 7 shows a typical fuel valve. They are normally electrically controlled with hydraulic actuation but electrically actuated valves are starting to become common.

Figure 7	Typical Fuel Gas Metering Valve

(Courtesy of General Electric)

ROUTINE MAINTENANCE

Fuel gas systems are relatively maintenance free and automatic protection is usually provided against common problems. Maintenance consists of:

- Checking for fuel gas leaks (usually daily)
- Monitoring pressures and temperatures (usually daily)
- Changing fuel filters at the required differential pressure
- Calibrating instrumentation and testing protective devices

Figure 8 shows a typical computer control system display used for monitoring a fuel system. Since the unit is stopped, the valves are in the closed position except for the vent valves. The 310 valve is a pressure regulator, the 20F12 valve is the main shutoff valve and the 65BA valve is the fuel metering valve.

Figure 8 Monitoring Screen for the Fuel Gas Control System

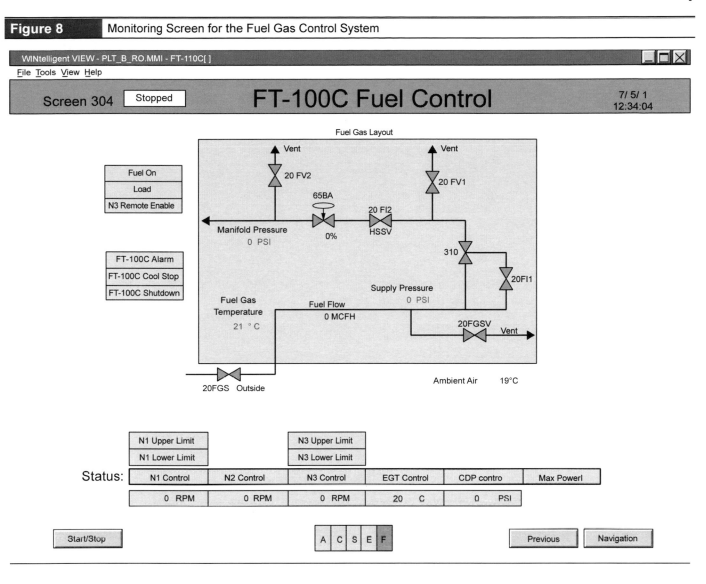

(Courtesy of Rolls-Royce plc)

OBJECTIVE 3

Describe and explain the operation and routine maintenance of a typical fuel oil supply system for a gas turbine.

LIQUID FUELS

The gas turbine can operate on a wide range of liquid fuels including:

- Distillates, such as kerosene, for which no fuel treatment is required
- Blended heavy distillates and low ash crudes, which require some treatment
- Residuals and heavy ash crudes that require considerable cleaning and treatment

The life of the gas turbine (in terms of time between maintenance actions and overhauls) is reduced as the quality of the fuel decreases. Maintenance costs increase as well.

FUEL OIL SYSTEM

A typical fuel oil system is shown in Figure 9.

The system starts with a fuel storage tank and fuel treatment.

| Figure 9 | Typical Liquid Fuel System |

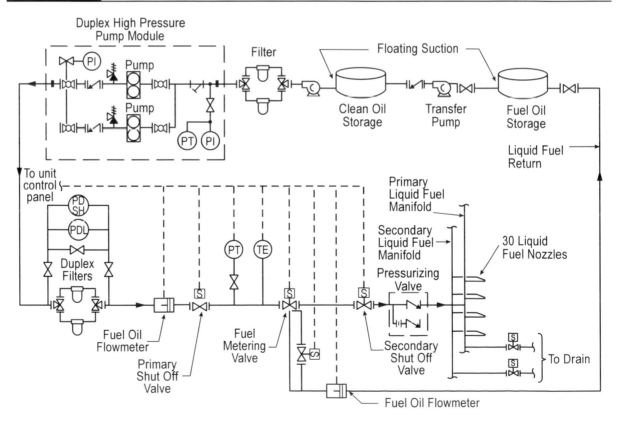

(Courtesy of General Electric)

Treatment varies with the type of fuel and may include centrifuges, filters, de-watering and chemical treatment. Chemicals that are especially harmful to the turbine section are sodium, potassium and vanadium since they cause rapid corrosion.

The cleaned and treated oil is then filtered and pumped to the gas turbine where it is filtered once more. There is a main metering valve with a primary and secondary shutoff valve. At the fuel metering valve, there is an overflow for unused fuel back to the fuel tank. Drains are provided on the fuel manifolds.

Protective instrumentation is installed for filter differential pressure and low pressure.

Dual Fuel Systems

Some gas turbine installations feature dual fuel capability so that the operator can switch to a less expensive fuel or as a backup.

An example of a dual fuel system is shown in Figure 10.

- Liquid fuel is shown entering at the top left of the diagram, while fuel gas is entering at the lower right.
- The electronic control unit in the centre of the system selects which metering and control system (liquid or gas) will be in operation, and therefore which fuel will be sent to the burners.
- A special fuel nozzle is required and the control system is more complex to manage the two types of fuels and to accommodate the switchover between them. With some systems, a mixture of gaseous and liquid fuels can be burned simultaneously.

Figure 10	Typical Dual Fuel System

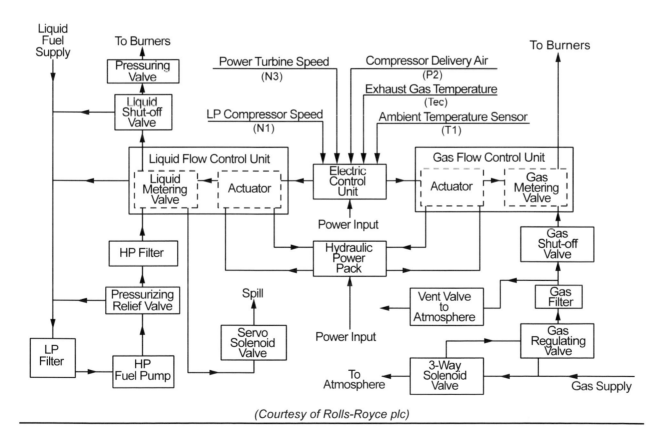

(Courtesy of Rolls-Royce plc)

ROUTINE MAINTENANCE

Fuel oil systems are relatively maintenance free and automatic protection is usually provided against common problems. If specialized fuel treatment is required (for example when waste products are being used as fuel sources) more maintenance is generally required.

Maintenance consists of:

- Checking for fuel oil leaks (usually daily)
- Monitoring pressures and temperatures (usually daily)
- Cleaning centrifuges and other treatment components and replenishing chemicals
- Changing fuel filters at the required differential pressure
- Calibrating instrumentation and testing protective devices.

OBJECTIVE 4

Explain the control of NOₓ from a gas turbine and describe the purpose and operation of water/steam injection and dry low NOₓ systems.

NOₓ EMISSIONS

NO_X refers to a family of compounds – NO and NO_2. They are formed during combustion from the reaction of the oxygen and nitrogen naturally occurring in the air, and are partially responsible for creating acid rain. As can be seen in Figure 11, the rate of NO_X formation decreases exponentially as the temperature decreases. The main way to decrease NO_X is to decrease the fuel to air ratio and operate with a lean fuel mixture. However, a decrease in combustion temperature also increases the undesirable formation of CO (carbon monoxide) so a balance has to be achieved.

Figure 11	Chart of NOₓ Emissions vs. Combustion Temperature

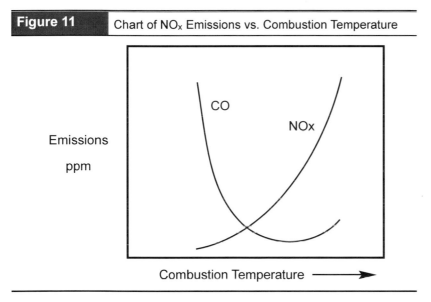

WATER OR STEAM INJECTION SYSTEMS

Water or steam injection reduces NO_X by dropping the combustion temperature, which drastically reduces the formation of NO_X. Either steam or water can be used depending on what is most easily available. Cleanliness and purity of the water or steam is of paramount importance to prevent corrosion of hot section components.

The water or steam can be injected into the combustion section through the fuel nozzles or can be premixed with liquid fuels in a separate manifold.

Aside from increased corrosion, the main disadvantage of water or steam injection is that, as more water or steam is injected to further reduce NO_X, the thermal efficiency is reduced because of the energy transferred to the water or steam. There is also an increase in combustion activity and pulsation, which reduces the life of hot section components. There is, however, an increase in power output that is important to some users.

The practical limit for NO_X emissions achievable with water or steam injection is 25 ppm for natural gas and 42 ppm for liquid fuels.

DRY LOW NOX COMBUSTION SYSTEMS

The standard scrubbing method for limiting NO_X is now mostly being replaced by dry low NO_X (DLN for dry low NO_X or DLE for dry low NO_X emission) technology, which is able to achieve the lower levels now required. The standard maximum level for NO_X in many locations is now 25 ppm and some gas turbines are now able to reach levels of 9 ppm.

Dry low NO_X combustion systems operate on the principle of lean premixed combustion. Air and fuel are premixed to the proper lean proportion and then combusted at lower temperatures. This requires an increase in combustion area.

Figure 12 shows a DLE configuration. Instead of single fuel nozzles, a triple annulus arrangement is used. They are staged over the operation of the gas turbine so that only one is used at low speeds; another one is activated at medium load and the third one is added at maximum speeds. The extensive solenoid arrangement required to make this work can be seen in Figure 12.

Other manufacturers use variations on this approach but the basic principles are the same. In all cases, fuel control becomes more complicated to enable low NO_X to be achieved over the entire operating envelope. Some vendors are also supplying retrofit options for existing equipment.

Catalytic systems, either during combustion or after a combined cycle exhaust heat exchanger, offer future possibilities for very low levels of emissions. However, they are still in the research and development stages and will not be commercially viable for some time to come.

Figure 12	Pneumatic Starter Installation Fuel Manifold and Solenoids for Low NO_X Combustors

(Courtesy of General Electric)

OBJECTIVE 5

Explain the purpose, location and operation of the gas turbine starting motor and turning gear.

STARTING SYSTEMS

Gas turbines must have a source of power (other than the compressor or load turbines) to provide the initial compression needed for ignition. This power source is used to rotate the large mass of the compressor, and bring it up to the speed necessary to supply combustion air to the combustor. The starting system engages the compressor shaft at the beginning of the start-up. Once ignition has been obtained, this system is disengaged from the compressor shaft. A variety of devices can be used to provide the initial rotation of the main compressor, including:

- pneumatic starters using compressed air or gas
- electric motors
- small diesel engines
- steam turbine expanders

Of these, pneumatic starters and electric motors are the most common.

Pneumatic Starters

High pressure air or gas can be expanded in a small turbine (called a starter motor) to drive the main gas turbine compressor up to ignition conditions. This is a particularly convenient system in remote gas pipeline applications (where the gas turbine itself is used to drive large transmission compressors). The high pressure pipeline gas is used as the starting gas supply.

Figure 13 and 14 illustrate a pneumatic starter system.

In this case a dual starter configuration is used. The user has the option of using air or gas depending on the most convenient source. The exhaust of the starter motor is normally vented to the atmosphere. The starter transmits power to the front end of the gas turbine rotor by means of an overrunning clutch. The shutoff valve is also pneumatically operated.

Figure 13	Pneumatic Starter System Diagram

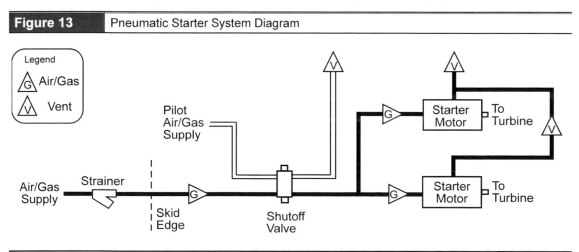

Figure 14	Pneumatic Starter Installation

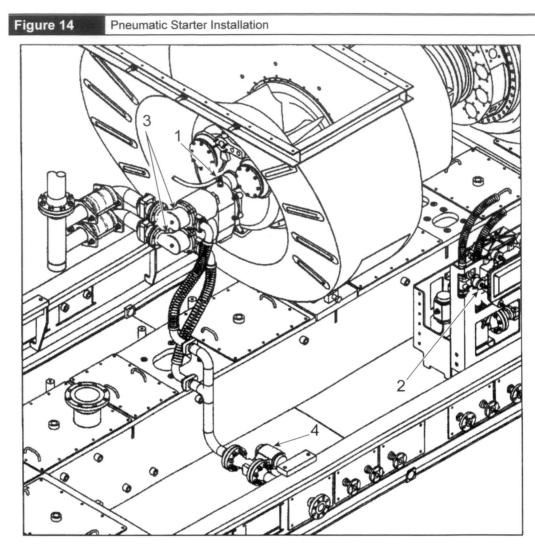

1. Clutch Lubrication Fixed Orifice
2. Gas Shutoff Pilot Solenoid Valve
3. Pneumatic Starter Motor
4. Gas Shutoff Valve

Electric Starters

Electric starters consist of an AC motor and a variable frequency drive as shown in Figures 15 and 16, but otherwise operate in the same fashion as a pneumatic starter. The variable frequency drive enables the motor speed to be controlled while still maintaining motor efficiency.

Figure 15	Electric Starter Diagram

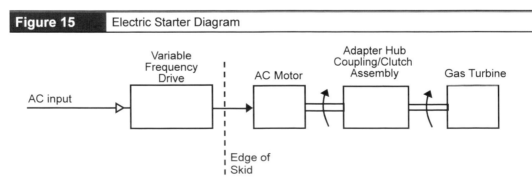

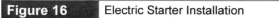

Figure 16	Electric Starter Installation

TURNING GEAR

On larger gas turbines, especially of the heavy-duty type, the rotors are quite heavy and they develop a sag or bow when they cool down after shutdown. If a rotor becomes bowed, the rotor may lock and prevent startup or it may result in high vibration until the bow slowly disappears.

To prevent this, a special turning motor is provided to slowly turn the shaft for a number of hours after shutdown. This is sometimes a hydraulic ratchet or a slow turning electric motor. The motor and the turbine shaft have corresponding gears. The turning motor gear can be engaged or disengaged (normal turbine operation) with the shaft. A similar type of device is used on large steam turbines for their warm-up and cool-down periods.

OBJECTIVE 6

Describe the compressor intake and the turbine exhaust components.

AIR INTAKE SYSTEM

The air intake system ensures that clean air is provided to the gas turbine. To achieve this, air filters are installed in the intake to filter the air. The type of air intake system is dependent on the environmental conditions encountered at the gas turbine location. Special challenges are posed when a gas turbine is installed on an offshore platform, close to the ocean, in a desert or dusty location, or in an arctic environment. The intake system becomes more complicated if intake cooling (to increase power at high ambient temperatures) is required, or if icing conditions may occur.

A typical intake system is shown in Figure 17.

Note that in this design, the air intake is positioned above the enclosure both to save space and to place the intake in a higher position where the air may be cleaner. The intake is designed to allow the installation of intake cooling and/or anti-icing. The first stage of filtration is a stainless steel screen to prevent entry of major debris. The main filtration is achieved by a series of cylindrical filters mounted inside the air intake.

| Figure 17 | Typical Air Intake System |

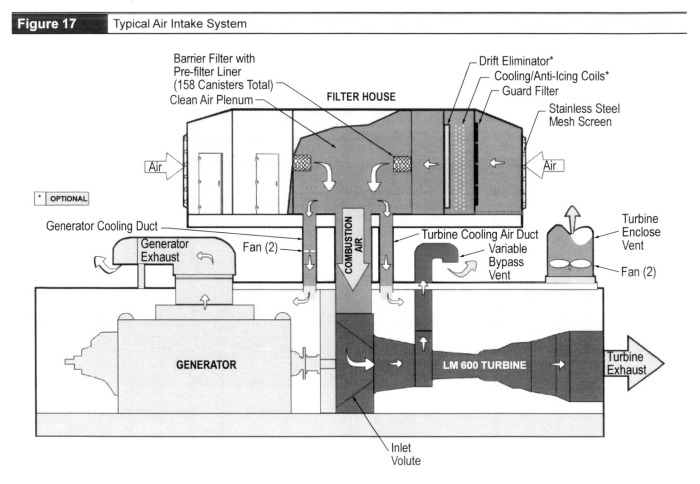

(Courtesy of General Electric)

In the past, many filter systems were based on inertial filtering which consisted of a series of vanes that deflected the air to separate the contaminants, using centrifugal force. The current approach is to use many small cylindrical filters such as the ones shown in Figure 18. In this system, compressed air is used to backflow individual filters and dislodge the dust that has collected on them. These "pulse cleaning systems" are commonly called "huff and puff", and operate automatically, based on pressure differential. They work well in both dusty and cold weather conditions.

Figure 18	Pulse Cleaning Filter

(Courtesy of Donaldson Company)

Inlet Cooling

Inlet cooling systems that decrease the temperature of the inlet air and thereby increase power output have been available for a long time but are now seeing renewed interest. They are based on the principle of evaporative cooling. When water evaporates, it requires a large amount of latent heat, which is provided by the warmer air. The result is a drop in air temperature.

Various methods are used today:

- Spray cooling where water is sprayed into the intake in fine droplets
- Fog cooling where a very fine fog is produced using a high pressure spray
- Special evaporative pads

Anti-Icing Systems

If chunks of ice are ingested into the compressor, major damage can result, including catastrophic destruction of the compressor section blading.

The formation of ice in the air intake or on the first few stages of the compressor can occur if a certain combination of temperature and humidity occurs. Figure 19 shows a chart relating relative humidity and ambient temperature. If the combination of these two falls within the shaded area, the condition is right for ice to form.

Figure 19	Range of Icing Conditions

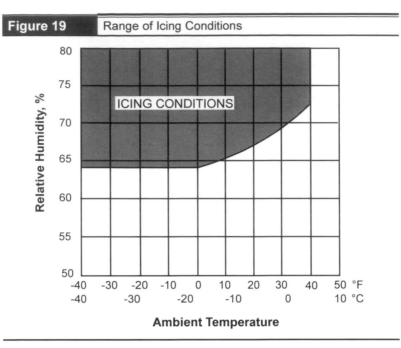

Ambient Temperature

In climates where icing is possible, gas turbine intakes are usually fitted with an anti-icing system, which may include:

- bleeding air from the compressor and injecting it into the front of the compressor through the nose cone and the first few stator vanes (see Fig. 20)
- installing heating coils in the air intake
- feeding heated air from some other source (such as the exhaust) into the air intake

Introducing warm air into the gas turbine intake will reduce the capacity of the unit, because warm air is less dense than cold air. The increase in air temperature means less mass will flow through the turbine. Therefore, anti-icing systems are used only when necessary.

Figure 20	Anti-Icing System

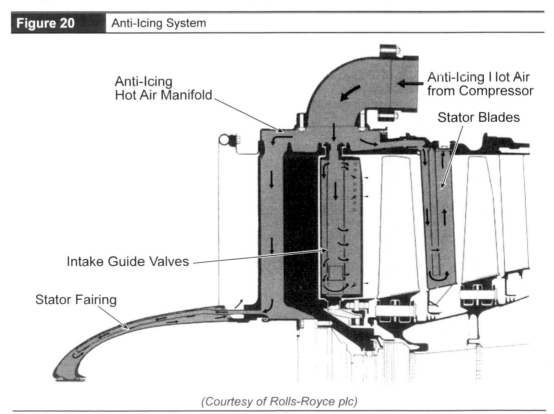

(Courtesy of Rolls-Royce plc)

EXHAUST SYSTEM

The exhaust system directs the hot turbine exhaust, at the lowest possible pressure, to a location that is safe for employees and other equipment. It must be designed for the high temperature of the exhaust and be structurally sound. Noise attenuation and silencers may be required to meet local requirements. Care must be taken that the exhaust air does not re-circulate into the air intake since this will result in a loss of turbine power.

The exhaust may incorporate a heat exchange for regeneration or combined cycle installations. An example is shown in Figure 21. Two gas turbines (GTA and GTB) exhaust into a common duct going to the water wall section of a boiler. The Heat Recovery Steam Generator (boiler) tubes are not shown, but they are connected to two steam drums. After leaving the boiler section, the exhaust gas provides heat to an economizer section, which preheats the boiler feedwater, and then travels to the stack and the atmosphere.

Immediately downstream of each of the turbine outlets, there is a diverter damper that permits the air to be exhausted directly to the atmosphere if the steam system is not operative. Prior to the heat recovery system, there is also a supplemental burner system to increase the exhaust temperature and thereby the recovery capacity of the boiler.

Figure 21	Combined Cycle Exhaust System

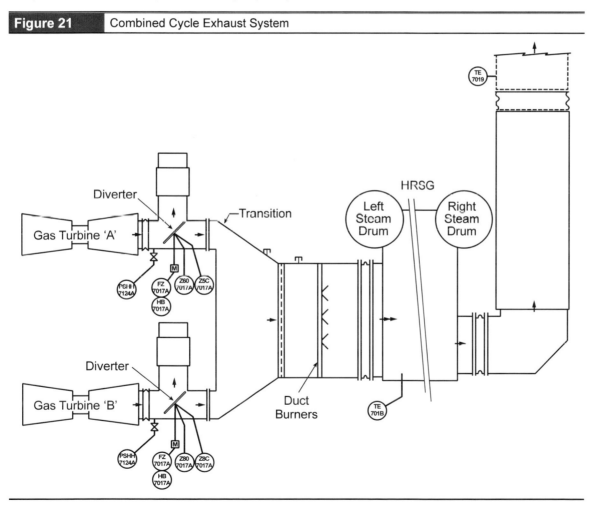

OBJECTIVE 7

Describe the preparation and complete start-up sequence for a gas turbine.

GAS TURBINE STARTUP PROCEDURE

The basic steps in starting a gas turbine are:

- Preparation for startup
- Start initiation
- Crank and lightoff
- Warmup
- Loading

These steps must occur in a specific sequence and at certain time intervals. They are usually managed by the control system and the operator often has no role except to watch the process. If certain conditions occur or specific requirements are not met at some point in the startup sequence, the startup will be aborted and the unit stopped. The progress of the startup is displayed on a control panel such as the one shown in Figure 22.

Figure 22	Typical Control Panel used to Monitor Startup, Shutdown and Operation

Preparation for Startup

When a start is initiated, it is assumed that all electrical, pneumatic, air, instrumentation and control systems are activated and energized. These systems will usually be active and will only need to be turned on if the equipment has been shut down for maintenance or an extended period of no demand. In remote applications, startup normally occurs automatically without human participation and intervention unless an abnormal situation requires response.

The operator may need to reset the system if a previous malfunction or abnormal condition has occurred. This is done by pressing a reset switch on the panel, or on a computer screen.

There are also a number of 'permissives' that need to be satisfied before the start sequence will be allowed by the control system. Some of these will pertain to the gas turbine, such as a minimum oil reservoir temperature, and others are related to the requirements of the particular load being driven by the turbine (typically an electrical generator or process/transmission gas compressor).

Figure 23 shows an example of a startup screen for a gas turbine driving a gas compressor.

Figure 23	Startup Screen with Permissives

(Courtesy of Rolls-Royce plc)

Start Initiation

A gas turbine is normally in one of two modes of operation: remote or local. The mode of operation is set either by a switch on the control panel or a selection box on a computer screen. When in remote, a higher level process control system has the ability to initiate a start. When in local, the start can only be initiated from the control panel.

During the startup sequence, a number of operating conditions must be met as determined by various pressure, temperature and status switches. Timers are used to ensure these conditions occur in the expected time period, or else the startup will be aborted. An example of a startup sequence screen is given in Figure 24. Notice the sequence of steps and the descriptions in the two left columns.

| Figure 24 | Startup Screen with Sequencing Status |

(Courtesy of Rolls-Royce plc)

When the start button is pressed (locally or remotely), the following occurs:

- The ventilation fans starts which vents the building or enclosure.

- Pre-lubrication occurs. Depending on the design of the lube oil system, the backup pump will start, and if adequate pressure is achieved within a certain time period, the pre-lube pump will start and the pre-lube timer resets to ensure adequate pressure.

- There may be a check of the fuel gas system to ensure that the fuel valves are operating properly and adequate fuel pressure is available.

Crank & Lightoff

Once these steps have been completed, the starter begins to rotate the gas turbine rotor (see Fig. 25). The first portion of this process purges the gas turbine for several minutes to ensure no explosive vapors are present. The rotor then coasts down to light-off speed.

Fuel is then admitted to the combustion chambers, the igniters are energized and lightoff occurs. This results in a rapid increase in speed. The overrunning clutch disengages the starter, which then shuts down, and the igniters are de-energized.

Figure 25	Startup of a Typical Gas Turbine

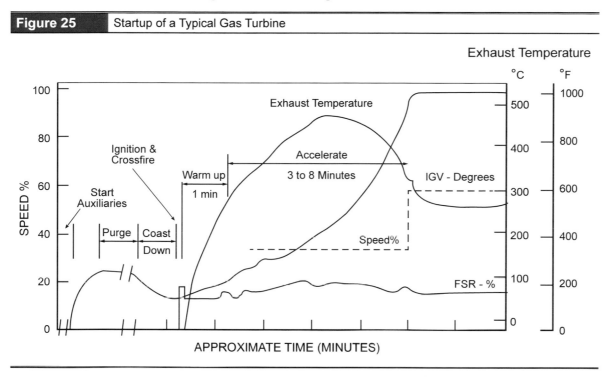

Warmup

Once idle speed is reached, the engine is allowed to warm up. For backup power generation, especially for small gas turbines, this may be very short. When time is not as critical, it is best to permit the engine to warm up slowly. Heavy-duty gas turbines take longer to start and warm up than aero-derivatives.

On start initiation, the bleed valve(s) will be open and the inlet and variable guide vanes will be in their closed position. The bleed valves will close either at a certain speed or over a specified range of speeds. The guide vanes will open to their optimum position over a range of speeds as designated by a specified schedule (based on a control program that relates guide vane position to turbine speed).

Loading

After the warm-up is finished, the fuel flow is increased and the load is applied. For a generator, this will require synchronizing the speed, phase and voltage, and then closing the breaker.

If the gas turbine drives a compressor, the compressor will have been de-pressurized prior to the purge crank, and the suction and discharge valves will have been opened. The compressor is started in the unloaded position, with the recycle valve open. Loading is accomplished by slowly closing in on the recycle valve. The actual operating point will be determined by the control system.

The acceleration and deceleration of the gas turbine is limited to a certain rate. Sudden increases in speed will cause rapid increases in turbine temperature that could easily be above the limit. A rapid decrease in speed could cause combustion to be interrupted and any re-lighting, without going through the required start-up procedure, would be catastrophic.

OBJECTIVE 8

Describe the shutdown sequence and procedure for a gas turbine.

NORMAL SHUTDOWN

Shutdown of a gas turbine is most often initiated by an operator although some systems do have an automatic shutdown when the gas turbine is no longer required. To a large extent, a shutdown is the reverse procedure of a startup.

- The first step in a normal shutdown is to reduce speed to idle so the gas turbine can cool down. In this step the power turbine is unloaded, for example, by opening the breaker that connects the generator to the power system or opening the recycle valve of the compressor. The gas turbine cools down as much as possible to minimize the negative thermal effects. During this time, the engine can easily be restarted, according to the specified procedure.
- When the cooldown timer times out, the fuel valve is closed which extinguishes combustion. The rotor speed decreases until the rotor stops.
- As the speed drops, the main lube oil pump (if driven off the rotor) will lose pressure. At a specified point, usually based on oil pressure, the postlube pump starts up and continues to lubricate and cool the bearings for a specified time period.
- The enclosure or building fans shut off.
- On some gas turbines, the turning gear activates once the rotor stops.

FAST SHUTDOWN

In certain situations a fast shutdown will be initiated. This occurs when a protective device detects an abnormal condition such as high vibration, or when an operator initiates an emergency stop. In this case, the cooldown period is eliminated and the fuel valve is closed immediately. The rest of the shutdown sequence is the same as for a normal shutdown.

This type of shutdown increases the wear on the gas turbine because of the rapid cooldown it entails and is reserved for emergency conditions only.

OBJECTIVE 9

Explain the purpose and describe typical on-line and off-line waterwash procedures for gas turbine blades.

INTRODUCTION

The major cause of deterioration in gas turbine performance is fouling of the compressor blading. Fouling results in a decrease in compressor efficiency which reduces overall thermal efficiency and maximum power. It will also result in compressor surging and acceleration problems.

The source of contamination is usually dust, salt and other airborne particles that are not trapped by the intake filters. Contamination can also come from other machinery close to the gas turbine or even the gas turbine exhaust being re-ingested under certain wind conditions. Sometimes, a compressor front bearing oil leak will make the problem worse.

Compressor cleaning can be accomplished by using either a liquid or an abrasive material. In the past, it was quite common for walnut shells or even rice (or other abrasive materials sometimes called carbo-blast) to be injected into the intake to abrasively clean the compressor blading. This is done while the unit is running and the materials are burnt up in the combustion section and then pass through the engine. Since it is not as effective as the waterwash method, it is not utilized as often any more. It also has the disadvantage of plugging up cooling passages in the compressor and cooling holes in the turbine blades.

The most effective method of compressor cleaning is the off-line waterwash. This method consists of stopping the unit, injecting waterwash fluids into the intake of the compressor while running on the starter and then restarting. It is also referred to as the crank-soak method.

On-line waterwashing is not as effective as off-line although it is still a viable alternative if downtime is not acceptable.

WATERWASH FLUIDS

The water used must be very clean and must conform to quality standards specified by the gas turbine vendor. Using hard water or water contaminated with sodium, potassium, vanadium or other chemicals can cause further fouling and increased corrosion.

To remove oily substances, additional cleaning agents and solvents need to be used. These are mixed with water and acceptable cleaners are often specified by gas turbine vendors. However, the most effective cleaning agents are also the most toxic and require special handling.

If the temperature is less than 4°C, a 1:1 mixture of water and ethylene glycol is recommended to prevent icing. Again the gas turbine vendor has to be consulted since commercial and automotive anti-freeze products are usually not acceptable.

Off-Line Waterwash

To perform the off-line waterwash, the engine is stopped and allowed to cool. Some vendors specify that various instrumentation, bleed and drain lines be disconnected prior to water washing. The engine is then run at maximum crank speed with the fuel valve and igniters deactivated. Once all of the wash fluid has been sprayed into the intake, all disconnected lines are reconnected and the unit can be restarted.

The waterwash fluid is injected through either a pre-installed waterwash ring or a hand-held sprayer. The waterwash may be installed on the intake bellmouth as shown in Figure 26 or on the intake volute.

As seen in Figure 26, due to the difference in airflow there are two spray ring assemblies, one for on-line wash and one for off-line wash.

Figure 26	Waterwash Connections

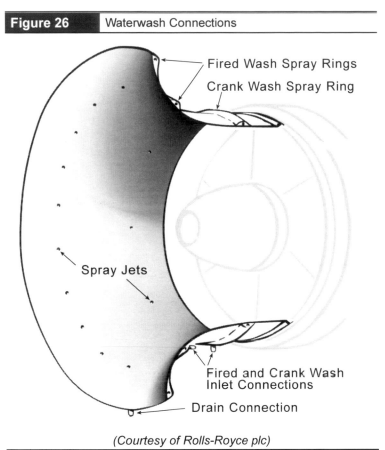

(Courtesy of Rolls-Royce plc)

In some cases, operators will actually go into the intake to manually scrub and wash the first few stages with a brush if deposits are especially stubborn.

The waterwash fluids are contained in a special tank and the spray pressure is provided by compressed air applied to the tank. This tank may be permanently installed or located on a special, portable cart, such as the one in Figure 27.

Figure 27	Waterwash Cart

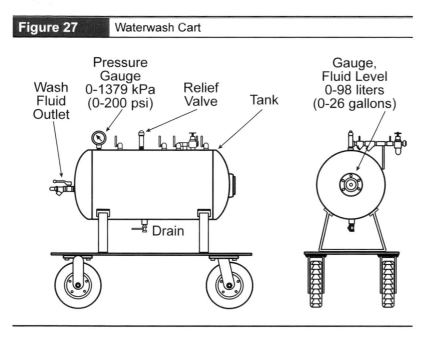

On-Line Waterwash

To perform an on-line wash, the gas turbine is brought to idle and allowed to cool. The waterwash fluid or abrasive material is then injected after which the engine is returned to the required operating condition. This method is sometimes used to increase the time between off-line washes.

If the waterwash procedure is successful, the operator should see an increase in compressor discharge pressure and a decrease in turbine inlet temperature.

CHAPTER 5 - QUESTIONS

1. Describe the components of a gas turbine lube oil system and explain its operation during startup, operation and shutdown.

2. List and describe maintenance tasks required for a gas turbine lube oil system.

3. Explain how a gas turbine fuel gas system functions.

4. Describe the operation of a gas turbine liquid fuel system.

5. List and describe maintenance tasks required for a gas turbine fuel system.

6. Explain the types of methods used to control NO_X emissions from a gas turbine.

7. Describe the design and components of a gas turbine air intake system.

8. Describe the functions and components of a gas turbine exhaust system.

9. List the steps in the startup of a gas turbine.

10. List the steps in the shutdown of a gas turbine.

11. Describe on-line and off-line waterwash procedures for a gas turbine.

ANSWERS: All answers are found within the content of the chapter.

Internal Combustion Engines

LEARNING OUTCOME

When you complete this chapter you should be able to:

Explain the operating principles, designs, support systems, and operation of industrial internal combustion engines (ICE).

LEARNING OBJECTIVES

Here is what you should be able to do when you complete each objective:

1. *Explain the principles of spark ignition and compression ignition; describe the operating cycles for two-stroke and four-stroke designs.*

2. *Identify and state the purpose of the major mechanical components of an internal combustion engine.*

3. *Describe carburetor, fuel injection, battery ignition, and magneto ignition systems for a spark ignition engine.*

4. *Describe individual pump, distributor, and common rail fuel injection systems for a diesel engine.*

5. *Explain the purpose and describe the operation of superchargers and turbochargers.*

6. *Describe and explain the operation of a typical cooling system for an industrial ICE.*

7. *Describe and explain the operation of a typical lubrication system for an industrial ICE.*

8. *Describe engine-starting devices/systems for diesel and gas engines.*

9. *Explain the monitoring, protection and control devices on a large industrial diesel or gas engine, including shutdowns and governing.*

10. *Explain a typical start-up procedure for a large industrial diesel engine, plus the routine monitoring requirements of a running engine.*

OBJECTIVE 1

Explain the principles of spark ignition and compression ignition; describe the operating cycles for two-stroke and four-stroke designs.

CLASSIFICATION OF INTERNAL COMBUSTION ENGINES

Internal combustion engines may be classified into general groups according to the type of fuel used, the method of ignition, and the number of strokes that constitute a working cycle. The three major types of fuels used are gasoline, gaseous fuels, and fuel oils.

Gasoline is in liquid form and is vaporized by being drawn through fine jets by the powerful suction of the engine during the intake stroke. At the same time, air is drawn in to mix with the vaporized fuel.

Gaseous fuels include natural gas, blast furnace gas, sewage gas, and producer gas. Of these, natural gas is the most common and engines burning natural gas are used in locations where the gas is plentiful and particularly as the drive units for gas compression machinery. Engines burning the other types of gaseous fuels have become common in sewage treatment plants and steel plants where gaseous fuels are readily available.

Fuel oils include light oils, such as kerosene, and heavier oils, such as diesel fuel. The diesel engine has many applications, such as a prime mover for electrical generation.

SPARK IGNITION

Internal combustion engines with spark ignition may be two cycle or four-cycle engines. In both designs, the compressed gas is ignited by a spark near the end of the compression stroke. A high voltage current jumping across the gap of a spark plug creates the spark. Most gasoline and gaseous fuel engines have spark ignition.

Four-Stroke Spark Ignition Cycle

The diagrams in Figure 1 show the operating principle of the four-stroke spark ignition engine. The four-cycle engine requires four strokes (two complete crankshaft revolutions) to produce one power stroke. The four strokes, designated as (a), (b), (c) and (d) in Figure 1 may be described as follows.

- **Intake or Suction Stroke** (a): The inlet valve is open while the piston moves down, drawing a mixture of gasoline and air from the carburetor into the cylinder.
- **Compression Stroke** (b): The inlet valve is closed and the piston moves upward, compressing the mixture in the combustion chamber. Near the upper end of this stroke the spark plug is timed to ignite the mixture.
- **Power Stroke** (c): The mixture burns, generating a high pressure, which forces the piston downward and produces useful power. Near the end of this stroke the exhaust valve opens to begin the removal of burned gases from the cylinder.
- **Exhaust Stroke** (d): The exhaust valve remains open while the piston moves upward and pushes out most of the remaining burned gases in preparation for the next intake stroke.

Figure 1   Four-Stroke Cycle Gasoline

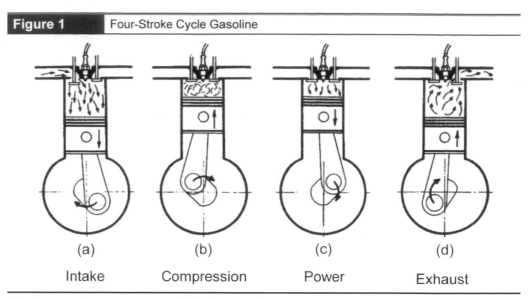

(a)	(b)	(c)	(d)
Intake	Compression	Power	Exhaust

The four-cycle engine is usually lubricated by a definite quantity of oil in its crankcase, which is either pumped under pressure to the bearing surfaces or is splashed onto them by rotation of the crank webs. The piston rings limit the amount of oil entering the combustion chamber and keep the carbon deposits to a minimum.

Two-Stroke Spark Ignition Cycle

As illustrated in Figure 2(a) and (b), the two-stroke engine functions by utilizing three openings or "ports" in its cylinder wall, which are covered or uncovered by the piston. There are no valves, no camshaft and no gearing.

Since the intake and exhaust functions are performed simultaneously during only a part of one stroke, the two-cycle engine has a power stroke every crankshaft revolution.

- Referring to Figure 2(a): The upward stroke of piston, F, compresses a mixture of gasoline vapor and air in the combustion chamber, D. The same piston stroke also creates a partial vacuum in crankcase, B, which draws in the next mixture charge through the carburetor and port, A.

- Near the upper end of the stroke, spark plug, G, is timed to ignite the compressed mixture.

- Referring to Figure 2(b): The pressure in the cylinder resulting from fuel combustion, forces piston, F, downward on its power stroke, closes intake port, A, and compresses the new mixture charge in the crankcase, B.

- Near the lower end of this stroke the piston uncovers exhaust port, E, which releases cylinder pressure and discharges most of the burned gases.

- Further piston movement then uncovers the transfer port, C, which allows the new, compressed mixture in the crankcase to flow upward into the combustion chamber where it assists in pushing the exhaust gases through the exhaust port, E. The head of the piston is usually shaped to direct the flow of new mixture upward so as to get maximum displacement of exhaust gas with minimum loss of new mixture out of the exhaust port.

The two-cycle engine is lubricated by thoroughly mixing a measured quantity of special lubricating oil with the gasoline in the tank. When this gasoline-oil mixture passes through the carburetor the gasoline is vaporized while the oil carries through as an oil fog and lubricates all parts of the engine in its passage through.

Figure 2	Two-Stroke Cycle

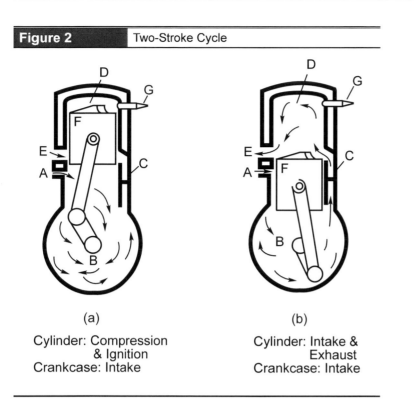

(a)

Cylinder: Compression
& Ignition
Crankcase: Intake

(b)

Cylinder: Intake &
Exhaust
Crankcase: Intake

COMPRESSION IGNITION

In the compression ignition system, only air is drawn into the cylinder during the suction or intake stroke. This air charge is then compressed by the engine piston and near the end of the compression stroke liquid fuel in an atomized form, or in some cases a gaseous fuel, is injected. The fuel ignites due to the high temperature developed by the compression of the air. Compression ignition is used in the diesel engine.

The major differences between the diesel engine and the gasoline engine are:

1. The charge drawn into the cylinder is air only.

2. The fuel is injected at high pressure at the end of the compression stroke directly into the engine cylinder in liquid form, though finely atomized.

3. Ignition is due to the high temperature resulting from the compression of the air and takes place without the aid of a spark. Thus diesel engines are known as compression ignition engines.

Four-Stroke Compression Ignition Cycle

Figure 3 shows the four strokes (Suction, Compression, Power and Exhaust) in sequence.

Figure 3	Four-Stroke Cycle Diesel Engine

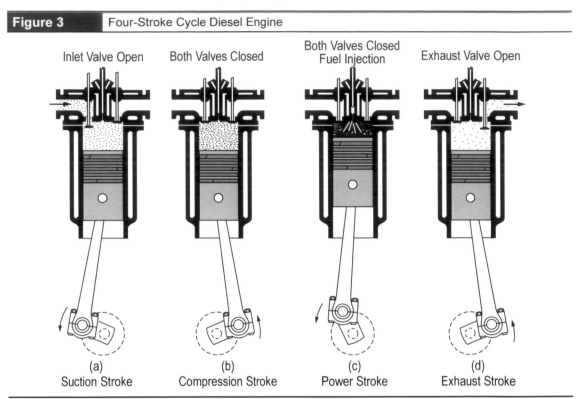

| | | Inlet Valve Open | Both Valves Closed | Both Valves Closed Fuel Injection | Exhaust Valve Open |

(a) Suction Stroke   (b) Compression Stroke   (c) Power Stroke   (d) Exhaust Stroke

(a) Suction Stroke

The inlet valve is opened just before the piston reaches the top dead-center position, and the exhaust valve closes just after the piston reaches top dead center. This allows a charge of air to be drawn into the cylinder through the inlet valve as the piston descends.

(b) Compression Stroke

After the piston has passed the bottom dead-center position the air inlet valve is closed and compression is begun as the piston rises. Shortly before top dead-center, fuel injection begins. Meanwhile compression of the air will have raised its temperature to the range of 540°C to 650°C, and its pressure in the range of 2750 kPa to 4100 kPa. Under these temperature and pressure conditions the fuel will ignite almost as soon as it enters the cylinder and mixes with the hot air. There will be a momentary increase of temperature and pressure as the fuel burns and the power stroke commences.

(c) Power Stroke

The hot gases of combustion expand and force the piston downwards. Before it reaches bottom dead-center, the burning gases have expended their energy and the exhaust valve is opened to allow them to escape from the cylinder.

(d) Exhaust Stroke

As the piston again ascends in the cylinder, the remaining exhaust gases are forced out through the open exhaust valve. Just before the piston reaches the top dead-center position, the inlet valve is opened and the whole cycle of events is repeated.

Two-Stroke Compression Ignition Cycle

In the two-stroke design there is a power stroke on each revolution of the crankshaft, which corresponds to two full strokes of the piston. There are two basic cylinder designs.

- Figure 4(a) shows a valveless cylinder with an air inlet on one side and the exhaust on the opposite side. When the piston is at the bottom of the stroke, both ports are uncovered, which allows exhaust out and fresh air in. When the piston moves upward it covers the ports and then compresses the air in the cylinder. At the top of the stroke fuel is injected and the heat of compression causes ignition. This forces the piston downwards again for the power stroke.

- Figure 4(b) shows a cylinder with two exhaust valves and the exhaust port at the top. When the piston is at the bottom the air inlet port is uncovered and the exhaust valves open. When the piston moves upwards it covers the air inlet and the exhaust valves close. Compression occurs, then fuel injection and ignition at the top of the stroke, causing the downward power stroke.

One difficulty in two-stroke engines is to completely clear the exhaust gases from the cylinder at the end of the power stroke and before the compression stroke. Removal of exhaust gases is called "**scavenging**." In larger engines, to more completely clear the cylinder the inlet air is supplied at a slightly increased pressure. This is called "scavenging" and the air is often supplied by a scavenge pump.

In Figure 4(a) the scavenging air must flow up into the cylinder, then back down and out the exhaust port. In Figure 4(b) the flow is upwards, through the exhaust valves, to the exhaust port. This is called "Uniflow" scavenging, since the flow is in one direction only.

Figure 4	Two-Stroke Cycle

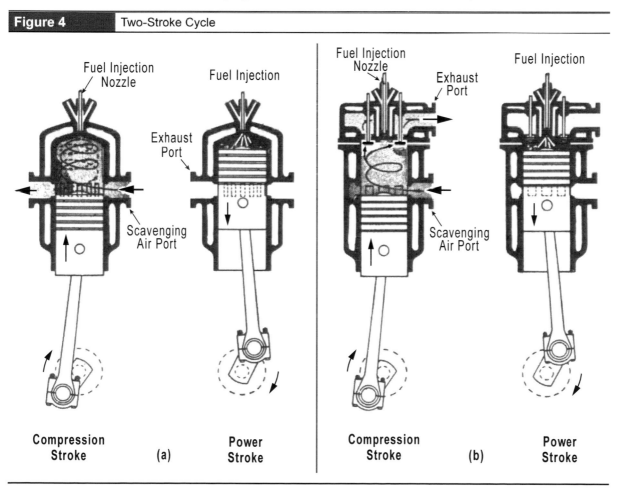

OBJECTIVE 2

Identify and state the purpose of the major mechanical components of an internal combustion engine.

INTERNAL COMBUSTION ENGINE COMPONENTS

There are many internal combustion engine types. This learning objective discusses a typical engine with construction features that are common to all internal combustion engines. It is a size common for stationary service, used to drive pumps or generators.

Figure 5 shows a diesel engine made by the W. H. Allen Co. It is a twelve-cylinder, Vee-style, four-stroke engine used to drive a 600 kW generator.

| Figure 5 | Twelve-Cylinder, Vee-Form Diesel |

Generator

Figure 6 shows a more detailed view of this engine and its components.

Figure 6	Typical Twelve-Cylinder Engine

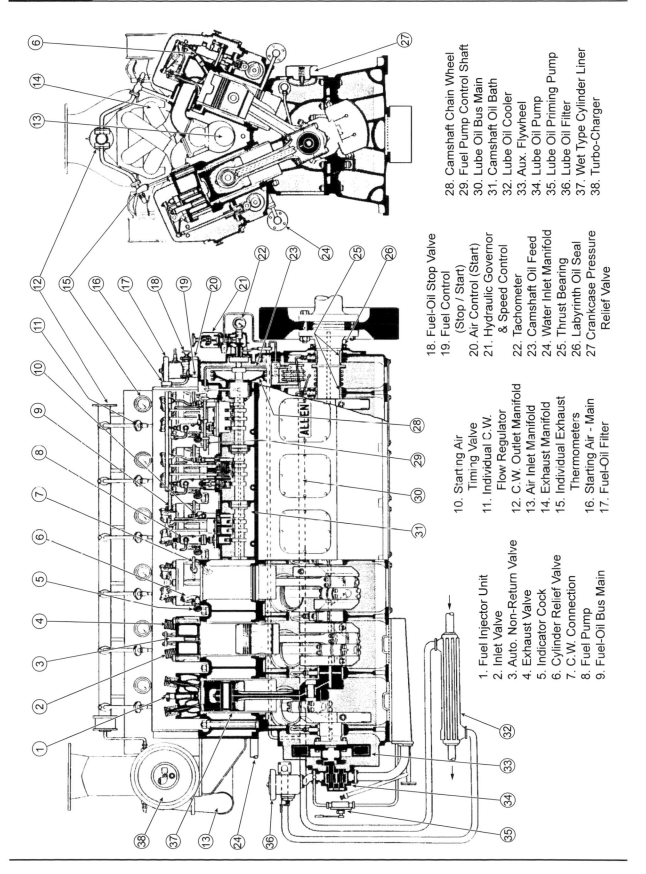

28. Camshaft Chain Wheel
29. Fuel Pump Control Shaft
30. Lube Oil Bus Main
31. Camshaft Oil Bath
32. Lube Oil Cooler
33. Aux. Flywheel
34. Lube Oil Pump
35. Lube Oil Priming Pump
36. Lube Oil Filter
37. Wet Type Cylinder Liner
38. Turbo-Charger

18. Fuel-Oil Stop Valve
19. Fuel Control
    (Stop / Start)
20. Air Control (Start)
21. Hydraulic Governor
    & Speed Control
22. Tachometer
23. Camshaft Oil Feed
24. Water Inlet Manifold
25. Thrust Bearing
26. Labyrinth Oil Seal
27. Crankcase Pressure
    Relief Valve

10. Starting Air
    Timing Valve
11. Individual C.W.
    Flow Regulator
12. C.W. Outlet Manifold
13. Air Inlet Manifold
14. Exhaust Manifold
15. Individual Exhaust
    Thermometers
16. Starting Air - Main
17. Fuel-Oil Filter

1. Fuel Injector Unit
2. Inlet Valve
3. Auto. Non-Return Valve
4. Exhaust Valve
5. Indicator Cock
6. Cylinder Relief Valve
7. C.W. Connection
8. Fuel Pump
9. Fuel-Oil Bus Main

Bedplate

The engine frame is mounted on a deep-section bedplate as shown in Figure 7. It is made of high-grade cast iron. The main bearings are steel-backed with white metal linings. It is provided with numerous internal joint bolts and studs to secure a rigid union of frame and bedplate. The last two flywheel end main bearings have white metal thrust faces for the axial location of the crankshaft. The bedplate forms a wet sump and contains all the engine lubrication oil. Provision for a dry sump system of lubrication is possible.

Figure 7	Bedplate

Crankshaft

The pistons of the engine are connected to the crankshaft by connecting rods. The crankshaft converts the linear, or back and forth movement, of the pistons to rotary movement. All the power of the engine is transferred through the crankshaft. The crankshaft is forged from steel, with balance weights as required. Oil feeds to the connecting rod bearings are taken through passages in the crankshaft from the adjacent main bearings.

Figure 8	Crankshaft

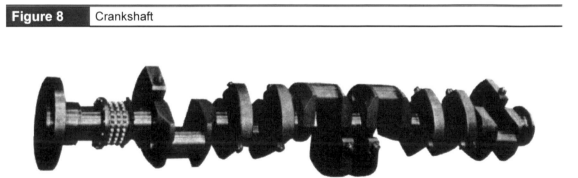

Frame & Crankcase

The frame is fitted over the bedplate and crankshaft. The frame has numerous, thick internal ribs to form a rigid framework for the cylinder bank. All working parts inside the crankcase are easily accessible through doors provided on both sides of the engine.

Figure 9	Frame

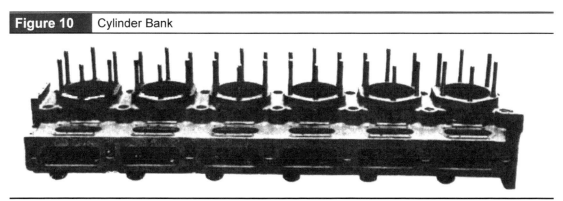

Cylinders and Liners

Separate cast-iron cylinder banks, each housing a chain driven camshaft, are mounted on either side of the engine frame. Cylinder liners (or sleeves) are fitted into the cylinder holes and provide a machined surface for the pistons and piston rings to fit into. The liners are replaceable inserts that protect the cylinder block from wear, since the piston rings wear the liner instead of the block.

Cylinder liners are of the "wet" type, which means that cooling water circulates next to the liner. "Dry" type liners, on the other hand, fit inside the cylinder bank or cylinder head, but there is no direct contact between the liner and the cooling water. The water cools the head, which in turn cools the liner.

Figure 10	Cylinder Bank

| Figure 11 | Wet-Type Cylinder Liner |

Connecting Rods

The connecting rods connect the pistons to the crankshaft. Each cylinder has one piston and one connecting rod. The wrist pins connect the piston to the rod. The connecting rods are of fully machined forged steel, and are hollow bored to convey lubricating oil to the bushings and gudgeon pins (wrist pins) of the small end. The large end bearing connects the rod to the crankshaft. It has a detachable bottom half with the top half forming a part of the forged connecting rod.

| Figure 12 | Connecting Rod |

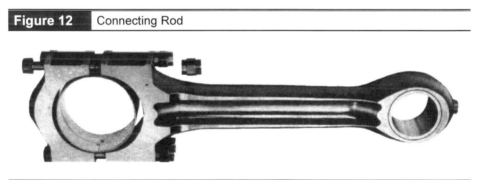

Pistons

The piston is designed with large bearing areas, and is fitted with four pressure rings and a scraper ring below the gudgeon pin. The case-hardened steel gudgeon pin is fully floating and retained by circlips. The piston is of cast iron or aluminum alloy, depending on the rated speed chosen for a particular application. The piston in Figure 13 is the type fitted to engines running at speeds, of approximately 750 r/min.

Figure 13 Piston

Piston Rings

Piston rings fit in the grooves in the piston. The four rings at the top of Figure 14 fit into the four top grooves in the piston in Figure 13. These are the compression rings. They seal the space between the piston and the cylinder, ensuring there is no leakage past the piston, which would reduce the compression inside the cylinder. They also conduct heat away from the piston to the cylinder wall.

The bottom ring in Figures 13 and 14 is an oil control ring. Its purpose is to distribute oil in a uniform film over the cylinder wall. It also prevents oil from leaking past the piston into the combustion chamber. Oil is scraped from the cylinder wall on the piston down stroke. It drains through the holes in the piston ring groove. These holes are visible in the bottom piston groove in Figure 13.

Figure 14 Rings, Gudgeon Pin, Circlips

Cylinder Heads & Valves

The cylinder heads are individually detachable, and made of a special heat-resisting cast iron. Ample waterways are provided with the water coming from the cylinder jackets through external connections. This cylinder head has an open type combustion chamber. The piston crowns are concave and the fuel is injected into the center of the combustion space.

| Figure 15 | Cylinder Head |

The interchangeable inlet and exhaust valves are actuated by push rods and rocking levers. Each valve has two concentric springs and a renewable seat of heat-treated nickel-iron alloy. Each head has a relief valve and provision for taking pressure measurements. The heads and valve gear have removable covers.

Camshaft

The camshaft is the link between the crankshaft and the valve train. It is driven through gears or a chain by the crankshaft. The lobes on the camshaft move the pushrods up and down. The pushrods through a rocker arm assembly move the intake and exhaust valves up and down.

There are two camshafts, one on the outward side of each of the two cylinder banks. Each is in a separate compartment with its own oil bath. Some engines have overhead camshafts, which are mounted above the valves, on top of the heads. They move the valves directly, with no pushrods or rocker arms. Overhead camshafts are usually belt or chain driven from the crankshaft.

| Figure 16 | Camshaft |

This arrangement allows easy access and short push rods. An oil-way, bored the full length of each shaft, delivers lubricating oil to the bearings. The camshaft is driven from the crankshaft by a triplex roller chain at the driving end of the engine. A geared extension from the camshaft operates the governor and tachometer through a flexible coupling. A set of cam blocks (for fuel pump, inlet valve, exhaust valve, and starting air valve) is provided for each cylinder. The cam followers are of the guided roller type. Each push rod has an individual return spring.

Flywheel

The flywheel is cast iron with timing marks on the periphery. The main coupling bolts pass through both the flywheel and crankshaft half-coupling flange. Two additional bolts retain the flywheel on the crankshaft when the driven machine is disconnected.

Governor

Figure 17 shows the basic principle of a governor for a diesel engine. A set of weights rotate in relation to the engine speed and centrifugal force moves the weights in and out. The position of the weights adjusts, through linkage and a hydraulic pilot valve, the operation of the fuel pump, which determines the speed of the engine. The governor may be driven from the camshaft (at camshaft speed) or at a lower speed through a reduction gear. A hydraulic governor controls the fuel pump rack rods through a short interconnecting linkage to each bank.

The governor must be sensitive enough to hold the engine speed within the required operating limits. The engine speed can be adjusted by changing the tension on the governor spring.

Figure 17	Simple Governor

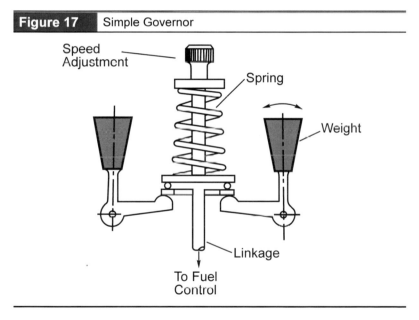

Fuel Pumps & Injectors

Individual fuel pumps are mounted on the top face of the frame at each cylinder and are directly actuated by the camshafts. This allows individual adjustment of each pump to equalize the load over all the cylinders. The proximity of each pump to its corresponding fuel injector and the use of short connecting pipes ensure that equal distribution of the load is maintained under all conditions.

The individual fuel pumps are of the reciprocating plunger type. Each has a rotating outer sleeve, which controls the fuel delivered per stroke. An anti-dribble, spring loaded, non-return delivery valve is part of the fuel pump discharge. The pump is designed to allow easy adjustment of both timing and quantity of fuel injected. A large diameter skirt over the cam follower prevents fuel from leaking into the lubrication system.

Injectors are of the multi-hole nozzle type, centrally located in the cylinder heads, and connected to the fuel pumps by short, rigid lengths of fuel delivery pipe. Atomization of the fuel at the nozzle is a result of passing through a spring-loaded needle valve.

Figure 18	Fuel Injection System Components

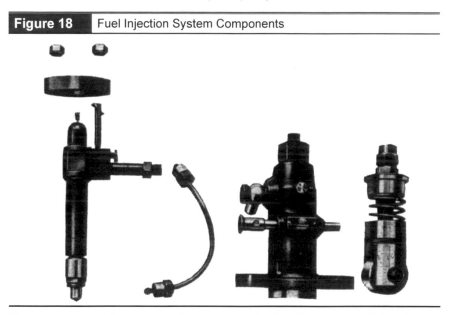

The quantity of fuel injected into the cylinders is controlled by the governor acting on each pump through a control rod that runs the length of each bank. Fuel passes through a filter as it enters the system. Edge-type filters may also be fitted at the inlet to each fuel injector.

OBJECTIVE 3

Describe carburetor, fuel injection, battery ignition, and magneto ignition systems for a spark ignition engine.

CARBURETOR

In the carbureted gasoline engine the fuel and air are mixed together before entering the cylinder. This mixing is carried out in a special device known as a carburetor, which not only causes the fuel and air to mix but also causes the fuel to be atomized before mixing.

Figure 19 illustrates the basic operating principle of a carburetor.

- During the intake stroke of a four-stroke engine, a vacuum is produced within the engine cylinder. This causes a flow of air through the carburetor.

- The air flows through a constricted passage called a venturi and creates a vacuum at the narrowest part or throat (F in Fig. 19) and this causes fuel to be drawn up from the reservoir A through the connecting tube D.

- The fuel is carried along in atomized form by the air stream.

- The fuel level in the reservoir is maintained by the float-operated needle valve C.

| **Figure 19** | Carburetor Principle |

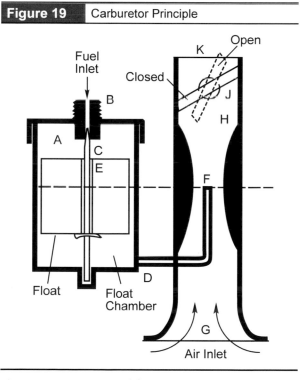

Figure 19 is a simplification. An actual carburetor requires many other features in order to provide efficient and economical operation of the engine. Figure 20 illustrates a more complicated, down draft, triple venturi carburetor.

Figure 20   Triple Venturi Carburetor

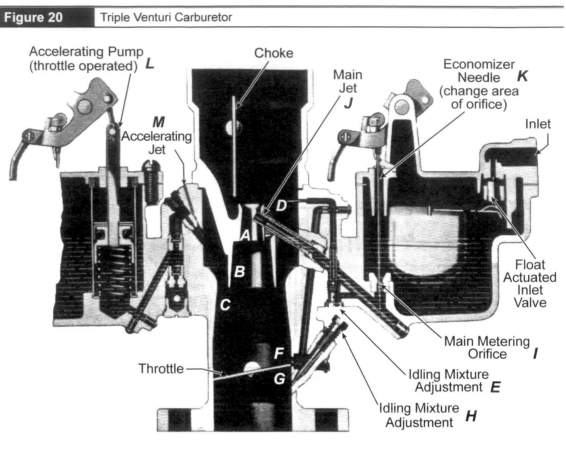

(Courtesy of General Motors)

- In this design, gasoline is pumped into a chamber, which is part of the carburetor. The level in the chamber is controlled by a float-actuated needle valve.

- The fuel is drawn from this chamber through the main metering orifice and to the main jet by the vacuum produced by the airflow through the triple venturi (marked A, B, and C in Fig. 20). The flow area of the main metering orifice can be changed for different engine loads by the economizer needle, which is moved by a linkage from the throttle. The accelerating pump comes into action when the throttle is opened suddenly. When this happens the piston of this pump will force extra fuel into the air stream through the accelerating jet.

- When the engine is running at slow speed (idling), the flow of air through the venturis is too low to cause a flow of fuel from the main jet. Therefore a special idling jet is used with its discharge just below the throttle valve where the vacuum is greatest when the throttle valve is closed or almost closed. This vacuum draws fuel into the engine through the idling jet and also draws in some air through the air bleed, marked D in Figure 20.

- A very rich air-fuel mixture is required to start the engine under cold conditions so a choke valve is used to reduce the air intake. The choke is a butterfly valve similar to the throttle valve and is operated manually by a lever or automatically by a thermostat. The throttle valve is operated manually or by a governor and controls the amount of the air-fuel mixture passing to the engine.

FUEL INJECTION

Fuel injection in spark ignition engines provides excellent atomization of the fuel and a homogeneous mixture for efficient combustion. This accomplished by pumping fuel through a nozzle producing fuel droplets that are as fine as possible. Atomization of fuel exiting a fuel injector nozzle is illustrated in Figure 21.

Figure 21	Fuel Injector Atomization

(Courtesy of Robert Bosch GMBH)

The fuel injection systems are classified as single point, multi-point or direct fuel injection. In single point (also called throttle body), the fuel is injected through a single injector situated above the throttle valve. This setup looks similar to a carburetor, and sits atop the intake manifold. With multipoint fuel injection, each cylinder has its own injector, which is situated in the intake manifold, upstream of the intake valve. Fuel is supplied to the injectors through a manifold. This type of fuel injection system is illustrated in Figure 22.

Figure 22	Multi-Point Fuel Injection

Multipoint Fuel Injection (MPI)
1. Fuel
2. Air
3. Throttle Valve
4. Intake Manifold
5. Injectors
6. Engine

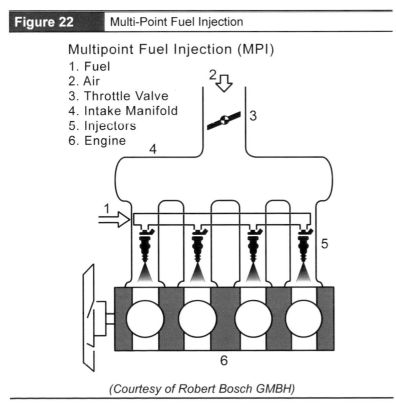

(Courtesy of Robert Bosch GMBH)

Direct fuel injection systems have injection valves, which spray fuel directly into the combustion chamber. Atomization of the fuel takes place in the cylinder. Each cylinder has its own injector as shown in Figure 23.

With a direct injection system, the engine draws in only air. This does away with any possible condensation of fuel in the intake manifold runners. Direct injection also makes it possible to burn a very lean mixture for idling and part-throttle operation.

Figure 23	Direct Fuel Injection

Direct Fuel Injection (DI)
1. Fuel
2. Air
3. Throttle Valve (ETC)
4. Intake Manifold
5. Injectors
6. Engine

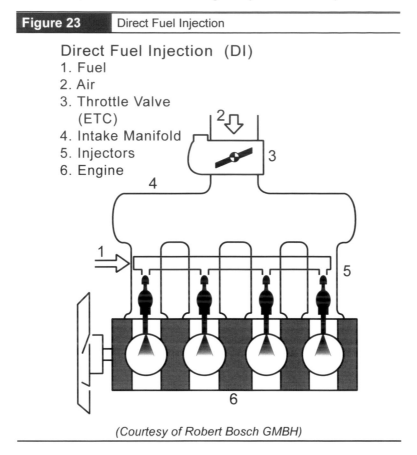

(Courtesy of Robert Bosch GMBH)

Figure 24 shows a typical fuel supply system.

It has an electric fuel pump, which pumps fuel through a filter to a manifold or rail supply system. The manifold supplies fuel under pressure to each fuel injector in the multi-point system. The fuel pressure regulator returns excess fuel to the fuel tank. The fuel pump is often situated in the bottom of the fuel tank. There is usually a screen on the suction of the pump.

Figure 24	Fuel Supply System

Fuel-supply System (Example using multipoint fuel injection)

With electric fuel pump:
1. Fuel tank **2.** Electric fuel pump **3.** Fuel filter
4. Fuel rail **5.** Fuel injector **6.** Fuel-pressure regulator.

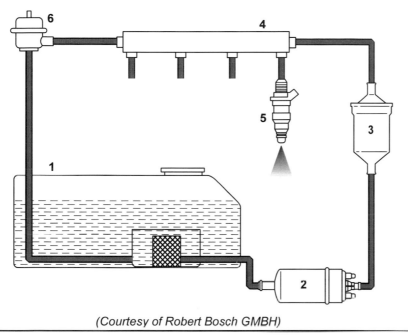

(Courtesy of Robert Bosch GMBH)

BATTERY IGNITION SYSTEM

The spark required for igniting the fuel in a gasoline or other spark ignition engine may be provided by a battery or by a magneto.

Figure 25 shows the circuit and components of a battery-operated system.

- In this system, the breaker points are opened and closed by a camshaft.
- When the points close, current from the battery flows through the primary winding of the induction coil establishing a magnetic field.
- When the points open, the magnetic field suddenly collapses inducing a high voltage in the secondary winding of the coil. This high voltage is applied to the desired spark plug in the correct sequence by the rotating distributor arm.

Figure 25 | Battery Ignition System

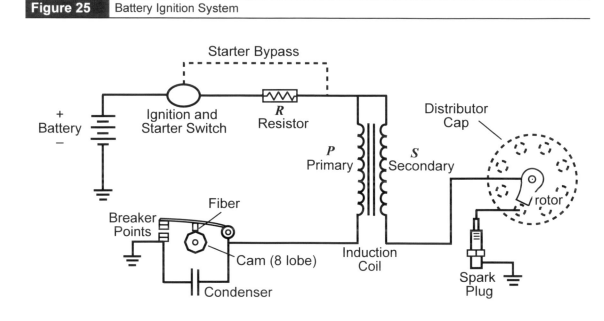

The purpose of the condenser in the circuit is to interrupt the primary current quickly. When the breaker points open, there is a tendency for the battery current to keep flowing causing an arc across the points. The condenser receives and stores electrical energy thus breaking the arc quickly.

The resistor in the circuit is used to obtain the correct primary current. When starting the engine, this resistor may be bypassed in order to give a higher current through the induction coil for the start-up period.

MAGNETO IGNITION SYSTEM

In this system, a magneto is used to generate the current necessary to produce the ignition spark. The magneto is a simple generator, which uses permanent magnets to produce its magnetic field rather than the electromagnets used in other types of generators.

Figure 26 shows the circuit for a magneto operated ignition system.

- Referring to Figure 26, the magneto is driven by the engine and when the points are closed a current flows in the primary winding of the induction coil.
- When the points open to break this current, a very high voltage is induced in the secondary winding of the coil and is directed to the appropriate spark plug by the rotating distributor arm.

Figure 26	Magneto Circuit

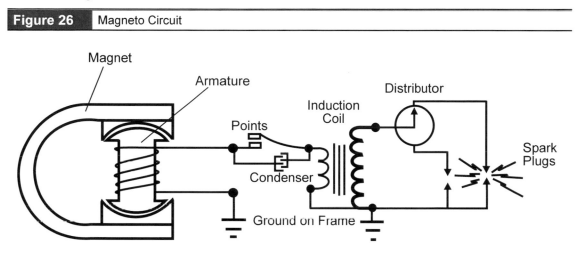

The magneto ignition system finds use in aircraft engines, industrial engines and in high performance racing engines. Its advantages are:

- it is lighter in weight than the battery ignition system.
- since the engine drives the magneto, it will produce a hotter spark at higher speeds when this is needed.
- it will produce a spark without the use of a battery.

OBJECTIVE 4

Describe individual pump, distributor, and common rail fuel injection systems for a diesel engine.

FUEL INJECTORS

The diesel engine does not use a carburetor to mix fuel and air, nor does it use a spark to ignite the fuel-air mixture. Instead, the diesel engine uses an injection system to spray the fuel into the engine cylinder. The fuel must enter against the pressure of the air that has been compressed in the engine cylinders.

The air may be at a pressure of 3100 kPa and at a temperature of 540°C. Therefore, when the fuel is injected into this high temperature air, it will ignite and burn. This type of fuel injection is called a **solid injection system**, since the fuel is pumped directly into each cylinder. The solid injection method has three different designs. They are the:

1) Individual pump system

2) Distributor system

3) Common rail system

1. Individual Pump System

The basic components of this system are shown in Figure 27.

This system has an individual high-pressure pump for each cylinder fuel nozzle. The fuel is supplied to the high-pressure pumps from a storage tank by a low-pressure transfer pump not shown in the diagram. The high-pressure pumps are operated by the engine through a camshaft arrangement and are of the plunger type. The camshaft controls the timing of each plunger so that injection takes place at the proper time. The control rod controls the amount of fuel injected by each plunger.

Figure 27	Individual Pump System

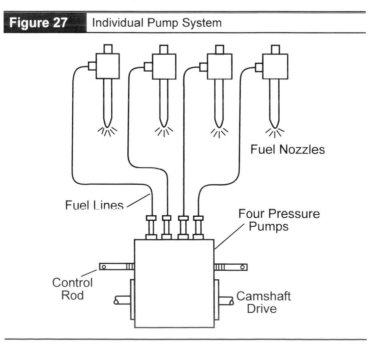

2. Distributor System

In the distributor system shown in Figure 28, the fuel is pumped from the storage tank to a single high-pressure pump by a low-pressure transfer pump. The high-pressure pump then injects the fuel to each cylinder nozzle in the proper firing order by means of a distributor. The distributor contains a rotating channel, which lines up the pump discharge with the fuel line to the desired fuel nozzle or injector.

Figure 28	Distributor System

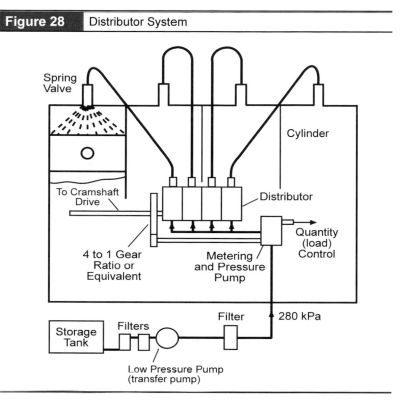

3. Common Rail System

The common rail system is illustrated in Figure 29. A low-pressure pump pumps the fuel from the tank to the injectors. A separate injector is located at each engine cylinder. Most of the fuel returns from the injector to the tank via the drain orifice B in the injector and via the drain manifold. Some fuel, however, passes through the metering orifice C into the cavity D under the injector plunger. When the proper firing point occurs in each cylinder, the injector lever, driven by the camshaft, pushes the injector plunger down and forces the fuel under high pressure into the cylinder.

Figure 29	Common Rail System

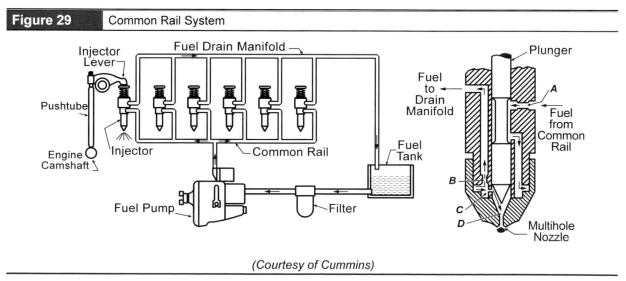

(Courtesy of Cummins)

OBJECTIVE 5

Explain the purpose and describe the operation of superchargers and turbochargers.

SUPERCHARGING

Supercharging involves the use of a blower to force more air into the cylinder of a diesel engine or more air-fuel mixture into the cylinder of a gasoline engine. In both cases the result is an increase in the power output, because the amount of fuel burned is increased.

The blowers used are usually the rotary lobe type or the centrifugal type. Gearing or a belt connects the lobe type blower to the engine shaft. The centrifugal type blower may be similarly driven or it may be driven by an exhaust gas turbine in which case it is called a turbocharger.

Figure 30 shows a rotary lobe blower used to supercharge a gasoline engine.

The air-fuel mixture is compressed to 35 to 140 kPa by the blower, which is driven from the engine shaft. The lobes in the compressor do not touch each other. They are constructed to fine tolerances so leakage is minimal. Similarly, there is no contact between the lobes in the blower and the blower casing. The lobe type blower requires little maintenance.

| **Figure 30** | Rotary Lobe Supercharger |

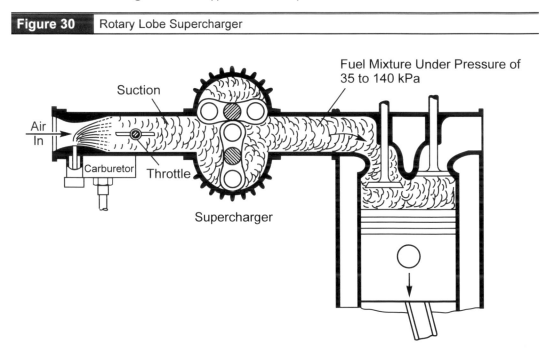

Figure 31 shows a similar lobe blower, but with 3 lobes per rotor.

The roots or lobe type of blowers are positive displacement air pumps. The airflow is proportional to engine speed. This is an advantage at low engine speeds, but may be a disadvantage if the engine starts to overload and slow down, since the blower also slows down, further reducing power output.

| Figure 31 | Rotary Lobe Supercharger |

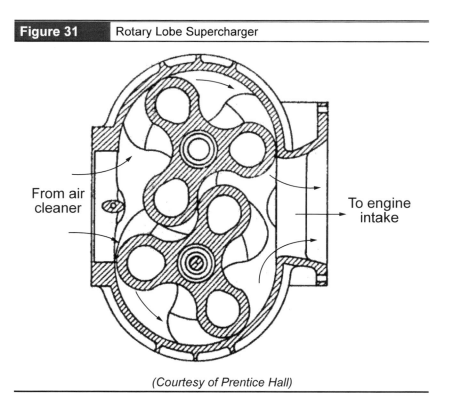

(Courtesy of Prentice Hall)

TURBOCHARGER

In the turbocharger, Figure 32, exhaust gases from the engine drive a turbine, which then drives the centrifugal blower. This arrangement forces air into the engine and as the engine load and speed increase the speed of the turbocharger also increases. As turbocharger speed increases the compressor forces more air into the engine, which allows more fuel to be burned.

| Figure 32 | Turbocharger |

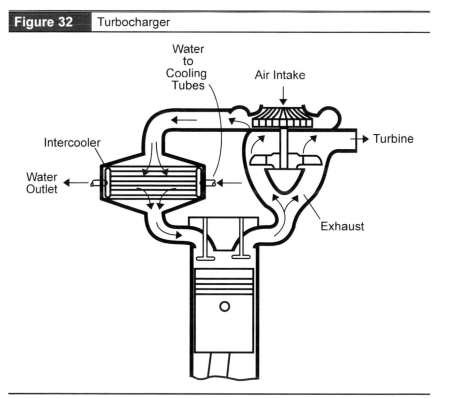

Using a turbocharger can reduce the exhaust temperature by 200°C (or, for large diesel engines, up to 300°C). It also increases the overall efficiency of the heat engine, with efficiency of over 40% possible.

Figure 33 shows the internal details of a turbocharger for a diesel engine.

Figure 33	Exhaust Driven Turbocharger

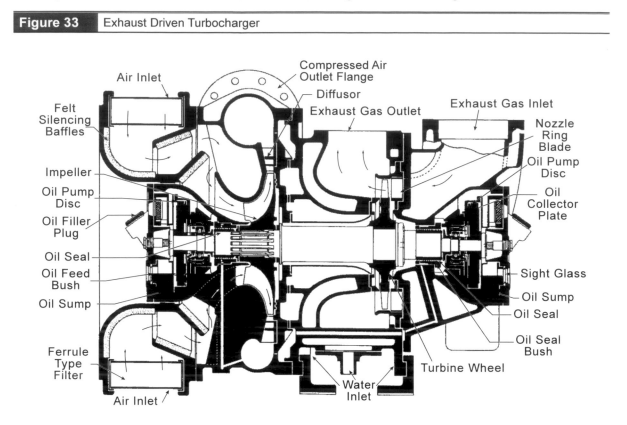

Turbocharger materials must withstand temperatures up to 600°C plus high centrifugal forces. Compresssor components are often made from aluminum alloys. The turbines are constructed of nickel or cobalt steel or ceramics. Most turbochargers use floating friction bearings (with a film of oil on both sides of the bearing), designed to rotate at about one third of the shaft speed. A thrust bearing limits the axial movement of the turbine rotor.

OBJECTIVE 6

Describe and explain the operation of a typical cooling system for an industrial ICE.

ENGINE COOLING

Small internal combustion engines are often air-cooled. Each cylinder or motor block is equipped with many thin fins, creating a large cooling surface. This has the advantages of being simple and cheap, but the disadvantage is lack of control of the engine temperature since cooling efficiency depends on the weather conditions.

In high compression diesel engines, the combustion temperature can exceed 2000°C, and only 30 to 35% of the heat is converted to mechanical work, leaving 65 to 70% to be removed by cooling. A small part of this heat is removed by radiation, but the bulk of it is removed by cooling water circulating through the water jackets of the cylinders and the cylinder heads.

Figure 34 illustrates the location of the cooling water jackets to the cylinders and heads.

Figure 34	Water Jackets in Cylinder Heads

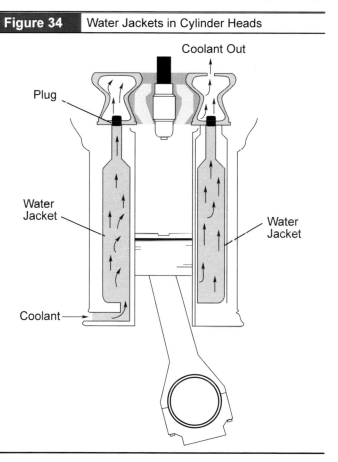

Radiator Cooling Water System

Most liquid-cooled engines use a circulating system, with a radiator that cools the liquid coolant (usually a mixture of water and glycol). The radiator is an air-cooled heat exchanger, which cools the coolant before it is pumped back through the engine.

Figure 35 shows this type of system.

The system operates at a positive pressure of around 100 kPa, which increases the boiling point of the coolant and reduces the likelihood of it boiling. The radiator cap maintains the pressure on the system. It is designed also to open and allow air into the system if a vacuum develops. The engine normally drives the circulating coolant pump and the radiator cooling fan.

The water temperature is controlled by a thermostat valve, located between the engine head and the radiator. It opens to allow more water flow as the water temperature increases. When the engine is cold the thermostat is nearly closed.

Figure 35	Radiator Cooling System

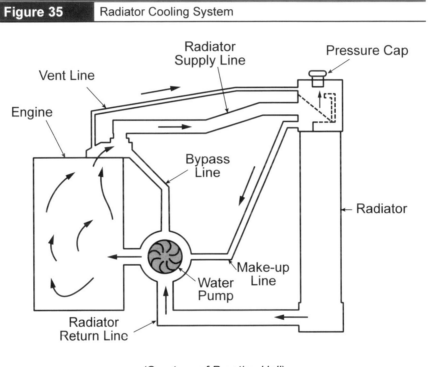

(Courtesy of Prentice Hall)

Figure 36 shows the cooling water system for a large diesel engine, using a separate cooling water (rather than a radiator) to cool the engine coolant.

It consists of a closed engine water system with circulating pump, expansion surge tank, and shell-and-tube heat exchanger. Engine coolant flows through the shell side of the exchanger, while cool water from a cooling tower flows through the exchanger tubes. With this closed system, the engine coolant can be treated and topped-up with ethylene glycol for corrosion and frost protection.

To obtain the most even engine cooling, the coolant circulating through the engine is kept at its maximum flow rate. The coolant temperature is controlled (usually between 60 and 75°C) by regulating the flow of water from the cooling tower.

An expansion tank, with a makeup valve, allows the engine cooling water to expand and contract safely as temperature changes.

The engine cooling water pump may be driven directly by the engine or it may be electrically driven. The advantages of an electric pump are that it can be kept running after the engine is shut down (to allow even cooling of the residual engine heat) and its startup can be delayed during an engine start (to allow the oil temperature to increase more rapidly to operating temperature).

| **Figure 36** | Diesel Engine Cooling System |

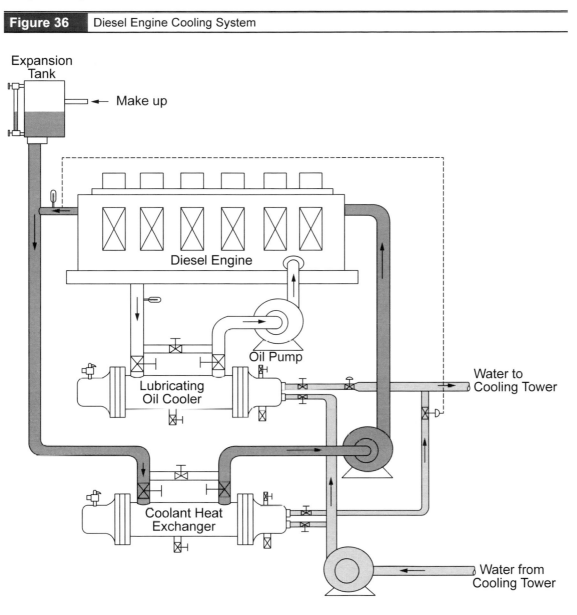

The pistons of large diesel engines cannot dissipate heat rapidly enough without some form of piston cooling. The piston is oil-cooled, using oil from the lubricating system. The oil is delivered to the piston through telescopic pipes or swinging elbow pipes, and returned the same way.

These telescopic and elbow pipes are weak points in the engine and are susceptible to failure. A solution to this problem is the crosshead engine. Here the piston cooling oil is circulated from the crank to the crosshead, then through a channel in the piston rod to the piston. It returns back through a second channel in the piston rod before draining out at the crosshead.

OBJECTIVE 7

Describe and explain the operation of a typical lubrication system for an industrial ICE.

LUBRICATING OIL SYSTEM

The importance of proper lubrication is obvious, since the majority of operating problems and damage to internal combustion engines are caused by improper lubrication. The lube oil forms a film around the shafts, separating the shafts and bearings to prevent metal-to-metal contact, thus reducing friction and preventing wear of the bearing metal. The heat due to friction in large bearings can be considerable, and large quantities of oil must be circulated through the bearings for temperature control.

A typical lubrication system for a medium sized diesel engine is shown in Figure 37. It is a forced-feed system of lubrication and uses the oil contained in the bedplate as a reservoir. A gear type oil pump is driven from the crankshaft.

Figure 37	Lubrication System

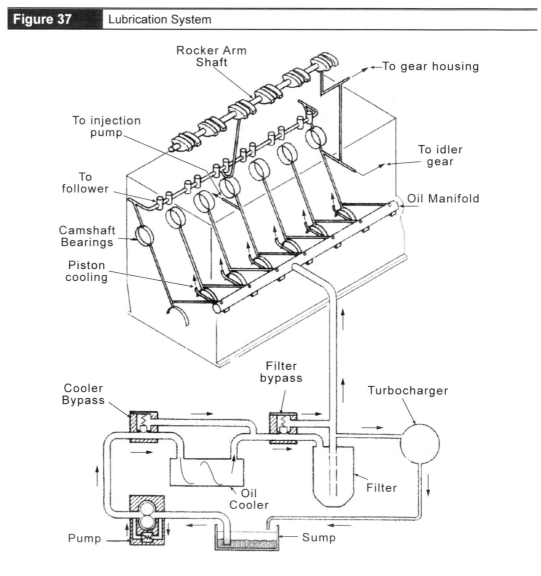

(Courtesy of Prentice Hall)

Oil is pumped from the bedplate through an oil filter and cooler into the lubricating oil manifold. The temperature of the oil leaving the cooler is used to control the engine oil temperature. A separate pipe supplies oil to the turbocharger. A supply of cooled oil is critical for the turbocharger to lubricate the high-speed bearings and to carry heat away from the rotor.

Connections from the pressure manifold go to each of the main, camshaft, and governor bearings and to the camshaft driving chain. Oil is also sent to the gear housing, the injection pump, and the idler gear. Oil is also fed via the connecting rods to the small-end bearings. The pistons also receive some oil for cooling in this design.

Figure 37 also shows a separately driven oil pump. A system with two separately driven pumps is often used on large engines to give full oil pressure during starting and stopping. This simplifies the engine because the oil pump and gears are omitted.

Figure 38 shows a gear type of oil pump. The oil enters the pump and is carried around the pump casing by the gear teeth. It is then discharged. The oil is prevented from returning to the inlet by the meshing of the gear teeth.

Figure 38	Gear Type Oil Pump

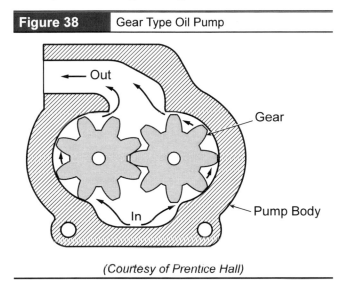

(Courtesy of Prentice Hall)

The cylinder lubrication on medium and large size diesels is applied at two, three, or four points on each cylinder. Each location is supplied by a small plunger pump with adjustable stroke, located in a central lubricator, with one to twelve such pumps operated by cams on a common camshaft.

The cylinders of smaller engines are generally lubricated by "splash lubrication", as seen in Figure 39.

The crankshaft is partly immersed in oil. As it rotates, oil is thrown from the crank into the skirt of the piston, and flows down inside the piston and through holes drilled in the piston into the groove for the lower piston ring (see Fig. 14) and seeps in over the top of the piston ring to the cylinder walls. On the down stroke, the lower piston ring scrapes the cylinder walls. Excess oil drains through holes just below the ring back to the inside of the piston.

Figure 39	Splash Lubrication

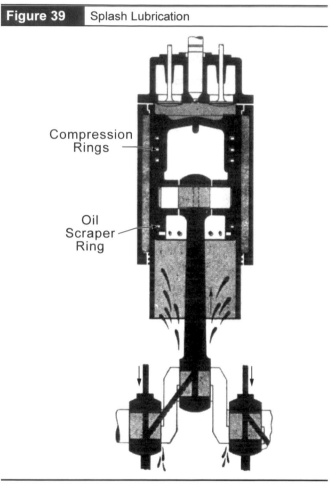

With splash lubrication the same oil is used for bearing and cylinder lubrication and it is very important that only the oil recommended by the manufacturer be used. The oil is a compromise between the two uses.

For large engines with separate cylinder lubrication systems, the lubricating oil is designed for very high temperatures and to withstand the products of combustion. The bearing lubrication can be separately specified, so can have the highest quality for that purpose.

Figure 40 shows the lubrication system for a six-cylinder diesel engine. It has a dual oil filter, and a shell and tube of oil cooler. The oil cooler uses cooling water to cool the oil. The oil supply piping to the camshaft and crankshaft can be seen in the figure.

Figure 40 | Lubrication System

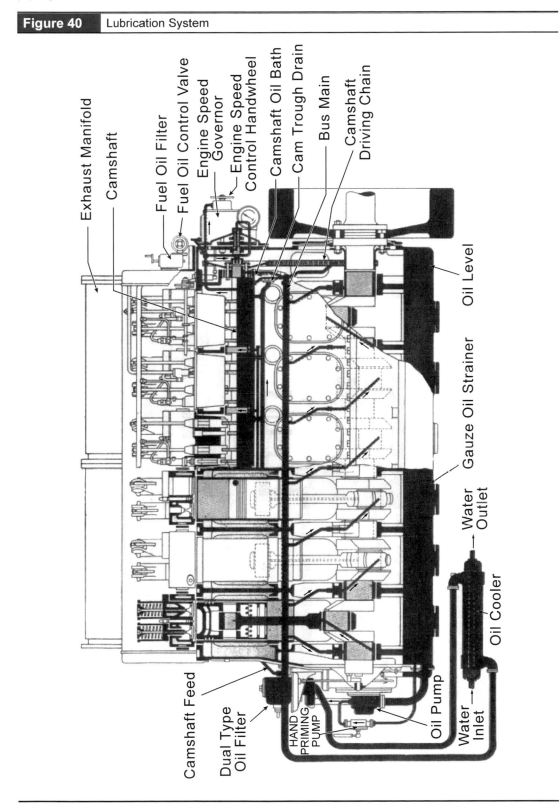

OBJECTIVE 8

Describe engine-starting devices/systems for diesel and gas engines.

STARTING METHODS

In order to start an internal combustion engine it is necessary to rotate the crankshaft by some means. This rotation will allow a charge of air (in a diesel engine) or air-fuel mixture (in a gasoline engine) to be drawn into the cylinders and compressed prior to firing. The rotation will also cause certain auxiliaries to operate, such as the fuel injection system in the diesel or the carburetor and ignition system in the gasoline engine.

Several different starting methods are used.

- Very small engine may use a manual crank.
- Medium sized engines usually have an electric motor driven starter, powered by a storage battery.
- Large diesel engines commonly use compressed air, which is admitted into one or more cylinders to drive the engine pistons.

Electric Starters

An electric starter motor powered by a storage battery may start engines up to 1000 kW. The motor cranks the engine until ignition takes place. When the engine reaches a certain speed, the starter disengages and power to the starting motor is de-energized.

Figure 41 shows an electric starter motor.

The drive pinion (gear) connects it mechanically to the engine flywheel. The motor is a DC type, enclosed to make it weatherproof.

Figure 41	Electric Starter Motor

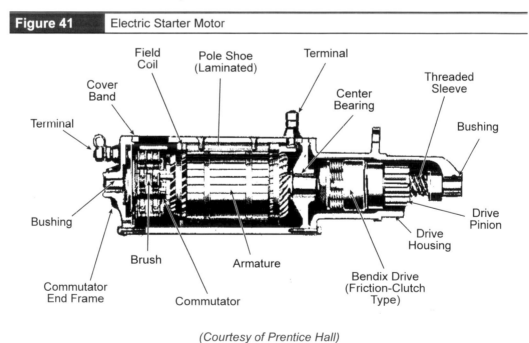

(Courtesy of Prentice Hall)

Air Starting System

Some medium sized and most large diesel engines are started with compressed air, which takes one of two forms:

- it may be led, through a distributing device, directly into the engine cylinders, or
- the air may be directed to a dedicated air motor, which cranks the engine, or

When starting air is fed to the engine cylinders, an air-distributing device (operated by the camshaft) directs the high-pressure air to each cylinder on its power stroke. The air, usually at about 2100 kPa, is fed through air-starting valves that are fitted in the cylinder heads. The air drives the engine in much the same way as steam drives a steam engine.

Unfortunately, the starting air cools the cylinders and makes ignition difficult. Therefore, only a few of the cylinders are used for starting. The engine is turned to a specified starting position indicated on the flywheel. Then timing valves (operated by the camshaft) supply starting air through starting valves (see Fig. 42) to the cylinders on their power strokes. The engine should fire after the first full compression stroke at which point no further starting air is supplied.

| Figure 42 | Air Starting Valve |

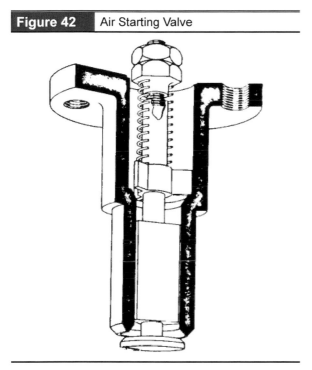

The air starting system includes a two or three-stage compressor and an air receiver. The compressor charges the air receiver to a pressure of 2000 to 2500 kPa. When fully charged, the air receiver should have sufficient capacity for at least twelve starts before recharging is necessary.

A starting system that uses a separate air motor is shown in Figure 43.

This system has its own tank, compressor and air drying system. A push button valve activates the flow of air to the starting motor via a relay valve. The air passes through the starting motor and is vented to atmosphere. Since the air is dry and has no lubrication qualities, lubricating oil must be added to the air motor. The air motor will rotate the crankshaft until the engine starts or until the air supply runs out.

The air motor system will turn the engine faster than an electric starter, which has the advantage of more quickly establishing the required ignition temperature.

Figure 43	Air Starting System

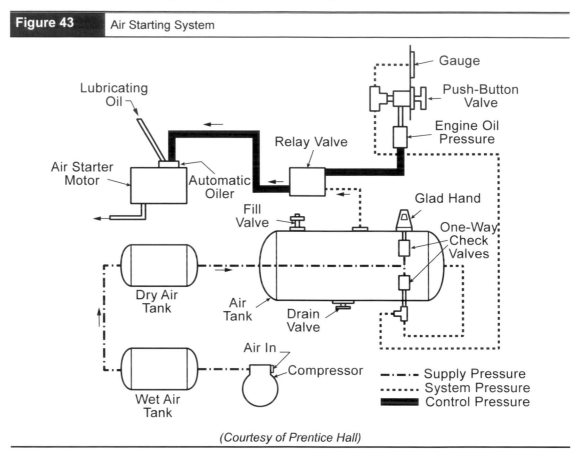

(Courtesy of Prentice Hall)

Hydraulic Starting System

The hydraulic starting system uses a hydraulic motor to turn over the diesel for starting. This type of system is shown in Figure 44.

The accumulator holds a quantity of oil under high pressure, 10 000 to 20 000 kPa. To start the motor the oil flows from the accumulator to the hydraulic motor, causing rotation. The low-pressure oil flows back to a reservoir.

The starter motor has a pinion, which turns the diesel engine flywheel. When the diesel starts, the flow of oil is shut off and the pinion drive disengages. The engine driven hydraulic pump restores the pressure in the accumulator. A hand pump is also supplied as a back up should the engine driven hydraulic pump fail.

Figure 44 Hydraulic Starting System

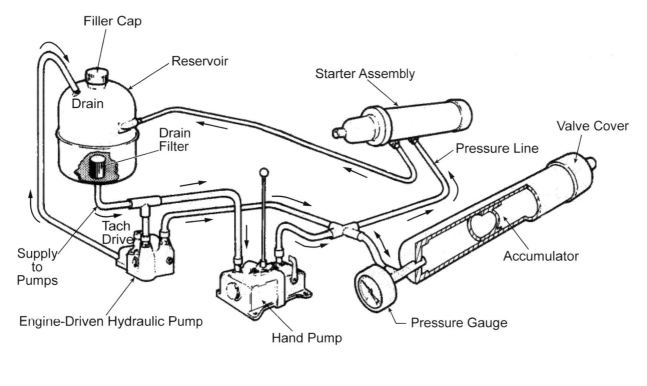

(Courtesy of Prentice Hall)

OBJECTIVE 9

Explain the monitoring, protection and control devices on a large industrial diesel or gas engine, including shutdowns and governing.

ENGINE MONITORING & PROTECTION

The systems necessary to keep a large engine running must be continuously monitored. The main systems, which must be monitored, are:

- The lubrication system including oil level, temperature, and pressure
- The cooling system temperatures and pressures
- The fuel system including fuel tank level, fuel filters and fuel injector pressure
- The air intake system including air filter differential pressure
- The exhaust system including temperature and pressure
- The electrical system including voltage, amperage, and charging conditions
- Engine speed
- Turbo or supercharger boost pressure

Figure 45	Diesel Engine Generator with Analog Control Panel

(Courtesy of Waukesha)

The monitoring system may consist of a field panel with analog gauges. This type of panel is usually mounted close to the engine. From this panel the operator can start the engine and monitor the gauges on the panel. This panel usually has a throttle and start and shutdown switches. The gauges on the panel incorporate shutdown switches. For example, the temperature gauge has a built-in switch, which will trip the engine if the temperature goes above a certain limit. The oil pressure gauge will also have a trip, which shuts down the engine on low oil pressure. An example of this type of panel is shown in Figure 45.

The digital system, as shown in Figure 46, monitors and controls most engine functions.

It has a microprocessor based control module (ECM), which takes inputs from engine sensors. It controls all engine functions such as engine speed, timing, boost pressure and exhaust gas recirculation. The digital system may be connected to a field mounted operator interface panel as shown in Figure 47, or a remote panel in a control room. The operator is able to input some control variables such as engine speed and load. Most functions are controlled by the microprocessor.

Figure 46	Engine Management System

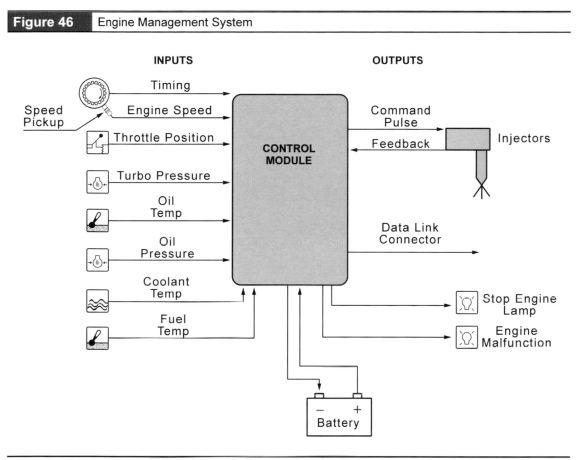

The safety and protective shutdown functions are also built into digital based systems. They are programmed to shut the engine down if limits are exceeded. The shutdowns are connected to an alarm panel, which makes the operator aware of the alarm condition that exists. The alarm must be cleared before the engine will restart. The engine may also shutdown if the microprocessor fails. Microprocessor problems can be difficult to troubleshoot, and repair involves replacing electronic components.

Figure 47	Control Panel for a Digitally Controlled Engine

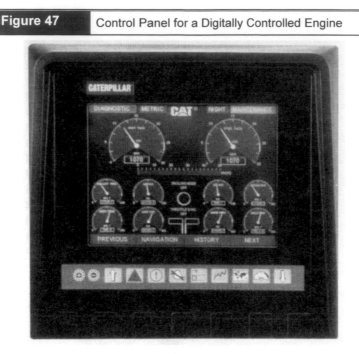

(Reprinted Courtesy of Caterpillar Inc.)

ENGINE GOVERNING

It is usually necessary to regulate the speed of an internal combustion engine, other than the automotive type, by an automatic device known as a governor.

In the case of a spark ignition engine, such as the gasoline engine, varying the amount of the air-fuel mixture entering the engine cylinder controls the speed. A throttle valve is linked to a governor. The governor consists basically of spring-loaded flyweights driven by gearing from the engine crankshaft. The weights produce a centrifugal force, which is balanced by the spring. Upon a change in engine speed, the weights will move the throttle valve by means of the linkage. With this method the quantity of the mixture entering the engine cylinder during the intake stroke is varied but the quality of the mixture, that is the ratio of fuel to air, remains practically the same at all loads.

In the compression ignition engine, such as the diesel, varying the amount of fuel entering the cylinder controls the speed. The amount of air entering on each intake stroke remains the same. Thus the quantity or ratio of fuel to air will vary but the quantity of the air entering the cylinder during each intake stroke will remain the same. The governor regulates the fuel entering the engine cylinder. The governor is usually of the flyweight type. By means of a linkage, any movement of the weights is transmitted to the fuel injector or pump mechanism and the fuel flow is thus varied. A diagrammatic representation of a simple governor fly-ball governor was shown in Figure 17.

The governor shown in Figure 48 has the fly ball connected to a hydraulic system. The fly ball output is connected to a pilot valve, which sends oil under pressure to the top or bottom of the power piston. The power piston moves the fuel control valve.

Figure 48 — Hydraulic Engine Governing System

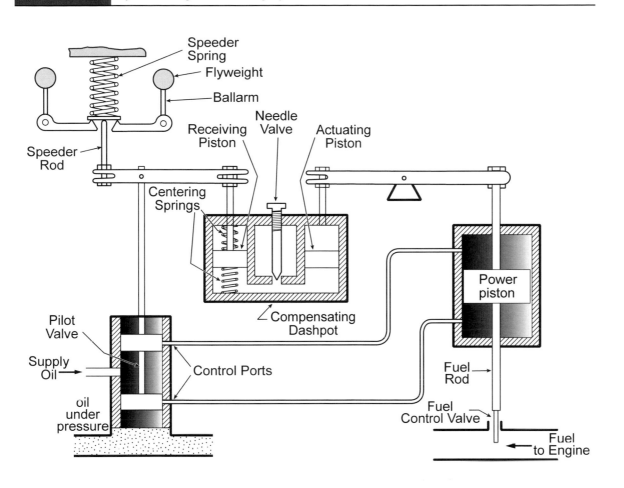

(Courtesy of Woodward Governor Company)

The speed control of a microprocessor-controlled engine has speed sensor pickups connected to the microprocessor. The microprocessor controls the fuel to the fuel injection system. The speed sensor, as shown in Figure 49 is mounted to a main engine shaft, such as the crankshaft. Pulses are created in the magnetic pickup when the teeth on the pickup rotor move past the pickup. The sensor sends out pulses to the electronic control module (ECM). Often an engine has more than one sensor, in case of sensor failure. If all sensors fail, the engine will shut down.

Figure 49 — Magnetic Pickup Speed Sensor

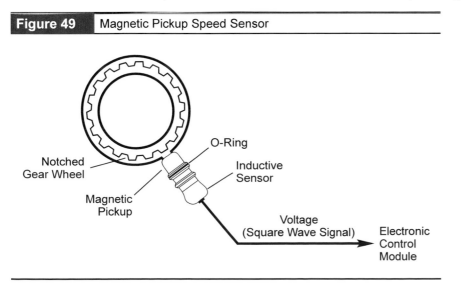

OBJECTIVE 10

Explain a typical start-up procedure for a large industrial diesel engine, plus the routine monitoring requirements of a running engine.

STARTING A DIESEL ENGINE

Before starting a diesel engine, special care should be taken to see that the fuel-injection pump is primed and that it will deliver fuel oil to the cylinders with the first revolution of the engine. Precautions should also be taken to ensure that all valves work freely in their guides. If the valve stems should appear sticky, a little clean kerosene applied with a brush will usually free them.

All lubricators, mechanical and otherwise should be filled, the feed opened and the pumps primed to ensure prompt delivery of the lubricating oil to all relative moving parts. In circulation systems the level of oil in the main reservoir should be checked and where independently driven circulating pumps are employed, they must be put into operation before starting the engine. In some designs manually operated semi-rotary pumps are fitted to the engine circulation system in order that oil can be manually fed to the bearings, etc. before the engine actually starts up.

The engine manufacturers instructions with regard to the cooling system arrangements should also receive detailed attention and any recommendations strictly observed. If air-cooling is used, the coolant level in the radiator should be checked. When water-cooling is used, cooling water flow to the cooler should be turned on.

A bypass switch or bypass button is usually provided to disable or override trips during the start-up mode. For example, the oil pressure may not go above the low oil pressure trip setting until the engine has started up. While starting the engine the bypass switch is turned to the startup position or the bypass button is pushed in to bypass the trips. Once oil pressure is above the trip setting, the bypass button may be released or the switch returned to the run position.

If possible the diesel engine should be run with little or no load until normal operating temperature has been reached. A cold diesel engine sounds rough or harsh and smoothes out as the engine temperature increases. When the engine operating temperature has been reached, the load can be applied slowly.

Once the engine is under load, it should be monitored until the operating variables have stabilized. It should be monitored both physically, at the location of the engine, and remotely by control room operators. Notes should be made of any problems and logged for communication to operators on other shifts and for follow up action if maintenance is needed.

ROUTINE MONITORING

Routine monitoring of a running engine involves monitoring the exterior of the engine for signs of problems such as oil leaks and smoke. It also involves monitoring the gauges on the control panel of the engine. Common operational variables to monitor include:

- Oil pressure
- Coolant temperature
- Exhaust temperature
- Air filter differential pressure
- Oil temperature
- Fuel supply pressure
- Fuel tank level

A log can be kept of values of required readings. If the engine is monitored remotely, the control operator can monitor these variables remotely. He may be able to graph up variables he chooses, to view trends. Alarms are usually set to alert the control operator of any variables out of normal operating ranges.

CHAPTER 6 - QUESTIONS

1. Describe the principle of operation of:

   a) The two-stroke cycle diesel engine.

   b) The four-stroke cycle gasoline engine

2. a) Make a diagram of a battery ignition system for a gasoline engine.

   b) Explain how a magneto ignition system differs from a battery ignition system and list any advantages that one system has over the other.

3. Describe a cooling system for a diesel engine

4. Explain "turbo-charging and "supercharging" and point out any differences between them.

5. Describe a common rail fuel system for a diesel engine.

6. Using a simple sketch, describe an air operated starting system for a diesel engine.

7. Describe the three types of governors: mechanical, hydraulic and electronic, which are used on diesel engines.

8. Using a simple sketch, describe a piston for a diesel engine, including the function of the piston rings.

9. List five common variables, which are monitored on a large diesel engine.

10. Describe a lubrication oil pump for a diesel engine.

ANSWERS: All answers are found within the content of the chapter.

Cogeneration Systems & Operation

LEARNING OUTCOME

When you complete this chapter you should be able to:

Explain cogeneration and describe common configurations, components and applications.

LEARNING OBJECTIVES

Here is what you should be able to do when you complete each objective:

1. *Define cogeneration and explain its purpose, advantages, and applications.*

2. *Explain the components and operation of simple-cycle cogeneration systems.*

3. *Explain the components and operation of combined-cycle, gas/steam turbine cogeneration systems.*

4. *Explain the components and operation of a fully fired, combined-cycle cogeneration system.*

5. *Explain single-shaft and dual-shaft combined-cycle power plants.*

6. *Explain the control strategies and components, for both power and steam production, including diverter and duct burner operation.*

7. *Describe the various designs of heat recovery steam generators (HRSGs) and explain their industrial applications.*

8. *Explain the environmental considerations and techniques in the operation of a cogeneration system.*

9. *Describe typical cogeneration systems that use internal combustion engines (gas or diesel) and heat recovery water heaters (HRWHs).*

10. *Explain a typical start-up procedure for a combined cycle cogeneration system.*

OBJECTIVE 1

Define cogeneration and explain its purpose, advantages, and applications.

COGENERATION

Cogeneration, in simplest terms, may be defined as the simultaneous production of two energy forms from a single energy source. More specifically, it is the generation of heat energy and electrical energy from a single fuel source. An equivalent term that is often used is "combined heat and power", commonly abbreviated as CHP.

The initial energy source (ie. fuel) may be natural gas, gasoline, diesel, oil, coal, biomass, or a variety of waste fuels from industrial processes. One energy output will be heat energy (the by-product of combustion), which is then utilized in a process for a particular purpose, such as heating or the production of steam in a boiler. The second energy output is electrical power, which involves the operation of an electrical generator. The generator may be driven directly by the machine (ie. gas turbine, diesel engine) that burned the fuel or by a steam turbine that utilizes the steam from the boiler.

Most modern cogeneration installations utilize a heat engine (gas turbine or internal combustion engine) to drive a generator and produce electrical power. Then the exhaust heat, rather than be wasted to atmosphere, will be used to produce steam or hot water in some type of heat recovery boiler.

Purpose

The primary purpose of cogeneration is to reduce energy costs by increasing the overall thermal efficiency of a system. A traditional plant with boilers, gas turbines, or internal combustion engines has an overall efficiency of less than 40%. Cogeneration can increase this efficiency to between 60 and 90%.

Advantages

Several advantages of cogeneration at both local and global levels have resulted in the ever-increasing popularity of cogeneration systems for business and industry.

Advantages at the local level include:

- A reduction in the total energy bill when electricity and heat are required at the site. Economics may be further improved with the ability to sell excess power back to the utility companies.

- Cogeneration facilities are generally more compact and require less maintenance compared to a conventional plant of similar capacity.

- A cogeneration facility usually has a much shorter start-up time than a conventional plant of similar capacity.

- A wide range of configurations and sizes to meet the requirements of almost any industrial facility.

Advantages at the global level include:

- Cogeneration facilities that utilize cleaner burning fuels will reduce the load demand on heavier polluting, coal-fired generation facilities.

- The greater efficiency of cogeneration facilities will result in less fuel being burned resulting in preservation of energy reserves and the subsequent reduction in the emission of green house gases (especially CO_2).

- Electrical production on site will reduce the requirement for the construction of new, large and expensive utility plants. Local production of electricity also results in a reduction of transmission line losses and capital costs of new transmission lines.

Applications of Cogeneration

Cogeneration serves a wide range of business and industry facilities. The applications of cogeneration can fall into three general areas:

- Schools, hospitals, hotels, universities, colleges, prisons, malls and other institutional or commercial establishments that have a heating, cooling and electrical demand twenty four hours a day. The heating requirements of these facilities can normally be met with a fairly low temperature heat recovery unit.

- Pulp and paper mills, petrochemical plants, refineries, gas processing plants, food processing plants and other large scale industrial processes. These types of plants may require high temperature energy for some processes or require low temperature from refrigeration units, or both.

- Localized central heating and cooling plants situated in city centers, supplying the electrical, heating and cooling requirements for a number of office and apartment buildings or small industrial plants.

OBJECTIVE 2

Explain the components and operation of simple-cycle cogeneration systems.

SIMPLE CYCLE COGENERATION SYSTEMS

"Simple Cycle" cogeneration means that the simultaneous generation of heat and power is accomplished using a single thermodynamic cycle. There are various types of simple-cycle cogeneration systems, including the following.

- Back Pressure Steam Turbine
- Waste Heat Cogeneration
- Internal Combustion Engine Cogeneration
- Gas Turbine

Back-Pressure Steam Turbine

The boiler and back-pressure steam turbine, as shown in Figure 1, is a type of a simple-cycle cogeneration system. The fuel, which may be gas, oil, coal, or waste fuel, is burned in the boiler to produce heat, which then produces steam. The steam drives the turbine, which in turn supplies mechanical energy to the generator. The LP (Low Pressure) exhaust steam from the turbine is controlled at a specific pressure to supply the required heat to the process.

Figure 1	Back Pressure Steam Turbine Cogeneration

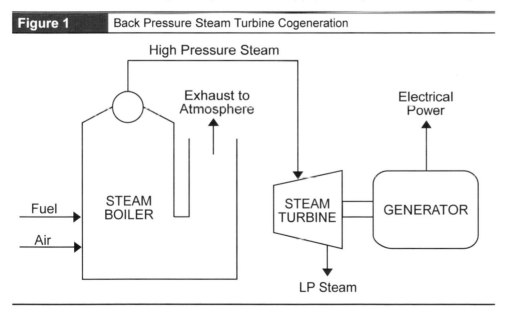

Waste Heat Cogeneration

Figure 2 shows a simple waste heat cogeneration system. The primary purpose is to burn a fuel to produce heat for a process and then to use the waste heat from the process to produce steam in the boiler. The steam from the boiler is fed to the steam turbine to rotate the generator and produce electrical power. The low-pressure exhaust steam from the turbine is used for feedwater heaters or other purposes. Examples of this system include municipal waste incineration or wood wastes from a pulp mill. The waste produced from the necessary processes can be used to produce electrical power for in-plant use or for sharing with an external power grid.

| Figure 2 | Waste Heat Cogeneration |

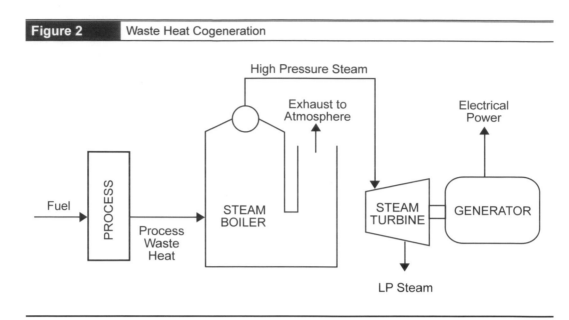

Internal Combustion Engine Cogeneration

Figure 3 show a simple internal combustion engine cogeneration system. The fuel used may be natural gas, oil, gasoline, or diesel. The engine rotates a generator for the production of electricity and the exhaust gases from the engine provide heat for the heat recovery water heater. The heater then transfers heat to a circulating fluid for building or process heat.

| Figure 3 | Heat Engine Cogeneration |

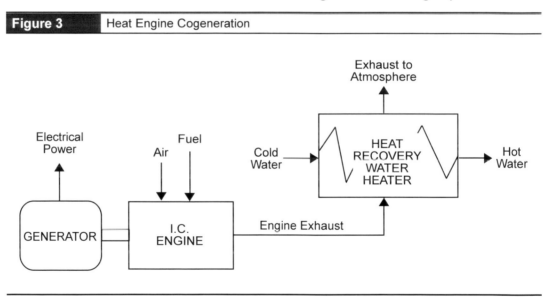

Gas Turbines

Figure 4 shows a simple gas turbine turning an electrical generator. The waste heat, produced by the gas turbine, passes through an exhaust heat boiler. The steam produced by the boiler is used for heating purposes and for an absorption refrigeration system. This unit may be used to provide heating and cooling for an office building, shopping center, or public institution.

Figure 4	Gas Turbine Cogeneration System

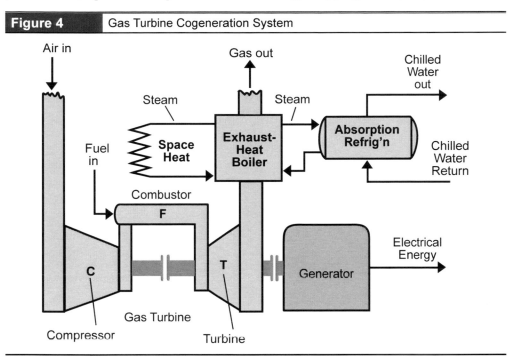

OBJECTIVE 3

Explain the components and operation of combined-cycle, gas/steam turbine cogeneration systems.

COMBINED-CYCLE COGENERATION SYSTEMS

"Combined cycle cogeneration" refers to the cogeneration of electricity and heat from a system that simultaneously utilizes two different thermodynamic cycles. Usually each cycle operates an independent electrical generator.

Figure 5 shows one example of a combined cycle.

- In this system, a gas turbine burns a fuel in its combustors to turn a power turbine, which then turns an electrical generator. The thermodynamic cycle used by a gas turbine is the Brayton Cycle.
- The exhaust from the gas turbine is used to heat the boiler and produce steam for the steam turbine.
- The steam turbine provides power for a second electrical generator. The thermodynamic cycle of the steam system is the Rankine Cycle. Steam is also bled off from sections of the turbine and used as a heat source in the feed heater

Since the boiler is "pressurized" by the gas turbine exhaust, neither forced draft (FD) nor induced draft (ID) fans are required. The combustion of fuel in the boiler is an entirely separate process and does not affect the gas turbine so that any boiler fuel may be used in this case.

| Figure 5 | Combined-Cycle Gas/Steam Turbine Cogeneration System |

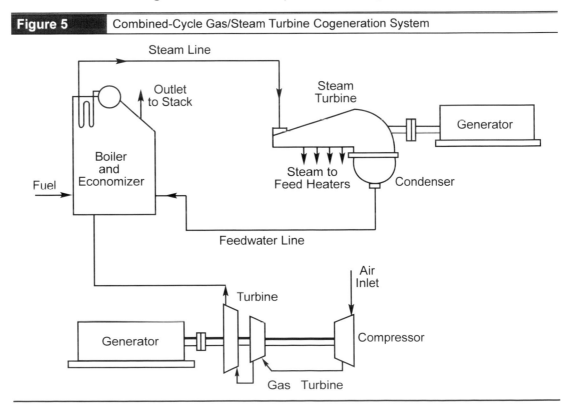

Figure 6 shows a different combined cycle configuration.

- The compressor supplies pressurized combustion air to the boiler, and the hot flue gases from the boiler are fed back to the gas turbine. Since the products of combustion in the boiler become the working gas for the gas turbine, the fuel used in the boiler must be acceptable for the gas turbine, to avoid blade fouling.

- The hot exhaust gases from the gas turbine heat the incoming feedwater in the economizer.

- The gas turbine is coupled to an electrical generator and the steam produced in the boiler drives a steam turbine, which also drives a generator. Again the Brayton and Rankine cycles have been combined to produce heat and electrical power.

Figure 6	Combined-Cycle Steam/Gas Turbine Cogeneration System

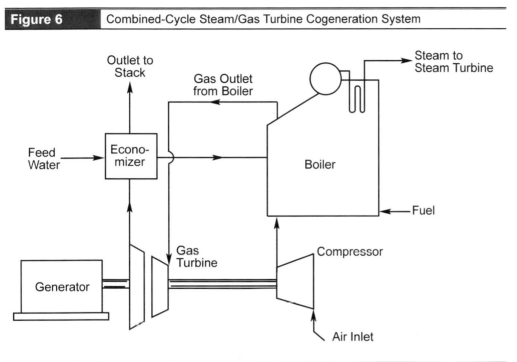

Figure 7 shows the most common combined cycle arrangement.

The gas turbine drives an electrical generator. The exhaust gases from the gas turbine pass through the heat recovery steam generator (HRSG) which generates superheated steam from feedwater. The steam expands through a steam turbine, which drives a second generator.

Figure 7   Combined Cycle System Schematic

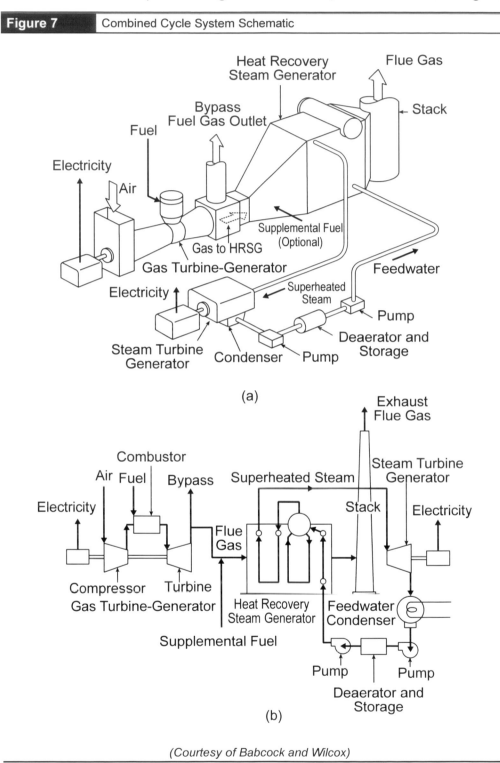

(a)

(b)

(Courtesy of Babcock and Wilcox)

OBJECTIVE 4

Explain the components and operation of a fully-fired, combined-cycle cogeneration system.

FULLY-FIRED COMBINED-CYCLE COGENERATION

A fully fired combined-cycle cogeneration system is shown in Figure 8.

This system consists of a gas turbine, steam turbine, generators and a fired heat recovery steam generator (HRSG). The gas and steam turbines are each coupled to a generator.

The steam generator (boiler) receives all the exhaust flow from the gas turbine and uses the air component of that flow for combustion air. The other products of combustion (from the gas turbine) pass through the boiler, but do provide heat for the boiler. The boiler has additional burners that are fired on a continuous basis and/or intermittently as steam load demands.

This arrangement allows the boiler to be fired separately at somewhat reduced load if the gas turbine is unavailable for service. When the gas turbine is in service the steam load is increased considerably. One application of this design is in the re-powering of existing plants, where additional output and efficiency can be achieved by adding the gas turbine.

Figure 8	Fully Fired Combined-Cycle Cogeneration System

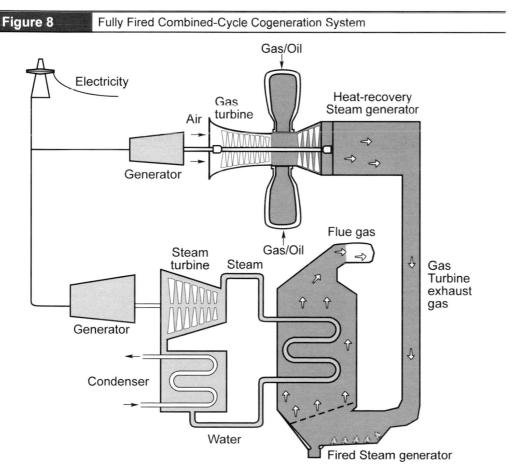

OBJECTIVE 5

Explain single-shaft and multi-shaft combined-cycle power plants.

SINGLE-SHAFT COMBINED-CYCLE POWER PLANT

Some large power plants use a single shaft, combined-cycle system, with the compressor, gas turbine and generator in tandem, which means they are, in effect, all on a common shaft. This requires the individual shafts of the three machines to be a straight line and joined together by couplings and, in some cases, reduction gears. The energy output of the gas and steam turbines are both applied to the generator.

The single shaft design has the most attractive operating and performance characteristics of all combined cycle plants. Some benefits, compared to multi-shaft combined cycle plants, include:

- Higher level of thermal efficiency
- Lower capital costs
- Higher operating flexibility (for example, fast start-up)
- Short project and construction times
- Lower operation and maintenance costs

Figure 9 shows one single shaft configuration.

Here the generator is located between the gas turbine and the steam turbine. This is common for smaller units (around 50MW or less) where the steam turbine is relatively simple, without reheat or several stages.

While it is compact and efficient, one disadvantage of this configuration is that the steam turbine must be removed for major maintenance on the generator, especially for removal of the rotor.

| **Figure 9** | Single Shaft Combined-Cycle Power Plant |

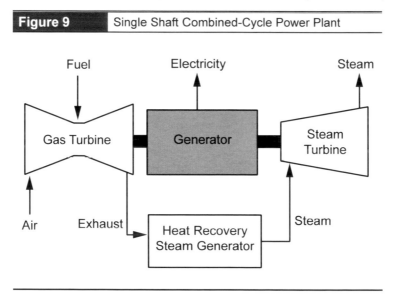

Figure 10 is a 3D computer rendering of a large single-shaft combined cycle plant, similar to that described above, with the generator between the gas and steam turbines.

| Figure 10 | Single Shaft Combined-Cycle Power Plant |

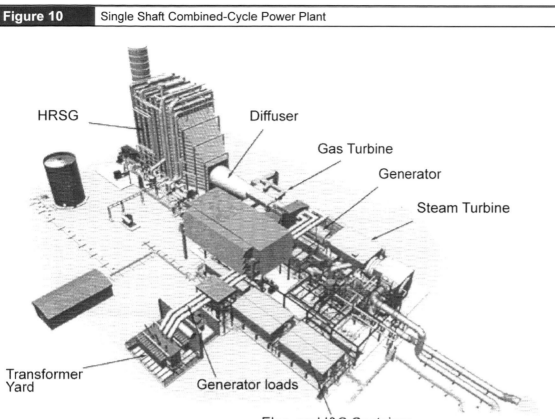

Figure 11 is a simplified sketch of a more common configuration for larger single-shaft systems. In this case, the steam turbine is located between the gas turbine and the generator. This design is used when the steam turbine is of a more complex design, operating with several stages and incorporating reheat. One obvious advantage of this configuration is that the rotor can be removed from the generator without having to remove part of the turbine.

| Figure 11 | Single Shaft Combined-Cycle Power Plant |

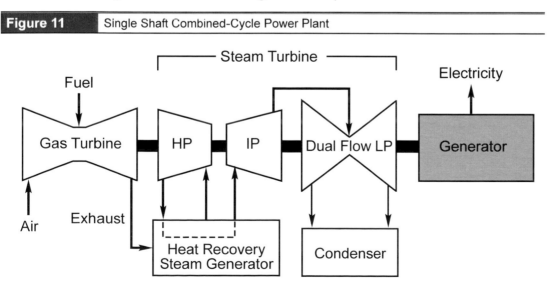

MULTI-SHAFT COMBINED CYCLE

A multi-shaft combined-cycle power plant has two or more gas turbines or steam turbines on separate shafts. Each machine is used to drive a separate generator. The exhaust gases from the gas turbines are routed to the heat-recovery steam generators to produce superheated steam for the turbines.

This is a popular configuration when flexibility of operation is required, particularly if power and steam loads vary too much to be efficiently handled by single-shaft systems. Multi-shaft is common when existing plants add cogeneration to their system. The gas turbine(s) and heat recovery generator(s) are easily added to supplement the existing steam supply plus increase the power generation capacity of the plant. The multi-shaft configuration also allows more flexibility and convenience for maintenance on the gas turbine or the steam turbine sections.

Figure 12 illustrates a simple multi-shaft arrangement, in this case called "dual-shaft" since there are two generators driven on separate shafts by the gas turbine and steam turbine.

| **Figure 12** | Dual Shaft Combined-Cycle Cogeneration Systems |

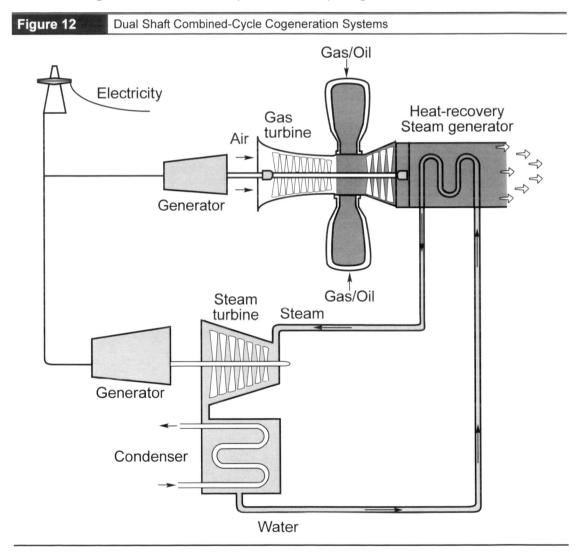

OBJECTIVE 6

Explain the general control strategies and components for both power and steam production, including diverter and duct burner operation.

CONTROL STRATEGIES

The selection of a control strategy will be dependant on the primary function of the cogeneration system as determined by the type of facility. The fuel supplied may first produce electrical power with the thermal energy produced as a by-product. This type of cogeneration system, called a topping cycle cogeneration, may be used in institutional or commercial establishments such as hospitals, colleges, universities, pulp and paper, and food processing. In a bottoming cycle cogeneration system, the primary fuel produces high temperature thermal energy for processes such as steel making, gas plants, and petrochemical facilities. The heat exhausted from these processes is utilized to produce electrical energy from a HRSG.

Electrical Load Control

The cogeneration system may be connected to the utility grid or be separated from the electrical utility grid. A system that is not connected to the electrical grid will supply all of the electrical requirements of the site, including that required for emergency backup and shutdowns. The process utilizes the waste heat from the electrical production. Some waste heat may be lost to the atmosphere if the heating requirements of the process are less than the heat produced by the system. Other heating systems, such as boilers or auxiliary firing, may be required if the waste heat produced is less than that required for the process.

A system connected to the electrical grid may be either a base loaded system or have a set electrical demand from the utility grid.

- The base loaded system has the electrical production from the cogeneration system fixed at its maximum production and changing electrical requirements met by the electrical utility grid.
- The set electrical demand has the electrical supply from the utility grid fixed and the cogeneration system looks after the changing electrical requirements. In both cases, the sizing of the system may require the ability to exhaust excess waste heat or to supply additional heat to the process from other boilers or from auxiliary firing.

Thermal Load Control

The thermal load control may be either a fixed production of a minimum thermal energy or varying requirement for thermal energy.

- With the first strategy, the production of the thermal energy is fixed at the minimum requirements for the site, and the prime mover will operate at full load, all the time. Further thermal requirements are met using other boilers or auxiliary firing.
- The second strategy involves the production of thermal energy to meet the changing requirements of the process at all times. In this case, the prime mover will have a varying output. Either purchasing or selling power to the electrical utility grid meets changes in electrical requirements for both of these strategies.

Diverter & Duct Burner Control

Figure 13 shows a control system utilizing a duct burner and a diverter.

Low thermal requirement may occur during startup, during times of low production in a process, or low electrical requirements in the case of a combined cycle.

- During low thermal requirements, the diverter valve is positioned to close off the exhaust gases to the HRSG. These exhaust gases are then vented to the atmosphere.

- As the thermal requirements increase, the diverter is positioned to allow more and more exhaust gases through the HRSG.

- If the diverter is positioned to completely close off the exhaust gases to the atmosphere, the duct burner (auxiliary firing) will begin to fire and modulate to control further changes in the requirements for thermal energy.

Figure 13	Cogeneration Control with Duct Burners and Diverter Valve

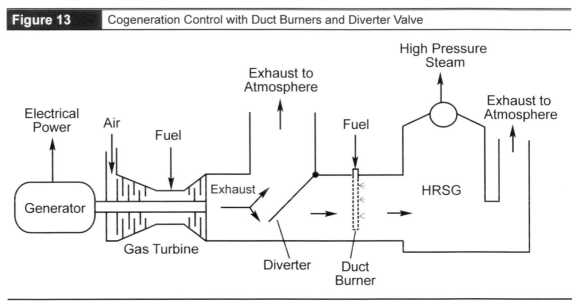

OBJECTIVE 7

Describe the various designs of heat recovery steam generators (HRSGs) and explain their industrial applications.

HEAT RECOVERY STEAM GENERATOR (HRSG)

The heat recovery steam generator (HRSG) is sometimes referred to as a waste heat recovery boiler (WHRB), or turbine exhaust gas (TEG) boiler. The main application for these boilers is steam generation using gas turbine exhaust as the primary heat source.

The specific design of the HRSG will be dependant on the electrical requirements of the plant (gas turbine size) and the thermal requirements of the plant site. The flexibility of the HRSG allows for different industrial configurations to meet the specific requirements of each specific plant site.

The gas flow can be either horizontal or vertical, depending upon the floor space available. The horizontal type is the most common. The HRSG may be designed for operation with multiple, separate pressure steam-water loops to meet application requirements and maximize heat recovery.

Circulation through a HRSG may be forced circulation or natural circulation, with most horizontal gas flow HRSG boilers using natural circulation. Some HRSG boilers are of the once through forced circulation design. Some have high alloy tubes, and can operate without water-flow through the tubes.

HRSG units may be unfired (waste heat only) or have auxiliary, or duct, burners to raise the gas temperature inlet of the HRSG coils. The duct burners can be used to:

- Increase the production of steam
- Control the superheater temperatures
- Meet process steam temperature requirements

The HRSG shown in Figure 14 has auxiliary burners. Heating surfaces include: superheater, boiler/evaporator tubes, and an economizer. It is a natural circulation boiler with a steam drum. This HRSG would be found at a plant site with a fairly high electrical requirement (larger gas turbine) and a requirement for superheated steam, possibly for steam turbines in a combined cycle cogeneration plant.

Figure 14   HRSG with Auxiliary Firing

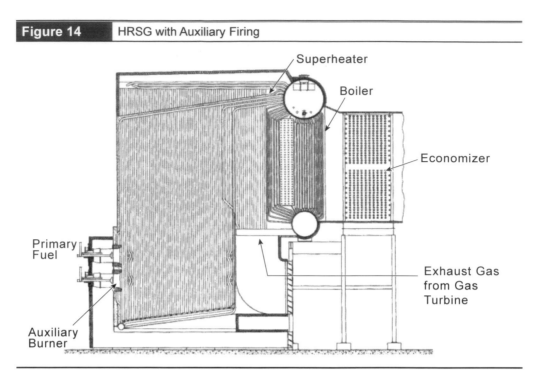

The vertical HRSG in Figure 15 has two ducts for gas turbine exhaust. There are three sections of horizontal tubes. The first, receiving the hottest exhaust gas, is the superheater section. This is followed by the evaporator tubes, which generate steam and discharge it to the steam drum, located outside the ductwork. A lower header, supplied by downcomers from the steam drum feeds the evaporator tubes and creates natural circulation. The final bank of tubes is the economizer section, which preheats the feedwater going to the steam drum.

Figure 15   Vertical HRSG

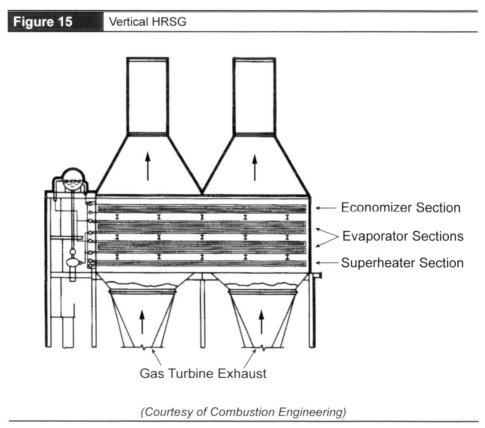

(Courtesy of Combustion Engineering)

Figure 16 is a simple sketch of a large, horizontal, multi-drum HRSG, used in a cogeneration cycle. It produces high-pressure steam from a high pressure steam drum (at 7000 kPa), which is fed through a superheater, then to a turbine generator. It also has intermediate (2400 kPa) and low-pressure (350 kPa) steam drums. The steam from these drums is used for process heating.

Figure 16	Horizontal Multi-Drum HRSG

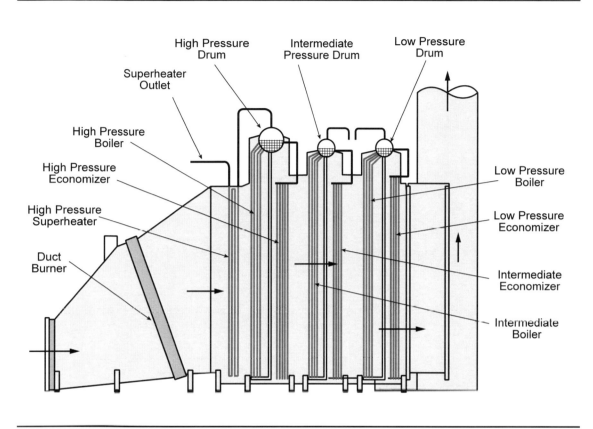

OBJECTIVE 8

Explain the environmental considerations and techniques in the operation of a cogeneration system.

ENVIRONMENTAL CONCERNS

The environmental impact of a cogeneration system will be dependant on the type of fuel used and the type of prime mover, either gas turbine or internal combustion engine. Cogeneration systems can be designed for coal, oil, gasoline, natural gas, and waste fuels. Each of these fuels has their own environmental impact, due to the formation of the following gases:

- Nitrous oxides
- Carbon dioxide
- Sulphur dioxide

Nitrous Oxides (NOₓ)

Oxides of nitrogen (NO_X) are produced by burning a fuel in air. The level of NO_X emissions is dependent on combustion conditions and particularly on temperature, pressure, combustion chamber geometry and the air/fuel mixture.

The primary environmental consideration for natural gas is the development of nitrous oxides (NO_X) due to the high temperature of combustion. The production of nitrous oxides leads to acid rain and are generally regulated by local environmental agencies. The newer combustor designs have greatly reduced the development of NO_X within the gas turbine. In locations where there is a greater environmental requirement for the reduction of nitrous oxides, the temperature of the flame can be reduced by the injection of steam into the combustion region, thereby greatly reducing the development of nitrous oxides. But, this has the disadvantage of reducing the temperature of the exhaust gases through the HRSG and therefore, reducing the efficiency of the unit.

The formation of nitrous oxides can also be reduced through the use of selective catalytic reduction (SCR). This involves the injection of ammonia prior to the catalyst. This process is extremely dependant on temperature and the flexibility of the HRSG allows the ammonia and catalyst to be installed at a precise location in the temperature profile of the exhaust gases exiting the gas turbine. The exhaust gases leaving the gas turbine are about 550°C and the optimal temperature for SCR is between 350°C and 450°C. The use of SCR with steam injection can reduce the nitrous oxides from 150 ppm to less than 10 ppm. Figure 17 shows the ammonia injection and SCR in a HRSG.

Figure 17	Selective Catalytic Reduction of NOₓ

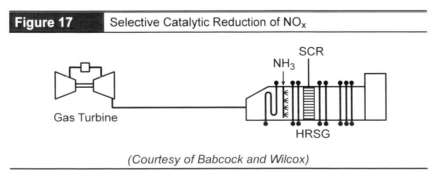

(Courtesy of Babcock and Wilcox)

Carbon Dioxide

The product of most concern in the combustion process is carbon dioxide, well known for its contribution to the greenhouse effect and climatic change. However, where cogeneration replaces the separate fossil fuel generation of electricity and heat, it reduces primary fuel consumption by about 35%. This means a similar reduction in CO_2 emissions.

Sulphur Dioxide

Emissions of sulphur dioxide vary directly with the sulphur content of the fuel. In the case of natural gas, this is negligible and condensing heat exchangers can be used to maximize heat recovery wherever appropriate. Diesel fuel and biogas do contain sulphur and where the sulphur content exceeds the limit set by the governing authority, some form of emission control is necessary. Furthermore, the cost of installing a stainless steel heat exchanger and exhaust flue to counter the corrosive nature of the condensate usually precludes the use of condensing heat recovery systems with these fuels.

OBJECTIVE 9

Describe typical cogeneration systems that use internal combustion engines (gas or diesel) and heat recovery water heaters (HRWHs).

INTERNAL COMBUSTION ENGINE COGENERATION SYSTEMS

For small facilities, an internal combustion (IC) engine with an electrical generator and heat recovery water heater (HRWH) may provide sufficient electrical and thermal energy to meet requirements. The IC engine may burn diesel fuel, propane, natural gas or gasoline, depending on local availability and cost.

The IC engine has the advantage of being capable of intermittent operation (ie. when required) and not being subjected to load changes due to changes in ambient temperature (as a gas turbine would be).

Figure 18 shows an internal combustion engine turning a generator (not shown) with the exhaust gases either passing to atmosphere or through a HRWH. The water flow from the process passes through an oil cooler, then an air cooler, and finally a water cooler before entering the hot water (or steam) coils in the heat recovery heater (or boiler). The heat recovery heater may be of the completely filled boiler (non evaporator) or of the once through tubular design.

This type of installation would be used where the electrical energy demand is higher than the thermal energy demand. Small businesses and institutions may find this type of system functional for providing all or part of the electrical and thermal requirements.

| **Figure 18** | Cogeneration using Internal Combustion Engine |

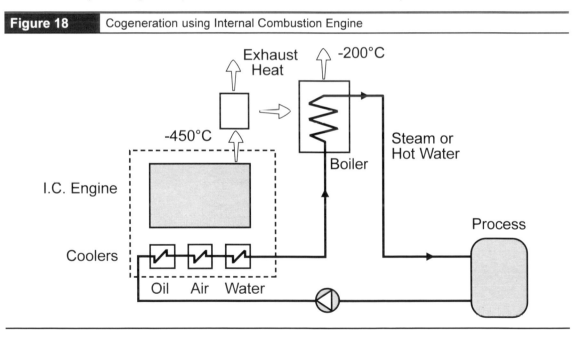

Figure 19 shows an arrangement that is very common in installations such as district or institution heating plants, where relatively small amounts of power are required (500 - 1500 kilowatt range) and the demand for heat is also relatively small.

In this arrangement, internal combustion engines, fueled by gas or light oil, are used to drive a number of generators. The hot exhaust from each engine discharges into a common header that carries it to a Heat Recovery Hot Water Generator (HRHWG). Water in the facility's heating system is heated and then circulated throughout the facility and returned back to the HRHWG.

| **Figure 19** | Hot Water Cogeneration System |

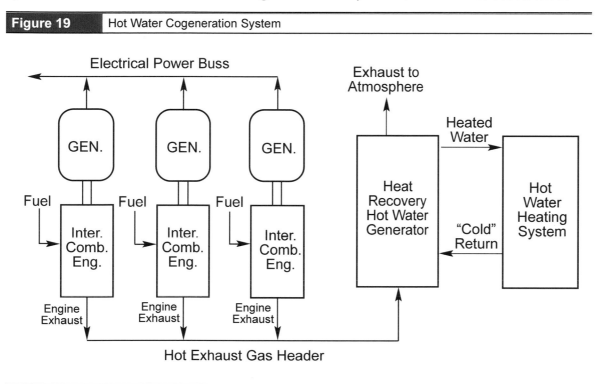

OBJECTIVE 10

Explain a typical start-up procedure for a combined cycle cogeneration system.

START-UP PROCEDURE

The start-up sequence of each cogeneration system will be unique to the specific design of the installation. The manufacturers guidelines and operating instructions should be consulted prior to attempting to start the system. The start-up sequence may be as easy as pushing a button and having electronic controls proceed through the start sequence or as complex as a major power plant start-up.

The start-up sequence below would be for a small (under 5 MW) electrical generation plant with the waste heat supplying a steam turbine attached to a generator, or supplying heat to an absorption refrigeration system, or supplying the heating system directly.

With reference to Figures 20 and 21, the following is a brief overview of the starting sequence of this particular system.

1. The operator initiates a turbine start up from the control room. A programmable logic controller (PLC) directs the starter motor through the start up and speed commands.

2. The PLC sends the following commands to the variable frequency driver (VFD).

    a) EY9016A - Close Starter Motor A Breaker

    b) EY9016B - Close Starter Motor B Breaker

    c) SC9015 A - Gas Turbine "A" Starter Motor Speed Control

    d) SC9015 B - Gas Turbine "B" Starter Motor Speed Control

3. The PLC receives the following information from the starter system

    a) ZSC9002A - Gas Turbine "A" Starter Breaker Closed

    b) ZSC9002B - Gas Turbine "B" Starter Breaker Closed

4. The turbine is rotated to about 55% of rated speed using a 480 V variable frequency drive electric motor. A clutch in the gearbox will keep the starter motor engaged until the torque from the driver is overcome by the torque of the turbine.

5. During start up, the diverter valve will be open to the atmosphere and the air from the turbine will pass up through the silencer, purging the gas turbine of combustibles. At 25% rated speed, the diverter valve will reposition to allow air to pass through the HRSG, purging any combustible gases from this region. The diverter valve is again repositioned to pass the exhaust gases to atmosphere through the silencer.

6. The turbine is then run up to starting speed (55% of rated speed) and the fuel is admitted to the combustor and ignited. The generator is then allowed to pick up electrical load.

7. Once the generator is stable, the diverter valve is slowly opened to allow hot combustion gases to enter the HRSG and slowly warm the water in the tubes. Once the HRSG is producing steam, the diverter valve is opened to allow 100% of the combustion gases to pass through the HRSG. The auxiliary burner may be started once the diverter is closed and steam demand is high enough to require the additional firing.

8. The steam turbine is started and its generator is allowed to pick up the additional electrical load, following the manufacturers recommended startup procedure.

Figure 20 Gas Turbine Starter Schematic

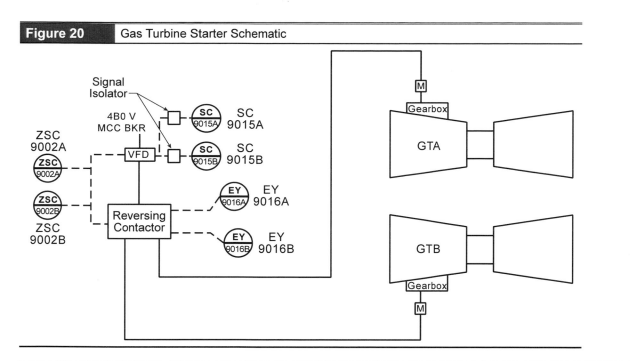

Figure 21 Gas Turbine Exhaust Schematic

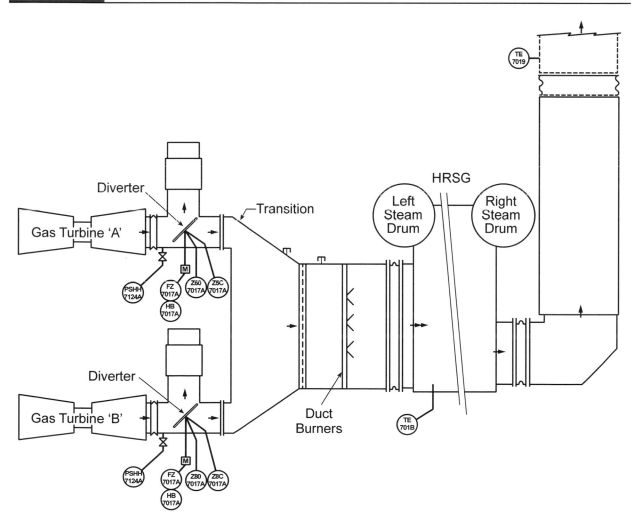

CHAPTER 7 - QUESTIONS

1. Define cogeneration.

2. State three advantages of cogeneration.

3. Briefly describe two types of simple-cycle cogeneration.

4. Briefly describe the typical components of a fully fired combined cycle cogeneration system.

5. Briefly describe single shaft and dual shaft cogeneration systems.

6. Sketch and briefly describe a diverter and duct burner control system.

7. Sketch and briefly describe a heat recovery steam generator with a superheater and economizer.

8. Describe how nitrous oxides are controlled with a gas turbine cogeneration system.

9. Describe how an internal combustion engine may be used as a cogeneration system.

10. Briefly describe a start up sequence for a cogeneration system.

ANSWERS: All answers are found within the content of the chapter.

Compressor Theory & Designs

LEARNING OUTCOME

When you complete this chapter you should be able to:

Explain the classification, designs, and operating principles of industrial air and gas compressors.

LEARNING OBJECTIVES

Here is what you should be able to do when you complete each objective:

1. *Explain compressor terminologies, including compression ratio, capacity, staging, intercooling and aftercooling. Explain the effects of moisture in compressed gases. Explain the effects of altitude on the compression process.*

2. *Describe the operation and common arrangements of reciprocating compressors, including single-acting, double-acting, and tandem arrangements.*

3. *Identify the components of a reciprocating compressor and describe the operation of plate and channel valves.*

4. *Describe internal and external lubrication systems for reciprocating compressors.*

5. *Describe the design and explain the operating principles of rotary compressors, including sliding vane, rotary lobe, and rotary screw.*

6. *Identify the components and controls for a packaged industrial screw compressor.*

7. *Describe designs and principles of centrifugal compressors/blowers, including single and multi-stage designs.*

8. *Describe designs and principles of axial compressors/blowers.*

OBJECTIVE 1

Explain compressor terminologies, including compression ratio, capacity, staging, intercooling, and aftercooling. Explain the effects of moisture in compressed gases. Explain the effects of altitude on the compression process.

COMPRESSOR TERMINOLOGY

Compression Ratio

A compressor receives a gas at a relatively low pressure and discharges it at a much higher pressure. The compression ratio of the compressor is the ratio of the absolute discharge pressure to the absolute intake pressure.

Capacity

The capacity of a compressor is the quantity of air compressed and delivered in a given time period. Capacity is expressed in terms of m^3/min of free air. It is also known as free air delivered (F.A.D.) or free air capacity. "Free air" is air at atmospheric pressure. So, the capacity is the volume (in cubic meters) of atmospheric air compressed in one minute.

Staging

A high compression ratio in a single cylinder of a compressor results in low volumetric efficiency and high discharge temperature. To overcome these undesirable features, compression may be carried out in two or more stages. Two or more cylinders are used to progressively increase the pressure to the final discharge pressure. Each cylinder discharges into the next higher pressure cylinder. This permits a more moderate compression ratio in each cylinder. The result is improved volumetric efficiency. The final discharge temperature may be lower if the air is cooled between the stages.

Compressor Displacement

Compressor displacement is the volume swept out by the piston of a reciprocating compressor and is expressed in cubic metres per minute. If the compressor has more than one stage, the displacement is the volume swept out by the first stage piston only, since the same air passes through all stages in series.

Intercoolers

Intercoolers are used to cool the compressed air between the stages of a multi-stage compressor. The primary purpose of this cooling is to reduce the density of the air, which improves the efficiency of the subsequent compressor stage and, ultimately, of the entire compressor.

Intercooling causes the compression to be more isothermal, rather than adiabatic and the work required for an isothermal compression is less than for an adiabatic compression. Intercooling reduces the power required for compression and increases the overall capacity of the system.

While not the primary purpose, in some cases an intercooler may also cause moisture to condense out of the air. This will prevent free moisture from entering the next stage. Moisture will only condense out if the air is sub-cooled, below the pressure dewpoint of the air.

Aftercoolers

Aftercoolers are used to cool the compressed air before it is delivered to either the point of use or to the air receiver. The temperature of the compressed air is reduced to significantly below the dewpoint at the discharge pressure. This facilitates the removal of moisture and oil vapour from the compressed air stream. (Note: If oil vapour is not condensed and removed, it will have a detrimental effect on air-operated instruments and any accumulation in pipes and reservoirs may ignite and explode). Further cooling of the air will occur in the air receiver, downstream of the aftercooler, usually to close to ambient temperature.

EFFECTS OF MOISTURE

Free or atmospheric air always carries moisture as water vapour. The amount depends upon the temperature of the air. Air that is carrying the maximum amount of water at a certain temperature is said to be saturated. Saturated air, at normal temperature and atmospheric pressure, contains about 0.5 kg of moisture for every 28 m^3 of air. This moisture will be carried into the compressor with the air. When the volume of the air is reduced by compression some of the moisture drops out. The water must be removed from the air because it has a detrimental effect on air-operated instruments and tools and may also freeze in the airlines.

EFFECTS OF ALTITUDE

As the distance above sea level (ie. altitude) increases, the atmospheric pressure decreases. This means that a compressor installed at a high altitude will require a higher compression ratio to produce the same discharge pressure as a machine at sea level. Furthermore, since one kilogram of air occupies a greater volume at higher altitudes than at sea level, a compressor will deliver less mass of air when operated in locations above sea level.

OBJECTIVE 2

Describe the operation and common arrangements of reciprocating compressors, including single-acting, double-acting, and tandem arrangements.

RECIPROCATING COMPRESSORS

A reciprocating compressor is one in which the air is compressed by a piston moving in a reciprocating manner within a cylinder. The cylinder is equipped with intake and discharge valves to control the flow of air entering and leaving. This type of compressor is used in a wide variety of applications including power plant service and commercial, industrial, and mining installations. It is suitable for all ranges of pressure.

Reciprocating compressors have a variety of designs or arrangements and are divided into types according to whether they are:

- Single-acting
- Double-acting
- Single-stage
- Two-stage
- Tandem

Single-Acting Compressors

In a single-acting compressor, compression takes place at one end of the cylinder only. There is only one compression stroke for each crankshaft revolution. The air is compressed only during the outward stroke of the piston. During the inward stroke, more air is drawn into the cylinder. A single-acting compressor, with a vertical cylinder, is illustrated in Figure 1.

Double-Acting Compressors

In a double-acting compressor, compression occurs on both sides of the piston. For each revolution of the crankshaft there are two compression strokes.

Figure 2 shows a horizontal, double-acting compressor. When the piston moves to the left, a partial vacuum is formed in the right end of the cylinder and air is drawn in through the right hand suction valve. At the same time, air is being compressed in the left end and forced out through the left hand discharge valve. When the piston reverses and moves to the right, it will compress the air and force it through the right hand discharge valve. At the same time, air will be drawn into the cylinder through the left hand suction valve.

Figure 1	Single-Acting Compressor

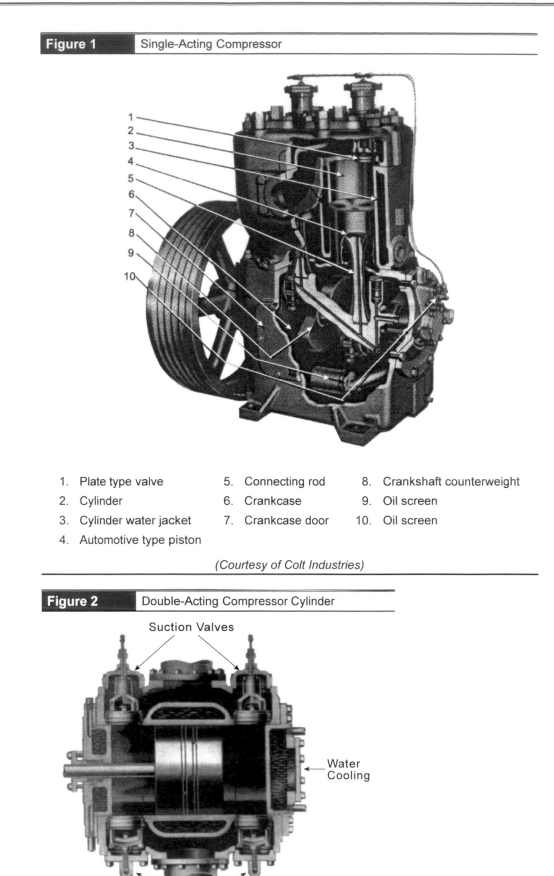

1. Plate type valve
2. Cylinder
3. Cylinder water jacket
4. Automotive type piston
5. Connecting rod
6. Crankcase
7. Crankcase door
8. Crankshaft counterweight
9. Oil screen
10. Oil screen

(Courtesy of Colt Industries)

Figure 2	Double-Acting Compressor Cylinder

Suction Valves

Water Cooling

Discharge Valves

(Courtesy of Worthington Corporation)

Single-Stage Compressors

A single-stage compressor may have one or more cylinders, as shown in Figure 3. For compressed air pressure up to about 1000 kPa the air is compressed in one cylinder, which may be either single-acting or double-acting. This arrangement is single-stage compression. If more than one cylinder is used, all will be the same size and all will discharge into a common outlet at the same pressure. Multiple cylinders increases capacity and helps to smooth out the discharge pressure.

Figure 3	Single-Stage Compressor Variations

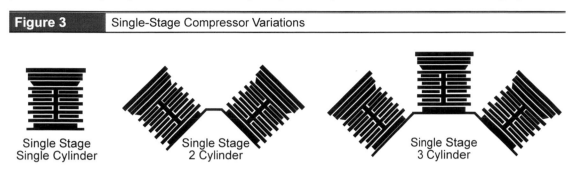

Single Stage Single Cylinder

Single Stage 2 Cylinder

Single Stage 3 Cylinder

Figure 4 is a single-stage, double-acting water cooled compressor, designed for heavy duty. Cushioned ring-plate valves are used, with the suction valves having diaphragm-operated valve lifters for unloading. Either constant-speed free-air control or automatic start-and-stop control, or a combination of the two, are used for the regulation of compressor output. Cylinders and heads have large water jackets for cooling. Shaft and rod seals and tight covers on all crankcase openings protect against leakage of oil and the entrance of dust and other contaminants.

Figure 4	Consolidated Pneumatic, Type T, Single-Stage Compressor

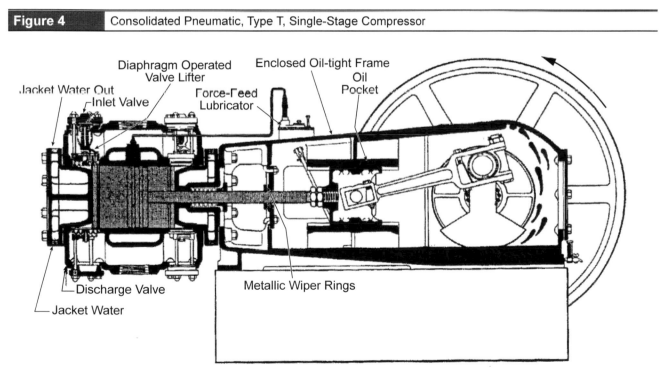

Two-Stage Compressors

A two-stage compressor consists of two or more cylinders, with the first stage being larger in diameter than the second. For pressures between 1000 kPa and 6900 kPa, the air is first compressed in a low-pressure cylinder and then further compressed in a high-pressure cylinder to the final discharge pressure. The cylinders may be either single-acting or double-acting. Larger compressors are usually double-acting.

Figure 5 shows two variations of the two-stage design.

- Figure 5(a) shows a two-stage, two-cylinder air compressor. Atmospheric air is drawn through a filter into the larger first stage and compressed to an intermediate pressure. It is then discharged into the inlet of the smaller second stage, where it is compressed to its final pressure before discharging into a storage tank. A finned intercooler is usually installed between the two stages to reduce the air temperature.

- Figure 5(b) shows a two-sage, 3-cylinder compressor that would be used when a larger volume of compressed air at a moderate pressure is required. Two low-pressure first-stage cylinders, acting in parallel, discharge into a single high-pressure, second stage cylinder.

Figure 5	Two-Stage Air Compressor Variations

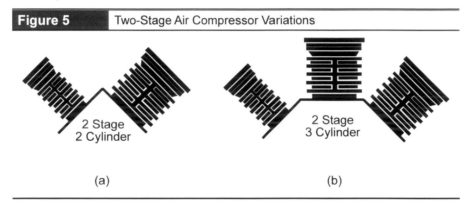

(a)   (b)

Figure 6 shows a more detailed section of a three-cylinder, two-stage compressor, equipped with an intercooler between stages. For compactness, the three cylinders are set at 60° between each other. After each low-pressure cylinder, the air passes through an intercooler before entering the high-pressure cylinder.

| Figure 6 | Two-Stage Three-Cylinder Compressor |

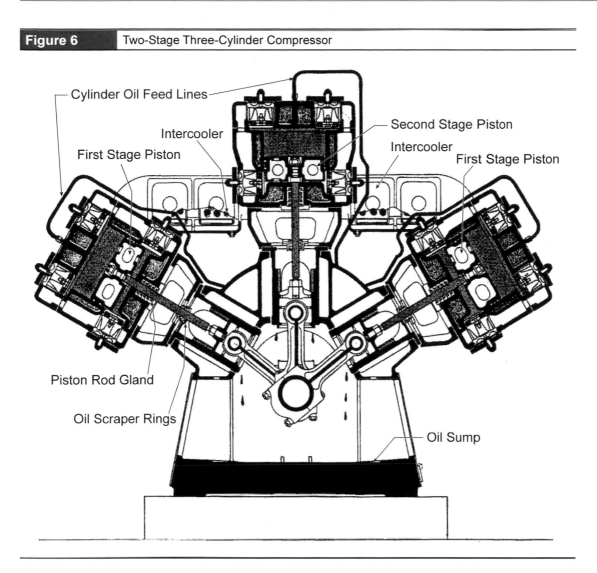

Tandem Compressors

Some dual-acting cylinders in high-pressure applications have a piston rod on both sides of the piston, to provide equal surface areas and to balance the load. Tandem cylinder arrangements help minimize dynamic loads by locating cylinders in pairs, connected to a common crankshaft, so that the movements of the pistons oppose each other.

Figure 7 shows a three-stage, tandem compressor design in which the first-stage cylinder is double acting, while the second and third stage cylinders are single acting. This results in the load being evenly divided between the outward and return strokes, which results in smooth operation. With this arrangement only one piston rod stuffing box is required.

The first and second-stage intercooler tubes are enclosed in a common shell. There is provision for the separation and draining of condensed moisture to prevent it entering the succeeding cylinders. Oil is supplied directly to the walls of the cylinders and to the stuffing box, when required, by a force-feed lubricator, which is driven from the crosshead.

| Figure 7 | Consolidated Pneumatic, Horizontal Tandem, Three-Stage Compressor |

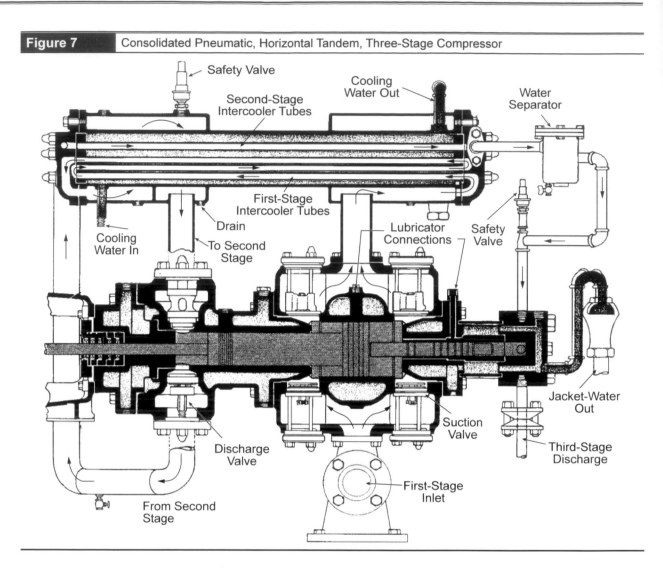

OBJECTIVE 3

Identify the components of a reciprocating compressor and describe the operation of plate and channel valves.

RECIPROCATING COMPRESSOR COMPONENTS

Cylinders

Compressor cylinders are made from cast iron for pressures up to 1000 kPa or cast steel for pressures up to 6900 kPa. Above this pressure, the material used is usually forged steel.

When the compressor is in operation, the cylinder is heated due to compression and the friction of the piston rings. It is necessary, therefore, to remove this heat and to maintain the cylinder at the manufacturers' recommended operating temperature. This is done by means of water-cooling or by air-cooling.

For water-cooling, the cylinder has a chamber or water jacket surrounding the cylinder barrel through which cooling water is circulated. A cross-section of a water-jacketed cylinder is shown in Figure 8. For air-cooling, the cylinder has integral cast fins, which provide an increased radiating area.

Water-cooling is more efficient than air-cooling. However, the air-cooled machine, has the following advantages:

- Simple construction
- Less piping requirements
- No freezing hazard

Figure 8	Water Cooled Cylinder

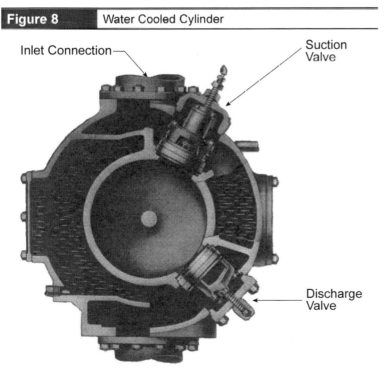

Inlet Connection

Suction Valve

Discharge Valve

Pistons

Pistons are constructed of steel, cast iron, or aluminum. Trunk type (automotive type) pistons are used for single-acting compressors. Double-acting compressor pistons may be solid or hollow. They are normally fitted on the piston rod with a taper fit against a machined shoulder on the rod and are locked in place by means of a nut. If the cylinder is lubricated, the piston rings are made of cast iron. If oil-free operation is desired, the piston rings are Teflon or carbon.

Figure 9 illustrates a single-acting piston and a double-acting piston. With the single-acting piston, the connecting rod also serves as the piston rod, while the double-acting piston is attached to a crosshead by means of a separate, steel piston rod.

Figure 9	Single-Acting Piston & Double-Acting Piston

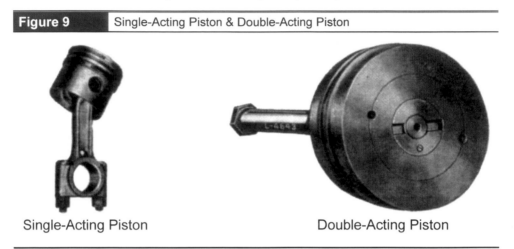

Single-Acting Piston   Double-Acting Piston

Crosshead

The crosshead is made of steel with upper and lower bearing surfaces, which contact the crosshead guides. The piston rod fits into the threaded hole in one end of the crosshead. The crosshead pin, to which the connecting rod is attached, is usually held rigid in the connecting rod. It moves within bearings or bushings in each side of the crosshead. However, in some designs, the crosshead pin is securely fastened in the crosshead. The bearing or bushing is in the connecting rod end. Figure 10 illustrates the construction of a compressor crosshead.

Figure 10	Compressor Crosshead

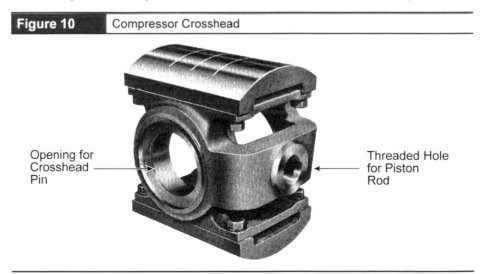

Opening for Crosshead Pin

Threaded Hole for Piston Rod

Connecting Rods

Compressor connecting rods are constructed of forged steel and have a crankpin bearing at one end and an opening for the crosshead pin (or for the piston pin of a trunk type piston) in the other end.

Figure 11 shows two designs of connecting rod.

Figure 11	Compressor Connecting Rods

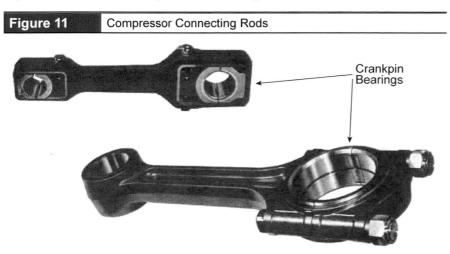

Crankpin Bearings

Figure 12 illustrates a connecting rod attached to the crosshead pin within the crosshead.

Figure 12	Crosshead and Connecting Rod

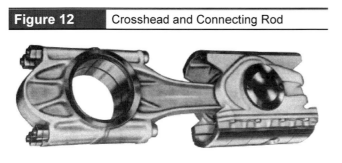

Compressor Crankshafts

Compressor crankshafts are of forged steel and are usually made from a single forging, which has been machined and ground to precision limits. They are drilled to provide oil passages for positive pressure lubrication. In order to balance reciprocating and rotating forces, the crankshaft may be made with counterweights, as shown in Figure 13. The crankshaft may be the type shown in Figure 14, which has opposing crank throws to provide balance.

Figure 13	Counterweighted Crankshaft

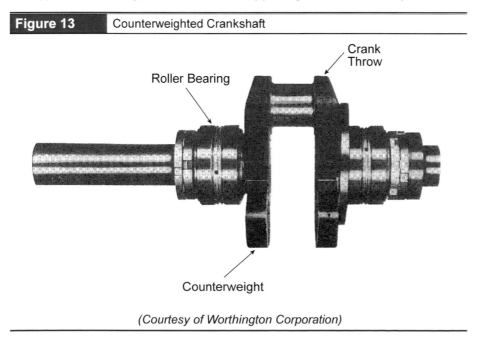

Crank Throw

Roller Bearing

Counterweight

(Courtesy of Worthington Corporation)

| Figure 14 | Crankshaft with Opposed Crank Throws |

Compressor Valves

Compressor valves are usually the automatic type, which open and close due to a pressure difference across them. Two common designs are the:

- Plate Disc type
- Channel type

Plate Disc Type

Figure 15 shows a plate disc type. The air enters through the ribbed upper body, forcing the circular valve discs downwards against the cushioning action of the valve springs. The air then passes between the valve discs and the valve seats and and out through the ribbed lower valve body. When the pressure on the discharge side of the discs becomes higher than the inlet, the springs force the valve close.

| Figure 15 | Plate Disc Type Compressor Valve |

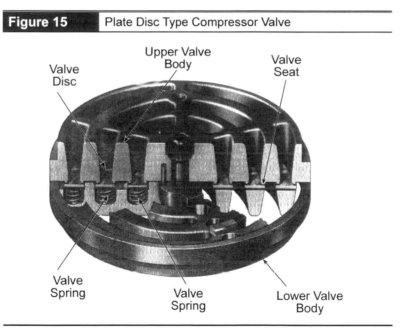

Channel Type

Figure 16 is an exploded view of a channel type valve. The port plate and the seat plate fit together with their passages or openings aligned. The valve channels fit over these openings and are held down against the seat plate by the valve springs. The valves springs fit inside the rectangular channels and are held in place by the stop plate. The air, entering through the port plate, pushes the channels up off the seat plate, against the force of the springs. The air then passes through the openings in the stop plate. Strips of self-lubricating material are placed within the channels to prevent metal-to-metal contact between the channels and the valve springs.

Figure 16 Channel Type Compressor Valve

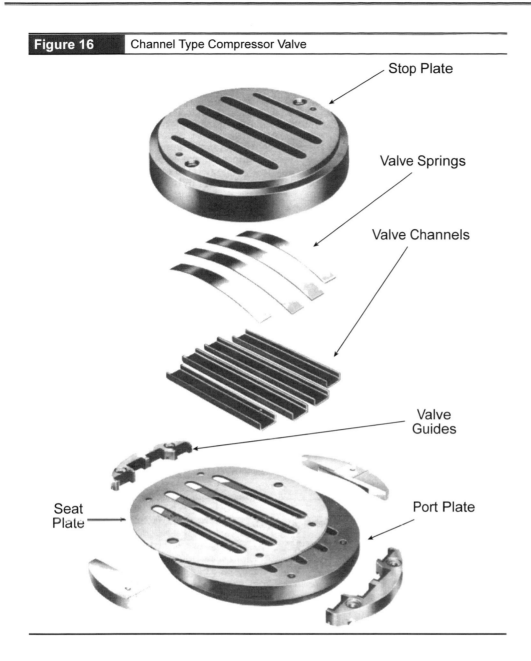

Stop Plate

Valve Springs

Valve Channels

Valve Guides

Seat Plate

Port Plate

OBJECTIVE 4

Describe internal and external lubrication systems for reciprocating compressors.

COMPRESSOR LUBRICATION

Lubricating oil is necessary in a reciprocating compressor to perform the following functions:

- Prevent wear by providing a film between surfaces
- Reduce friction and the resulting power loss by providing a film between surfaces
- Remove the heat produced by friction
- Reduce corrosion by providing a coating for metal surfaces
- Provide sealing around piston rings, vanes, and valves

External Lubrication

External lubrication is the lubrication of moving parts that are external to the compressor cylinder or casing. On reciprocating compressors, these parts include crankshaft bearings, connecting rod bearings and crosshead. A pump, driven by the compressor shaft, delivers oil to the crankshaft and connecting rod bearings. The oil is pumped from the crankcase to the bearings and then drains back to the crankcase.

For small, single-acting, reciprocating compressors, a splash lubrication system is used. The oil is splashed, due to the movement of the crankshaft, onto the various bearings. This method provides internal lubrication at the same time as some oil is splashed onto the cylinder walls.

Internal Lubrication

Internal lubrication provides lubricating oil to the cylinder walls and pistons of reciprocating compressors.

A mechanical lubricator, which is driven from the crankshaft or crosshead, feeds lubricating oil directly to the cylinder walls. Each cylinder has one or more points to which the oil is pumped. After the oil enters the cylinder through these feed points, the piston spreads the oil over the cylinder walls. In a single-acting compressor where the bottom of the cylinder is open to the crankcase, oil is splashed from the crankcase to lubricate the cylinder walls.

OBJECTIVE 5

Describe the design and explain the operating principles of rotary compressors, including sliding vane, rotary lobe, and rotary screw.

ROTARY COMPRESSORS

All rotary compressors have the following features in common.

- They provide energy to the fluid being compressed through the input shaft of one or more rotating elements or rotors.
- They do not have inlet or discharge valves.

Rotary compressors are classed as positive displacement. Several different designs are in use, the most common being the sliding vane, rotary lobe and rotary screw.

Sliding Vane Compressor

A sliding vane compressor is shown in Figure 17.

It consists of a cylindrical rotor in which flat, sliding vanes fit into radial slots. The rotor is contained within a water jacketed cylinder or casing. It is supported by bearings so that it is eccentric to the casing.

- As the rotor turns at high speed, the sliding vanes are forced outward against the casing wall, due to centrifugal force.
- Pockets of gas are trapped between the vanes and the wall and carried around the casing. Due to the eccentricity, these pockets decrease in volume, thus compressing the gas as the vanes move around the casing from the intake to the discharge.

Figure 17	Sliding Vane Compressor

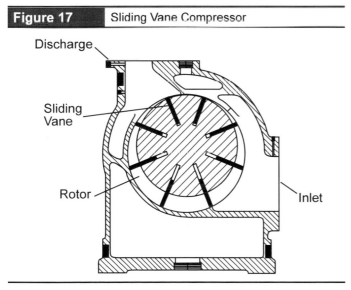

Sliding vane compressors operate at speeds up to 3000 r/min with discharge pressures as high as 1000 kPa.

Figure 18 shows a side view of a large sliding vane compressor. Notice the cooling water jacket surrounding the casing and the lube oil supply to the bearings.

Figure 18	Side View Cutaway of Large Sliding Vane Compressor

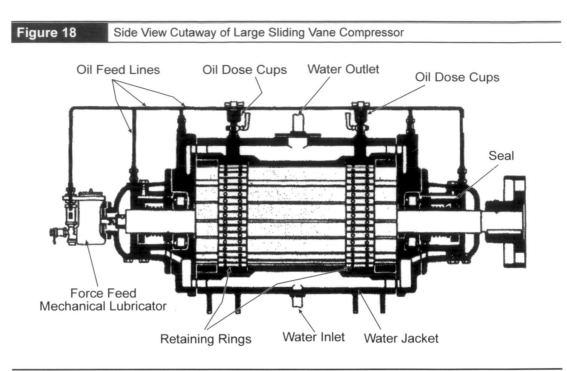

Sliding vane compressors often have two stages. The gas is compressed in a low-pressure casing, which discharges it through an intercooler and into a high-pressure casing. The two casings have separate rotor elements and the shafts are connected by a flexible coupling and share a common drive motor.

Rotary Lobe Compressor

A rotary lobe compressor, shown in Figure 19, has two rotors, with a figure eight cross-section, revolving in opposite directions within a casing. The rotors always intermesh so that no air can pass between them. Timing gears are used to maintain the rotor positions relative to each other. One rotor is driven directly by the driver while the other is driven through the timing gears. As each lobe sweeps past the inlet, a pocket of air is trapped between the lobe and the casing wall. The lobe carries the air around to the discharge on the opposite side of the casing.

Casing lubrication is not required, since the rotors do not touch each other or the casing. Rotary lobe compressors operate at speeds up to about 1750 r/min. Discharge pressures are relatively low, about 100 kPa for single-stage, and 200 kPa for two-stage.

The lobe compressor has the advantages of being compact, requiring no inlet or discharge valves and producing an even flow of oil free air.

Figure 19	Rotary Lobe Compressor

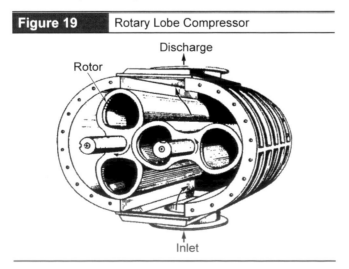

Rotary Screw Compressor

A rotary screw compressor consists of two intermeshing rotors, machined in the form of an axial screw and enclosed in a close-fitting casing. One rotor has four convex lobes and the other rotor has six concave flutes. The rotors do not come in contact with each other or with the casing, thus internal lubrication is not required. The convex rotor is usually driven and it, in turn, drives the concave rotor, through timing gears.

Figure 20 shows the principle of operation.

The driven rotor has four convex lobes and the follower has six concave flutes. The two rotors trap and smoothly compress the air until it passes the discharge outlet. Continuous compression takes place and pulse-free delivery is assured by having another lobe-flute space reach the outlet before the previous space has completely emptied. The drive rotor, being smaller, turns faster than the follower.

Referring to Figure 20:

- In (a), air is drawn in through the compressor inlet into the inter-lobe space.
- In (b) further rotation seals the space off from the inlet.
- In (c), as rotation proceeds, the lobes occupy the space in the flutes, thus displacing the air and forcing it toward the outlet.
- In (d), continued rotation brings the compressed air to the outlet port which is shown by the dotted lines.

The advantages of the rotary screw compressor include compactness, vibration free operation, smooth flow, oil-free air, and no suction or discharge valves required. However, like other rotating types, efficiency is less than that of a reciprocating compressor.

The rotary screw compressor is suitable for installations requiring large capacity at low pressure or small capacity at high pressure. Single-stage machines are capable of discharge pressures up to 700 kPa. Multi-stage machines supply much higher discharge pressures. Capacities range up to 700 m³/min and operating speeds vary from 1500 to 12 000 r/min.

Figure 20	Principle of Operation of Rotary Screw Compressor

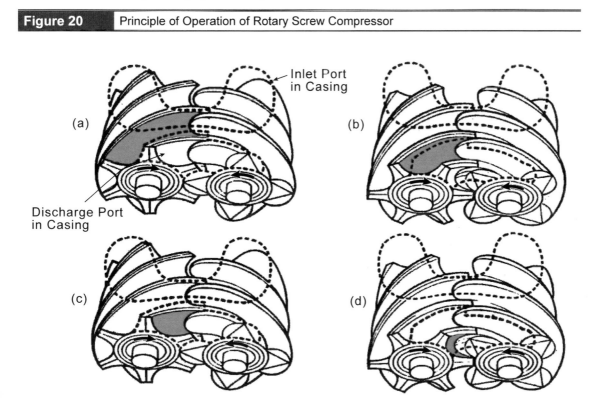

OBJECTIVE 6

Identify the components and controls for a packaged industrial screw compressor.

COMPONENTS

The packaged skid mounted industrial screw compressor, shown in Figure 21, is manufactured by Sullair Corporation. It consists of the following components (refer to both Fig. 21 and 22).

- Compressor driver
- Air filter (on air intake)
- Air inlet valve
- Air compressor
- Fluid/air separator
- Fluid cooler/air after cooler
- Moisture separator
- Water/oil separator
- Prefilters
- Air dryer
- After filters

Figure 21	Packaged Industrial Screw Compressor

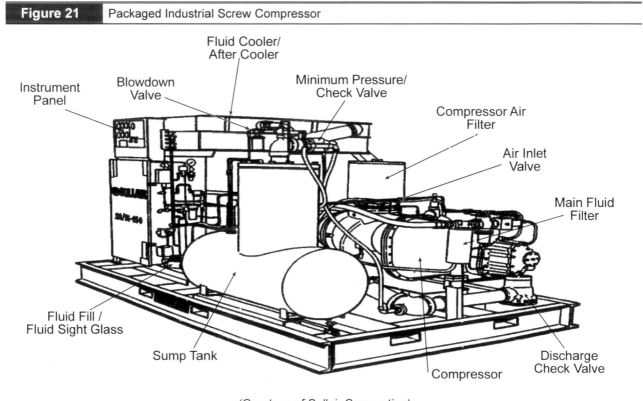

(Courtesy of Sullair Corporation)

Figure 22 shows the basic compressor flows.

| Figure 22 | Packaged Industrial Screw Compressor |

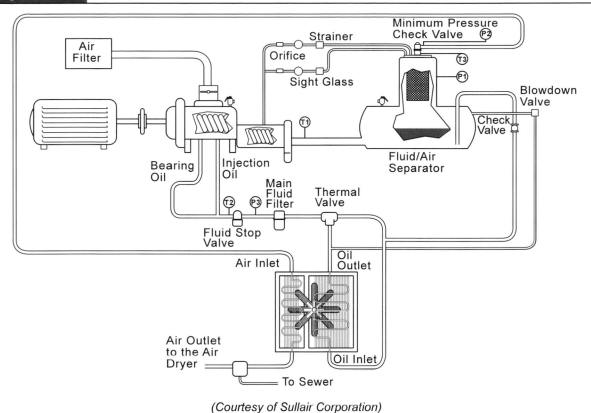

(Courtesy of Sullair Corporation)

Compressor Driver

The driver usually consists of an electric motor, but could be a diesel engine or a steam turbine.

Air Filter

The air intake filter, required to prevent dust and dirt from contaminating the compressor lubricating fluid, is a two stage heavy duty, dry type.

Air Inlet Valve

The air inlet valve is a butterfly valve, which is part of the variable capacity control system for the compressor. By positioning the inlet valve, the Sullicon control system regulates the amount of air to the compressor unit according to service air demand.

Spiral Valve

The spiral valve is used to open and close by-pass ports in the stator, which varies the volume of compressed air produced. The bypass ports return air to the suction before it can be compressed.

Air Compressor

Sullair Tandem Air Compressors feature a two stage, positive displacement, fluid lubricated type compressor. This unit provides continuous pulse free air at a maximum output pressure of 793 kPa. The only major moving parts are the two lobe rotors in each stage. Tandem compressors achieve high efficiencies by using two sets of rotors to stage compression. Rotors turn in a flood of lubricating fluid allowing contact only on a lubricated pitch line, so wear is virtually eliminated.

Fluid/Air Separator

As atmospheric air is drawn into the compressor, a silicone-based fluid is injected into the rotor cavity. In flooded rotary screw compressors, the fluid is necessary to lubricate, seal rotor clearances, and to remove the heat of compression. This entrained fluid is then removed from the air in the fluid/air separator.

Fluid Cooler/After Cooler

This system consists of a radiator type cooler accompanied with an electric powered fan for cooling. The radiator type cooler is split in two sections. Compressor fluid is circulated and cooled in one half of the cooler. Discharged compressed air is cooled in the other half. The air-cooling fan moves air across both sections, at the same time. This cooler is required to remove the heat of compression from both the air and the compressor fluid.

Moisture Separator

Compressed air leaving the air cooler passes into the moisture separator. Any entrained moisture is removed via centrifugal force due to air path changes. The condensate recovered flows to the water/oil separator and the compressed air to the prefilters. The moisture separator will remove the bulk of any moisture in the compressed air and take the load off the prefilters.

Water/Oil Separator

The water/oil separator is constructed of polyethylene with a 144 litre holding capacity. A translucent 5 litre capacity oil reservoir is also included. Inputs to the separator come from the moisture separator and the two prefilter drains. Oil is collected in the 5 litre reservoir and clean water is discharged to sewer. An adjustable oil funnel is specially designed to allow the oil to be continuously skimmed off the surface.

Prefilters

Two prefilters are located in series on the inlet of the air dryer. Both filters are the coalescing type. "Coalescing", by definition, means to come together and form one mass. Fine oil and water aerosols, which are entrained in the compressed air, collect within the microfibre filter media of the filter element. They agglomerate (coalesce) to form drops of continuously increasing size. The drops fall to the bottom of the filter bowl and are subsequently drained away.

The first filter is a coalescing oil filter and will remove particles down to 1 micron including entrained liquid water and oil, providing a maximum remaining oil aerosol content of 0.5 ppm at 21°C.

The second filter is a high efficiency coalescing oil filter and will remove particles down to 0.01 micron including water and oil aerosols, providing a maximum remaining oil aerosol content of 0.01 ppm at 21°C.

Electronic condensate drain valves dump any collected liquids from both prefilters to the water/oil separator.

Air Dryer

This air dryer assembly consists of the air dryer, a dew point analyzer and associated electric and pneumatic controls. Dryers are modular construction and are filled with a high performance zeolite molecular sieve desiccant.

Compressed air enters the dryer and is directed by the inlet valve into one of the chambers in the lower manifold. From the lower manifold, the air passes up one side of the columns and is dried through contact with the desiccant material contained in the columns. The dried air then enters the upper manifold and is directed via a check valve, via the outlet housing into the after filter. The afterfilter will remove any dust particles should the desiccant break down. The dry, clean air passes now to the air receiver and the distribution system.

CONTROL PANEL

| Figure 23 | Rotary Screw Air Compressor Control Panel |

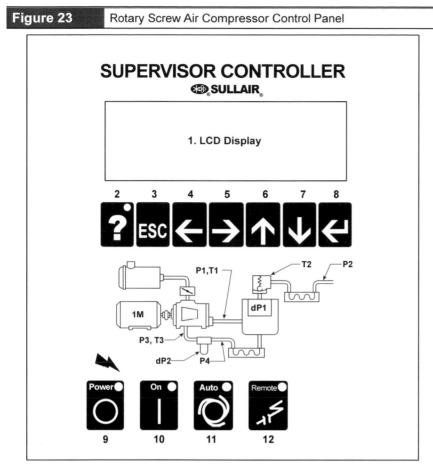

(Courtesy of Sullair Corporation)

Touch Keys (Figure 23)	
1.	Liquid crystal display readout
2.	Help key, used to display possible causes and correction for an alarm or fault
3.	Return to main display
4.	Used to edit text or numbers, moves cursor left
5.	Used to edit text or numbers, moves cursor right
6.	Used to change numbers or text, or scroll
7.	Used to change numbers or text, or scroll
8.	Used to select an item from a menu
9.	Stops machine. Clears faults and warnings if machine is stopped
10.	Starts machine. Clears warnings if machine is running
11.	Toggles auto mode
12.	Toggles local/remote mode

Points			
1M	Drive motor windings temperature	dP1	Air/fluid separator differential pressure
P1	Compressor discharge pressure	P3	Fluid injection pressure
T1	Compressor discharge temperature	T3	Fluid injeciton temperature
P2	Unit discharge pressure	dP2	Fluid filter differential pressure
T2	Unit discharge temperature	P4	Fluid filter inlet pressure

CONTROLS

Start Mode (0 to 345 kPa)

Referring to Figure 23, when the compressor start pad is depressed, the sump pressure will quickly rise from 0 to 345 kPa. During this period, both the pressure regulator and the solenoid valve are closed and the Sullicon control is inoperative. The spring on this control holds the butterfly valve fully open. The spiral valve is fully closed (maximum position) and the compressor pumps at full rated capacity. The rising compressor air pressure is isolated from the service line in this phase by the minimum pressure valve, which is set at approximately 345 kPa. To prevent motor overload, the inlet butterfly valve is held closed for six seconds at start-up to reduce the starting current load.

Full Load Mode (345 kPa to 690 kPa)

When the compressed air pressure in the sump rises above 345 kPa, the minimum pressure valve opens, allowing compressed air to flow into the service line. The Supervisor continually monitors the line air pressure. The pressure regulator and the solenoid valve remain closed during this phase, keeping the Sullicon Control inactive. Both the spiral valve, as well as the inlet butterfly valve, remains in the full load position as long as the compressor is running at 690 kPa, or below. The spiral valve solenoid is energized when the compressor is running. The spiral valve is modulated by the spiral valve differential pressure regulator, and is not affected by the loading control solenoid, the inlet valve, or the loading pressure settings.

Modulation (690 kPa to 793 kPa)

As air demand drops below the rated capacity of the compressor, the line pressure (P2) will rise above 690 kPa. As a result, the differential pressure regulator for the spiral valve gradually opens, applying air pressure to the spiral valve actuator. Air pressure at the actuator expands the diaphragm. The rack, in turn, engages with the pinion mounted on the spiral valve shaft assembly. This results in a rotary motion. As the spiral valve rotates, it starts opening the bypass ports gradually. Excess air is then being returned back internally to the suction end of the compressor unit. The compressor is now fully compressing only that amount of air that is being used. As air demand drops, the spiral valve opens further until all the bypass ports are fully open. At this point, the spiral valve has moved into the unload (minimum) position.

The spiral valve provides a modulation range from 100 to 50%. During this period, the pressure rises from 690 to 738 kPa.

As the air pressure exceeds 738 kPa, the differential pressure regulator controlling the Sullicon Control opens. This allows the air pressure to expand the diaphragm chamber of the Sullicon Control, which starts partially closing the inlet butterfly valve. The inlet butterfly valve provides modulation range from 50% to 40%. During this period, the pressure rises approximately from 738 to 793 kPa. During this range, the spiral valve remains in the unload position.

Unload Mode (Excess of 793 kPa)

When a relatively small amount or no air is being used, the service line pressure continues to rise. When the line pressure exceeds 793 kPa, the Supervisor de-energizes the solenoid valve. When de-energized, the loading solenoid valve bypasses the inlet valve differential pressure regulator. This applies line pressure directly to the inlet valve and the blowdown valve to unload the compressor. The blowdown valve opens the sump to the atmosphere. This reduces the sump pressure to approximately 207 to 345 kPa, which results in low horsepower consumption. The check valve in the air service line prevents line pressure from returning to the sump while the compressor is running in the unloaded mode. The butterfly valve will remain in the unload position. The spiral valve will also be in its unload position but will modulate as air header pressure changes.

When the line pressure drops back to 690 kPa, due to an increase in the air demand, the supervisor energizes the solenoid valve. This action allows the air pressure behind the Sullicon control to be vented through the solenoid valve exhaust port. The blowdown valve closes, and the inlet butterfly valve opens. The air pressure at the spiral valve actuator diaphragm is also reduced through a vent hole at the spiral valve differential pressure regulator. A spring in the actuator causes the spiral valve to return to the full load (maximum) position.

OBJECTIVE 7

Describe designs and principles of centrifugal compressors/blowers, including single and multi-stage designs.

CENTRIFUGAL COMPRESSOR

Centrifugal compressors accelerate the velocity of a gas (ie. increase the kinetic energy), and then convert this energy into pressure.

A centrifugal compressor consists of an impeller, which rotates at high speed within a closed casing. The impeller has several radial or backward-curved blades, enclosed by a shroud on the front and/or the back.

Air is drawn in at the center (eye) of the impeller and is discharged at the impeller periphery with high velocity, due to centrifugal force. The impeller is surrounded by a volute shaped casing and, in many cases, by a ring of diffuser vanes in addition to the casing. As the impeller spins in the compressor casing, gas is forced outward between the blades. As the gas moves radially outward, away from the center of the impeller, energy is transferred from the impeller blades to the gas in the form of both velocity and pressure.

Only part of the velocity energy in the gas is converted to pressure in the blades. The balance of the velocity energy is converted upon leaving the tip of the impeller. The portion of the velocity to pressure conversion, which takes place as the gas moves through the impeller, is a function of the degree of curvature of the impeller blades. The straighter the blades, the less pressure is converted in the impeller.

On leaving the impeller, the high velocity air passes through the diffuser vanes attached to the casing where some of the air velocity is converted to pressure. The air then passes through the volute shaped casing where a further conversion of velocity into pressure takes place.

Figure 24(a) show the arrangement of a compressor having a volute casing only, while Figure 24(b) has both a volute casing and diffuser vanes.

Figure 24	Volute and Diffuser Arrangements

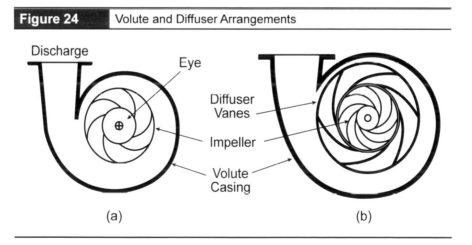

(a)   (b)

Single-Stage Centrifugal Compressors

A single-stage centrifugal compressor, having a volute casing with a single impeller but no diffuser vanes, is illustrated in Figure 25. This type of compressor is able to compress atmospheric air to a discharge pressure of 350 kPa.

Figure 25	Single-Stage Volute Compressor

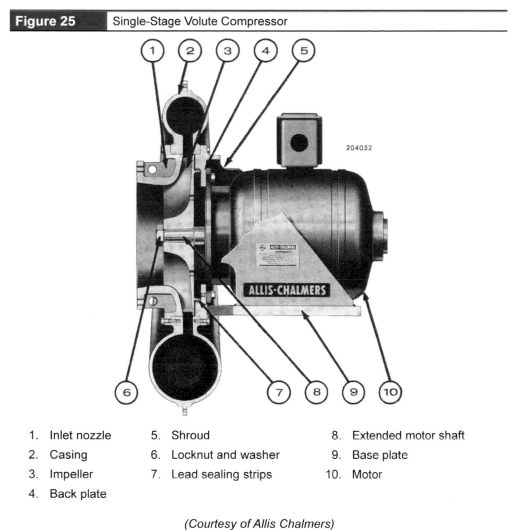

1. Inlet nozzle
2. Casing
3. Impeller
4. Back plate
5. Shroud
6. Locknut and washer
7. Lead sealing strips
8. Extended motor shaft
9. Base plate
10. Motor

(Courtesy of Allis Chalmers)

Figure 26 shows a single-stage compressor having both diffuser vanes and a volute casing.

The impeller is the over-hanging type that is mounted on the shaft end and only requires one shaft seal. The diffuser vanes are adjustable, allowing a change in the operating characteristics of the compressor, when required. In addition, adjustable inlet vanes are provided to allow control of the amount of air flowing to the impeller and thus the capacity of the compressor. The impeller itself has vanes at the eye. These are shaped so as to provide shockless entry to the impeller.

Figure 26	Centrifugal Compressor with Diffuser Vanes

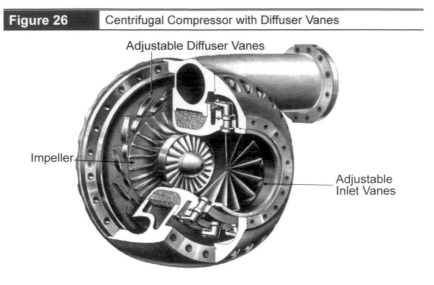

(Courtesy of Worthington Corporation)

Two-Stage Centrifugal Compressor

Figure 27 shows a sectional view of a two-stage centrifugal compressor.

Figure 27	Two-Stage Centrifugal Compressor

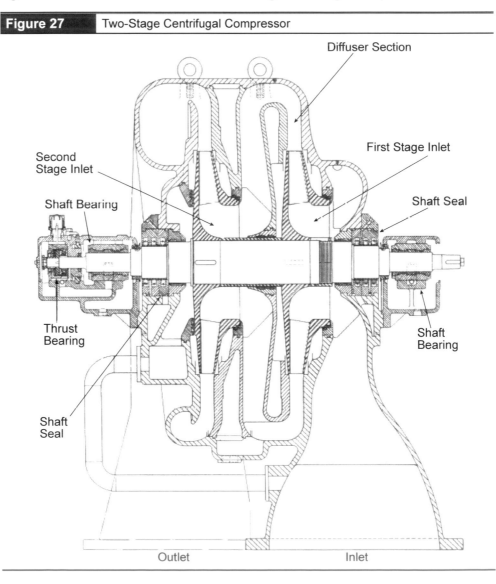

Multi-Stage Centrifugal Compressors

A diffuser type compressor, with nine stages producing air at 1500 kPa and 4000 m³/min, is shown in Figure 28. The compressor is water cooled by circulating water in the diaphragms holding the diffusers.

Figure 28	Multistage Centrifugal Compressor with Horizontally Split Casing

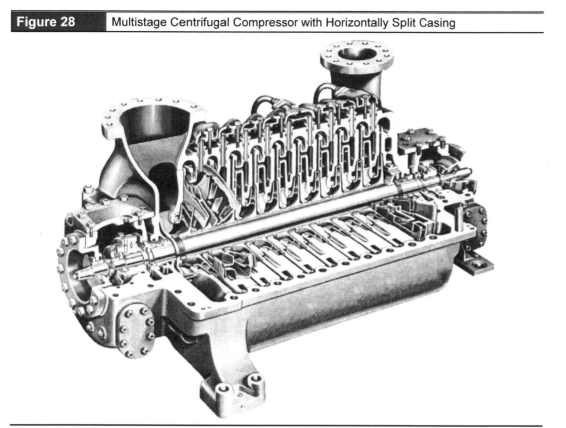

Centrifugal Compressors Advantages

Advantages of the centrifugal compressor are:

- Large volumes of oil-free air
- Simple, rugged construction
- Low maintenance requirements

Centrifugal Compressors Disadvantages

Disadvantages of the centrifugal compressor are:

- Lower efficiencies than positive displacement types
- Unsuitability for low capacity work

OBJECTIVE 8

Describe designs and principles of axial compressors/blowers.

AXIAL FLOW COMPRESSOR

In axial compressors, the gas travels in an axial direction, along the length of the shaft, from inlet to discharge. Rows of blades are attached, radiating outward from around the circumference of the rotor, and fixed blades are attached around the inside of the casing.

The rotor rotates, carrying the moving blades at high speed between the alternating rows of fixed blades. As the rotor turns, the moving blades increase the velocity and pressure of the air. When the air passes through the fixed blades its pressure is further increased by the conversion of velocity energy to pressure energy.

Another way of saying this is that the energy from the rotating shaft of the compressor is transferred to the gas by the series of moving blades. The gas passes through alternating sets of moving and stationary (stator) blades as it passes along the complete gas pass from inlet to discharge. Each pair of moving and fixed blades constitutes a stage. Since the pressure rise per stage is small, a large number of stages are required in order to attain high discharge pressures.

The sketch in Figure 29 shows a sectional view of an axial flow compressor.

Figure 29	Axial Flow Compressor

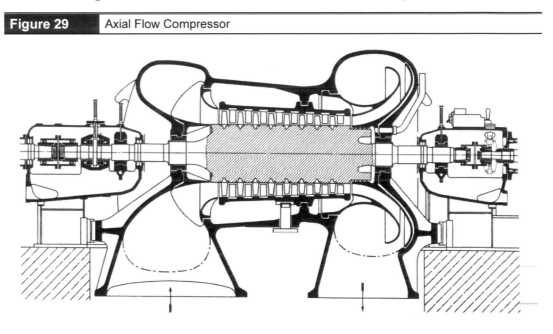

Figure 30 shows a partial cutaway of one type of axial design, with the rotor assembly shown slightly lifted from the casing. The rotor consists of individual disc-like units, which are fitted tightly to each other on the shaft. The diameter of the outer casing is constant over its length. However, the blades get gradually shorter toward the discharge end.

Figure 30	Split Casing Axial Flow Compressor

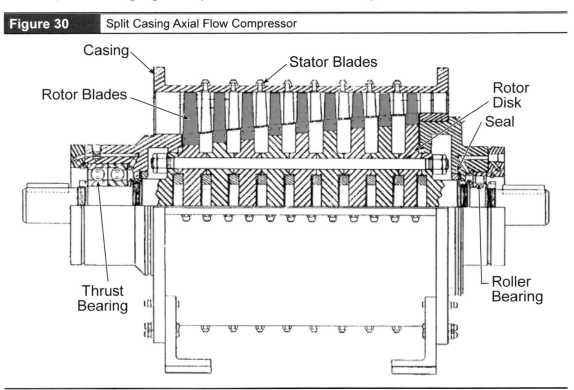

Axial compressors are suited to supplying large volumes at medium pressures and for high-speed operation, up to 20 000 RPM. They can be directly coupled to high-speed motors and turbines. Their free air capacities range from 2.8 m³ to 3700 m³/min.

The efficiency of axial compressors is about 10% greater than centrifugal compressors. However, axial blades are more subject to corrosion and erosion than the impellers of centrifugal compressors.

CHAPTER 8 - QUESTIONS

1. Explain what is meant by the following terms:
   a) Single-stage compression
   b) Two-stage compression
   c) Single-acting
   d) Double-acting

2. Question intentionally deleted.

3. Explain the operation of a sliding vane compressor.

4. Explain the principle of operation of a rotary screw compressor

5. Describe the principle of operation of the following.
   a) Centrifugal compressor, having a volute casing with diffuser vanes.
   b) Centrifugal compressor, having a volute casing without diffuser vanes.

6. Explain the operating principle of a rotary lobe compressor.

7. Explain the principle of operation of an axial flow compressor.

ANSWERS: All answers are found within the content of the chapter.

Compressor Auxiliaries & Operation

LEARNING OUTCOME

When you complete this chapter you should be able to:

Explain the controls and system auxiliaries for a typical instrument air system and explain startup procedures for air compressors.

LEARNING OBJECTIVES

Here is what you should be able to do when you complete each objective:

1. *Describe the control devices and strategies for air compressors, including start-and-stop, variable speed, constant speed; describe pilot and unloader devices.*

2. *Explain the design and operation of an anti-surge system for a dynamic compressor.*

3. *Describe the designs of water and air-cooled aftercoolers and intercoolers, with separators.*

4. *Describe the components, arrangement, and parameters of a typical, complete instrument air system, including wet and dry receivers, dryers.*

5. *Describe the components and operating principles and sequences of instrument air dryers. Explain dewpoint monitoring of air systems.*

6. *Describe the design, fittings, and operating consideration for air receivers.*

7. *Explain the start-up procedure for a positive displacement compressor.*

8. *Explain the start-up procedure for a dynamic compressor/blower.*

OBJECTIVE 1

Describe the control devices and strategies for air compressors, including start-and-stop, variable speed, constant speed; describe pilot and unloader devices.

AIR COMPRESSOR CONTROLS

The demand for compressed air in most industrial operations varies widely. Therefore, the compressor requires a means of regulating its output in accordance with the volume of air required. Some method of control is necessary over the compressor output to maintain the receiver pressure within operating limits. Compressor regulation systems fall into three main types: Start-and-Stop Control, Variable Speed Control, and Constant Speed Control.

Start-and-Stop Control

In start-and-stop control, the compressor will start at a set minimum receiver pressure, run at constant speed and then stop at a set maximum receiver pressure. For example, to supply a system with air at 700 kPa, the control may start the compressor when the pressure drops to 650 kPa and to stop the compressor when the pressures rises to 750 kPa.

This system is normally only used on small compressors driven by electric motors. The most common use is for utility air systems where the load demand is generally steady, but may be reduced for prolonged periods of time. An example would be a small reciprocating or sliding vane compressor. In a sliding vane compressor the starting torque is small in comparison to the full load torque, since the sliding vanes don't begin to function until about 40% of full-load speed.

There are two conditions that can make start-and-stop control uneconomical: an almost continuous demand for air and an air receiver that is too small. Both conditions would cause a very rapid drop in system pressure after the compressor stops and the compressor would start and stop much too often. This would cause excessive power consumption, since the starting load current of an electric motor is greater than its normal full load current. For this reason, the compressor should be automatically unloaded during motor start-up.

Variable Speed Control

Variable speed control is useful when a steam engine, turbine, internal combustion engine, or variable speed electric motor drives the compressor. To maintain a constant system pressure, the compressor speed is increased or reduced according to system pressure. If the demand for air decreases, then the receiver pressure will increase, causing a pressure-actuated control to slow down the driver. If the demand increases, the receiver pressure will drop and the control will increase the driver speed.

Variable speed control can be used with rotary and dynamic compressors. The disadvantage with dynamic compressors is that if the speed is reduced too much, the compressor may go into a surge condition.

Constant Speed Control

As the name suggests, this control method is used on a compressor that runs at constant speed. In this case, the output from the compressor is varied by some type of unloading device. "Unloading" means a situation is created by the compressor controls, whereby the compressor cannot compress the air even though it is running at a constant speed.

Constant speed control is used for both positive displacement and dynamic air compressors. Since there are several methods of constant speed control, this method will be discussed specifically for reciprocating, rotary, and dynamic compressors.

RECIPROCATING COMPRESSOR CONTROL

There are three constant speed control methods for reciprocating compressors, including:

- Inlet air unloader (suction valves open)
- Suction line unloading valve
- Suction valves closed

Inlet Air Unloader

An inlet air unloader holds the inlet valve in the open position. This prevents air from being trapped inside the cylinder, so the air passes freely in and out of the compressor inlet without being compressed.

Figure 1 shows an inlet valve unloader. It consists of fingers, which can be moved by a shaft connected to a diaphragm. When the air receiver pressure rises to the preset cutout pressure, a spring-loaded pilot valve (see Fig. 2) opens and admits air to the underside of the diaphragm. The diaphragm moves upward, causing the fingers to hold the inlet valve open.

Figure 1	Inlet Valve Unloader

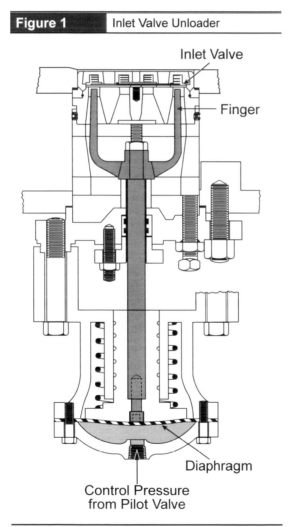

The advantages of the inlet valve unloader are:

- When the inlet valve is open the power consumption is minimal. The only power required is used to overcome the friction of the machine.

- It can be used where the compressor load changes frequently.

- The operating range of the compressor can be easily changed by adjusting the pilot spring.

The disadvantage of the inlet valve unloader is the extra time required to repair the main compressor valves. The unloader must be removed before the valve can be repaired and this results in extra repair costs and longer downtime.

Figure 2 shows a typical pilot valve, which operates as follows.

- The piston is held in the closed position by a spring. The top of the piston is exposed to air receiver pressure.

- When the air receiver pressure rises to the preset pressure (set by adjusting the spring), the piston is forced downwards. This allows the air to flow to the diaphragm of the inlet unloader.

The manual unload handle on the side of the pilot valve is used for start up of the compressor. The lever forces the piston down, allowing the receiver pressure to hold the inlet valves open so the compressor starts in the unloaded position. The handle can also be used to unload the compressor before shutting it down.

Figure 2	Pilot Valve

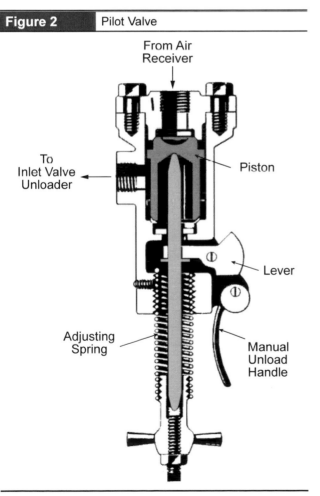

From Air Receiver

To Inlet Valve Unloader

Piston

Lever

Adjusting Spring

Manual Unload Handle

Suction Line Unloading Valve

Figure 3 shows a suction unloading valve, which is inserted in the intake pipe to the compressor. When the receiver reaches the set pressure, the valve shuts, preventing more air from entering the compressor.

- A small piston, actuated by the pressure in the receiver, moves sufficiently to open a small port (air passage), which admits air to a plunger of larger area.
- Force on the plunger pushes the plunger valve against its seat.
- When the pressure in the receiver falls to a preset minimum the pressure is relieved from the plunger and the valve spring pushes the plunger valve open.

| **Figure 3** | Cross-Sectional View of a Suction-Unloading Valve |

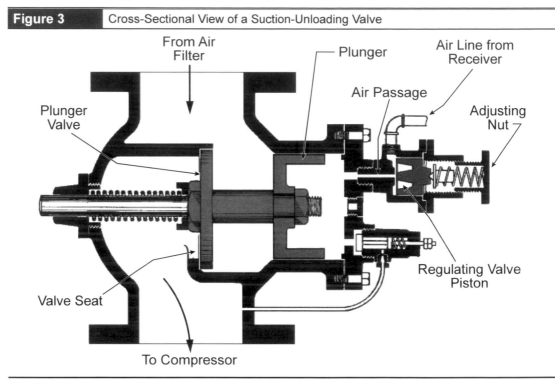

There are several advantages with the suction line unloader.

- When the suction-unloading valve is closed the power consumption is minimal.
- It can be used where the compressor load changes frequently.
- The operating range of the unloader can easily be adjusted with the adjusting nut.
- The compressor suction valves can be changed more quickly, since there is no unloader to remove first.

The disadvantage of this unloader is that the compressor and suction piping (from suction unloading valve to compressor) is operating under a vacuum whenever the unloading valve is closed. This can result in gasket leaks on the compressor and suction piping.

Suction Valves Closed

One method of unloading a compressor, often used with mechanically operated suction valves, is to close the valves so no air can enter the cylinder. This is shown diagrammatically in Figure 4. When both valves are closed there is slight compression in each end of the cylinder but no work is done and no air will be delivered.

Figure 4	Compressor Cylinder Unloading – Suction Valves Closed

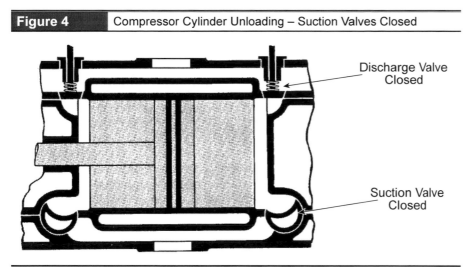

Discharge Valve
Closed

Suction Valve
Closed

The advantages of this method of control are:

- The control range can vary from 0% to 100%
- It is energy efficient

The disadvantages of this method of control are:

- Danger of the compressor cylinder over heating due to the slight compression of air in each end of the cylinder while the suction valves are closed
- The control strategy can be very complex

ROTARY COMPRESSOR CONTROL

The methods used to control the load for Rotary Compressors are:

- Start-stop control
- Load-unload control
- Modulating inlet valve
- Microprocessor-based control system

Start-Stop Control

This type of control is used for a sliding vane compressor. It is similar to a start-stop control for a reciprocating compressor. The driver of the compressor is started at a preset low pressure in the receiver and then restarted at a preset high pressure.

Load-Unload Control

Load-unload control for a rotary compressor, involves a pilot-operated inlet valve which opens and closes the inlet line to the compressor. Referring to Figure 5, the operation of the valve is effected by the high-pressure air, which is controlled by a pilot valve. This pilot valve is fitted with a spring, against which the pressure has to operate.

- When the delivery pressure exceeds the required setting, the pilot valve opens and admits air to the top of the piston. The piston moves downwards to its seat, thus shutting off the suction of the compressor from the atmosphere.

- At the same time the release valve is opened. The underside of this valve is connected to the discharge of the compressor, and when it is opened, air that may be inside the machine is discharged to atmosphere, and the compressor runs under vacuum. This reduces the power absorbed at the shaft to about 20% of the full load value, depending on the working pressure.

- When the pressure in the delivery air main has fallen by the required amount, usually from 35 to 85 kPa, the spring on the pilot valve causes it to close. The space on top of the operating piston is opened to the atmosphere, and the spring opens the main valve and closes the release valve.

This method of load control is suitable for steady load demands. The pressure at which the compressor loads and unloads can be manually adjusted by means of an adjustment screw.

You will notice that there is a handle on the pilot valve diagram labeled "handle in start position" This is used to start the compressor in an unloaded position, and to unload the compressor before shutting it down.

Figure 5	Rotary Compressor Inlet Valve with Pilot

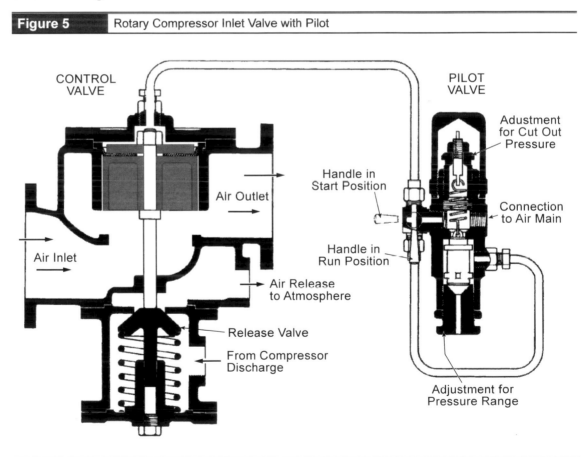

Modulating Inlet Valve

Figure 6 shows a modulating system, which allows the compressor capacity to be adjusted to match the load demand.

- A pressure transmitter senses the discharge pressure and sends a signal to the regulating valve controller.
- The controller positions the inlet valve to the compressor. Partially closing the inlet valve reduces the mass flow of air to the compressor.
- Some systems that require very precise control also have a discharge vent valve, which relieves excess discharge pressure to atmosphere (through a silencer).

This method of compressor load control is energy efficient as power consumption is directly linked to load demand. The system air pressure is also very steady, compared to an on-off control.

Figure 6	Modulating Inlet Valve Control

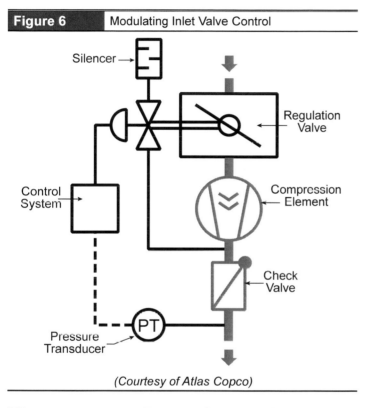

(Courtesy of Atlas Copco)

Microprocessor-Based Control System

The three previous methods of rotary compressor control systems described can be done by means of microprocessors. Most rotary air compressors now incorporate this type of control. The microprocessor takes the place of the analog controller. The microprocessor control system relies on electrical transducers and sensors, which sense variables such as air pressure and flow, and will load and unload the air compressor accordingly. A microprocessor can also monitor large numbers of variables. This type of control will also modulate the inlet valve according to the air discharge pressure. The microprocessor control system is faster and more accurate than pneumatic control systems.

CONTROL OF DYNAMIC COMPRESSORS

The methods used for dynamic compressor (ie. centrifugal and radial) load control are inlet vane control, electro-pneumatic control, and microprocessor-based control.

Inlet Vane Control

This method is used on smaller sized dynamic air compressors. The inlet vanes are controlled by a signal from the air receiver. The disadvantage with this type of control is that if the load demand is reduced significantly the compressor can go into a surge condition, with the possibility of compressor damage.

Electro-Pneumatic Control System

Most air compressors in use today utilize electro-pneumatic control systems. These compressors feature electric and mechanically controlled devices such as pressure switches, and solenoid valves. They adjust the loading and unloading through the use of an inlet throttle or bypass valve. These control systems typically rely on mechanical pressure switches to monitor the compressor's discharge pressure. In addition, electro-pneumatic systems typically feature a series of mechanical trip switches that will discontinue compressor operation when pressures or temperatures reach critical levels.

Microprocessor-Based Control System

This is the latest and fast becoming the preferred method of control for dynamic compressor systems. Processes with complicated and varying demand cycles, which can include several compressors of different sizes and configurations to maintain system pressure, require a more sophisticated control system. Instead of common pressure and metering devices, the microprocessor control system relies on electrical transducers and sensors. These devices sense air pressure and temperature values, which are then transmitted to a central microprocessor. The microprocessor interprets the information and adjusts the compressor's output through an integrated control system.

OBJECTIVE 2

Explain the design and operation of an anti-surge system for a dynamic compressor.

SURGING

Surging is the reversal of flow within a compressor. Surging occurs when the flow through the compressor drops to a point where the pressure being generated is not sufficient to maintain flow out of the compressor. At this point, the direction of flow will reverse, and the inrush of air from the discharge piping causes a shock wave. This shock wave can be audible, and may be severe enough to damage the impeller or piping. Once the pressure in the discharge line drops below the surge point, the air will again flow through the compressor. The reversal of flow will rapidly repeat itself, until there is a sufficient volume flowing through the compressor.

Centrifugal and axial compressors are both subject to surging.

In the case of the centrifugal compressor, as seen in the pressure-volume curve in Figure 7, at low volumes (low flows or capacities) the pressure drops off. The curves first rise and then drop, with the highest point being the surge point.

Figure 7	Pressure-Capacity Graph for Dynamic Compressors

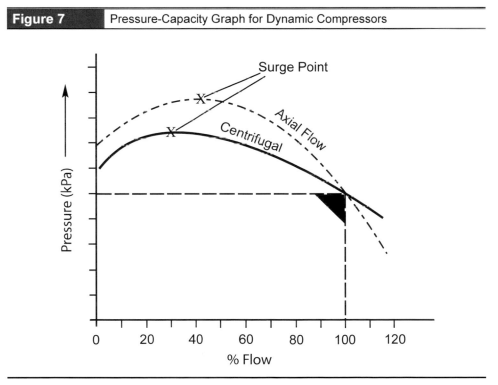

There are several methods used to prevent surging.

- One method is to open a discharge line blow-off valve to atmosphere when the flow through the compressor decreases to near the surge point. The blow-off valve can be operated automatically using a flow meter, so if the flow from the compressor reaches a pre-set low flow condition, the blow-off valve will be opened by a signal from the flow meter. This will increase the flow through the compressor, and keep it from going into a surge condition. Once the flow reaches a certain point, the flow transmitter will send a signal to close the blow-off valve.

- Another method uses a discharge recirculation valve (anti-surge valve), which opens and sends flow back to the suction of the compressor. This increases the mass flow through the compressor and keeps it away from the surge point. One problem with this method is that the compressor will eventually heat up and may shut down on high discharge temperature, unless the recirculated air goes through an air cooler.
- Modern surge control technology involves microprocessor controllers. The overall compressor control scheme, including discharge pressure control, anti-surge control, and start-up/shutdown control is implemented in an integrated system.

Figure 8 shows an anti-surge control system, which uses a flow valve to recirculate air from the discharge to the suction of the compressor (it also shows an alternate method, which discharges to atmosphere). The surge controller (SC) receives three inputs, the inlet air flow to the compressor, the suction pressure and the discharge pressure. If the discharge pressure falls below a certain value for a corresponding flow rate, the surge controller starts to open the recycle flow valve. Opening the flow valve causes the compressor to stabilize for that particular flow rate.

The purpose of the two pressure inputs is to ensure that a certain pressure differential is maintained across the compressor when operating. If the pressure differential becomes too high or too low, the compressor will shut down, since there may be a problem with the compressor.

When the compressor is shut down, or shuts down for any reason, the anti-surge valve will open. On start-up, after the compressor is up to speed, the anti-surge controller will begin to close the anti-surge valve.

Figure 8	Anti Surge Control System on a Centrifugal Compressor

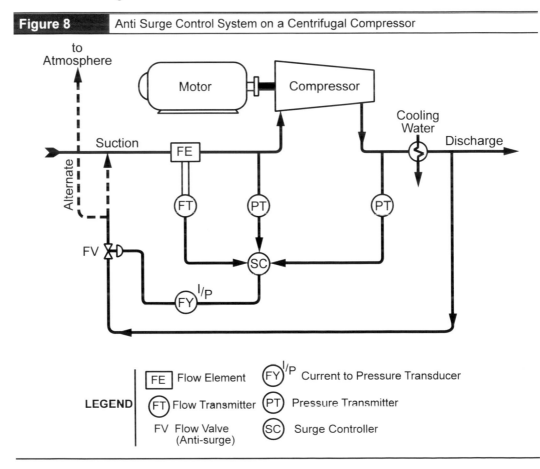

OBJECTIVE 3

Describe the designs of water and air-cooled aftercoolers and intercoolers, with separators.

INTERCOOLERS & AFTERCOOLERS

Intercooling is the cooling of air between the stages of a multistage compressor.

Aftercooling is the cooling of the air after it leaves the final compressor discharge.

The reasons for cooling the air are as follows:

- To remove water vapour and oil vapour from the air between compression stages and after the last stage. When the air is cooled, the water and oil vapours will condense and can be drained from the bottom of the coolers.

  If water vapour is not removed from the air, it may collect in pipelines and cause water hammer or damage from freezing. In the case of air driven tools and machinery, the water will wash away lubricating oil from the machine surfaces

  If oil vapour is not condensed and removed, it can have a detrimental effect on air operated instruments and may also build up deposits in pipes and reservoirs that could ignite and explode.

- Intercoolers decrease the amount of power required to compress the air by about 15%. Cooling the air during compression increases the efficiency of operation so that costs are reduced. For this reason, in addition to using intercoolers, compressors are usually water jacketed to aid in removing the heat of compression.

- Other purposes for cooling include: to make cylinder lubrication more effective, to reduce weakening of parts due to high temperatures and to reduce the possibility of an explosion of any air/oil vapour mixture.

Intercoolers

Intercoolers may be air-cooled or water-cooled. Finned tubing is used to increase the heat transfer area. A current of air is directed across the tubing by a fan, which is driven by the air compressor unit. When the air compressor cylinders are water-cooled, then the intercooler is usually also water-cooled. Except for the very small sizes, water-cooled intercoolers are often shell and tube heat exchangers.

Figure 9 shows a shell-and-tube intercooler that is integral to a two stage reciprocating compressor. The cooling water makes several passes through the tubes, while baffle plates direct the air flow around the tubes.

Figure 9	Two-Stage Compressor with Water-Cooled Intercooler

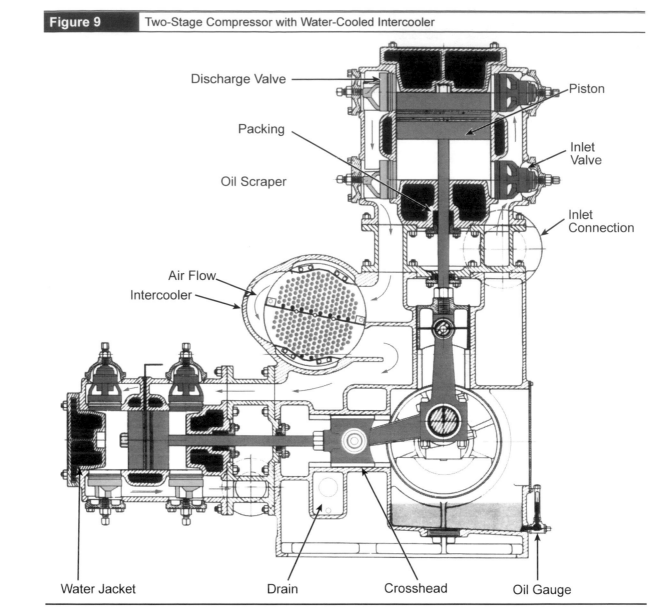

Air entering the first-stage cylinder contains a certain amount of entrained moisture. The moisture will not be deposited in the compression cylinder since the air is heated above its original temperature, thus increasing its water-carrying capacity.

After compression the hot air passes through the intercooler. Due to the temperature decrease in the intercooler, the air loses its water-retaining capacity and moisture condenses out on the cooling tubes. Oil vapour will also condense out. The water and oil ultimately fall to the bottom of the intercooler shell.

Drains must be provided on all intercoolers so that any condensed water and oil may be removed. This is usually done with a drip leg and a trap. The arrangement is shown in Figure 10.

It should be noted that only a small portion of the entrained moisture should condense in the intercooler, since the primary purpose of the intercooler is to reduce the air temperature, not to condense entrained moisture. A properly designed intercooler will maintain an outlet temperature that is slightly above the pressure dewpoint. The majority of the entrained moisture should be condensed in the aftercooler.

Figure 10	Automatic Condensate Drain or Trap

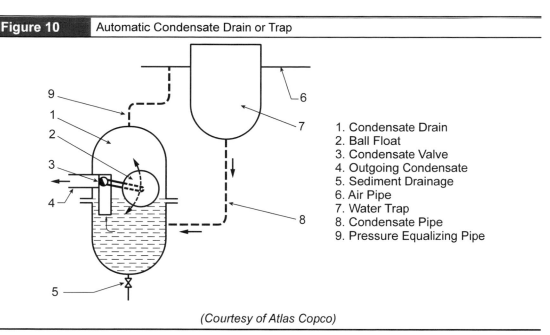

1. Condensate Drain
2. Ball Float
3. Condensate Valve
4. Outgoing Condensate
5. Sediment Drainage
6. Air Pipe
7. Water Trap
8. Condensate Pipe
9. Pressure Equalizing Pipe

(Courtesy of Atlas Copco)

All intercoolers must be provided with a safety valve, pressure gauges, and thermometers on the compressed air side. If the intercooler is water-cooled a thermometer is provided on the cooling water side.

Aftercoolers

Most aftercoolers are water-cooled. The finned tube type is used for the portable type of air compressors, like the ones that are used in private workshops, and portable rental units. The purpose of the aftercoolers is to cool the compressed air prior to being delivered to the point of use or to the air receiver. It is usual to bring the temperature of the compressed air to significantly lower than the pressure dewpoint, causing moisture to condense. Further cooling and condensing will occur downstream as the air sits in the air receiver.

Aftercoolers, like intercoolers, are fitted with pressure gauges and thermometers and, if there is a shut-off valve between the aftercooler and the air receiver, the aftercooler must also be fitted with a safety valve. Aftercoolers should always have a means of collecting the moisture that is condensed out of the air stream. A water separator, located at the outlet of the air cooler, usually accomplishes this. The water separator is often fitted directly to the aftercooler. It is constructed as an integral part of the aftercooler. When it is built as a separate vessel, it is installed as close as possible to the aftercooler.

The aftercooler shown in Figure 11 is known as the pipeline type. It is shell-and-tube construction and is arranged so the compressed air flows through the tubes and the cooling water flows through the shell. It has a water separator located at the air outlet as shown in the illustration. The moisture and other particles are removed from the air stream by the rapid change of direction of the air.

Water separators are often of the internal baffle type, where the direction of the airflow is changed to separate the moisture particles from the air stream. Another type is the Cyclone Separator, where airflow is given a swirling motion to separate moisture from the air stream.

Figure 11 | Pipeline Aftercooler

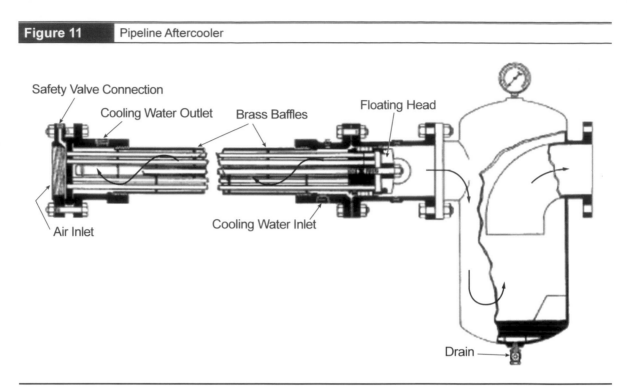

The aftercooler in Figure 12 is air-cooled. Hot compressed air enters at the bottom of the cooler. It then flows through the finned tubes, where cooling takes place. An electric motor driven fan moves air across the finned tubes. Moisture is drained off the bottom of the cooler by an automatic trapping arrangement.

Figure 12 | Pipeline Aftercooler

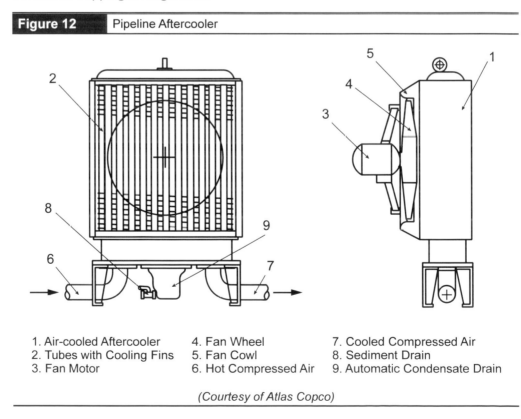

1. Air-cooled Aftercooler
2. Tubes with Cooling Fins
3. Fan Motor
4. Fan Wheel
5. Fan Cowl
6. Hot Compressed Air
7. Cooled Compressed Air
8. Sediment Drain
9. Automatic Condensate Drain

(Courtesy of Atlas Copco)

OBJECTIVE 4

Describe the components, arrangement, and parameters of a typical, complete instrument air system, including wet and dry receivers, dryers.

TYPICAL AIR SYSTEM

The air systems in a plant are designed to supply pressurized air for various purposes. The primary purpose is dry air for all instrumentation. This part of the system is called the instrument air system. Other users are also supplied, such as for power tools. The latter air is commonly referred to as plant air, maintenance air or utility air. The latter may not require the same dryness quality as the instrument air.

Figure 13 shows a simply sketch of one system that satisfies both instrument air and utility air. The air is all supplied from one (or more) compressors, but there are two air receivers. The wet receiver supplies plant air and the dry receiver supplies the instrument air. The air in the wet receiver, while not as dry as the instrument air, is still drier than atmospheric air since it has been compressed and cooled, with some of the entrained moisture knocked out.

Figure 13	Compressed Air System with Two Air Receivers

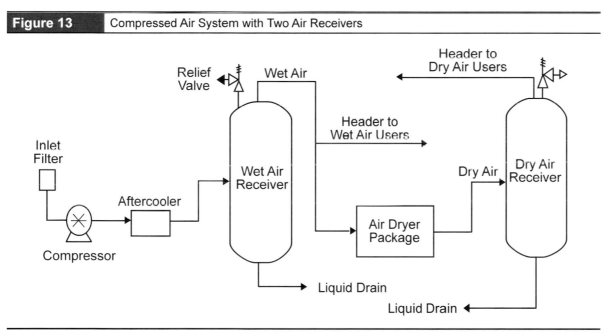

Air enters the system through the inlet filter. An air filter should always be installed in the inlet line of the compressor to prevent dust and other particles from being carried into the compressor. Wherever possible, the inlet air should be supplied from atmosphere at a location away from engine or process exhaust outlets. The inlet piping should be at least as large as the compressor intake connection to prevent inlet flow restriction.

The air is compressed and goes through the aftercooler to the wet receiver. Some moisture condenses when the temperature is reduced and this moisture drops out in the wet receiver. The large volume of the receiver creates low velocity which encourages the free water to drop to the bottom. A manual or automatic drain then removes the water. The cooled air leaves the wet receiver and goes to two places. A takeoff line delivers air to the wet air users, via a supply header.

The main air flow goes through the air dryer package, where entrained moisture is removed by adsorption into a dry dessicant. This lowers the dew point sufficiently to prevent freezing of moisture at low ambient temperatures and to minimize the deposit of water in lines and instruments. The air dryer package includes a prefilter and an afterfilter to ensure clean air to the instruments. The dried air goes to the dry air receiver, which serves as a demand reservoir for the instrument air system, helping to keep the pressure steady. Final traces of liquid are occasionally drained from the dry receiver.

INSTRUMENT AIR SYSTEM COMPONENTS

Air Compressor

The type of compressor chosen: reciprocating, rotary or centrifugal will depend on the load requirements of the air system, compressor operating costs, and if the air compressor is to be an oil-free or oil-lubricated air compressor. If the air compressor is to be oil-lubricated, then an elaborate and thus expensive filtering system must be used to ensure oil-free air. The air filters designed to remove oil from the air are called coalescing filters.

Figure 14	Packaged Compressor Rotary Screw Type

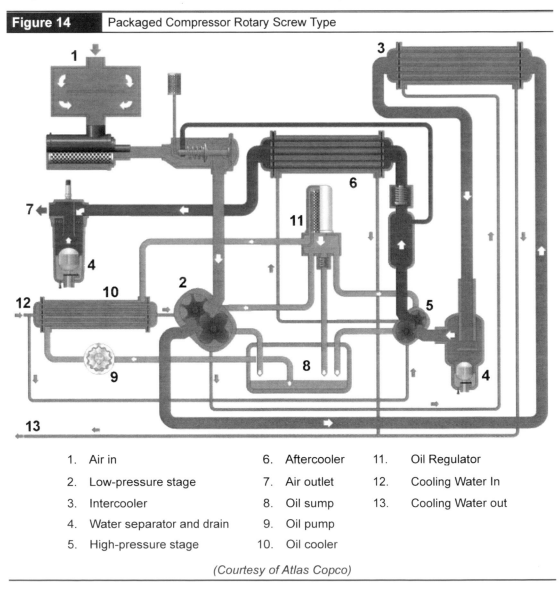

1.	Air in	6.	Aftercooler	11.	Oil Regulator
2.	Low-pressure stage	7.	Air outlet	12.	Cooling Water In
3.	Intercooler	8.	Oil sump	13.	Cooling Water out
4.	Water separator and drain	9.	Oil pump		
5.	High-pressure stage	10.	Oil cooler		

(Courtesy of Atlas Copco)

The air compressor in Figure 14 is a packaged two-stage Rotary Screw oil-free air compressor. The term "Packaged Air Compressor" means that the unit and its auxiliaries come in one unit. The package contains a two-stage compressor with an electric motor drive, lubricating oil system, coolers, and a control system. The intercooler, aftercooler and lube oil coolers are water-cooled. The control system for this compressor is microprocessor based. The compressor load is varied by means of a modulating inlet valve.

Moisture Separator

The moisture condensed in the aftercooler is removed from the air stream in a centrifugal or cyclone separator.

Air Receivers

There are two types of air receivers that are used in an instrument air system: the wet air receiver and the dry air receiver. If both the instrument air and the plant airflows are dried, one air tank is all that is required.

Wet Air Receiver

This receiver is located on the discharge of the air compressor, downstream of the moisture separator. This vessel acts like an air reservoir and thus provides three important functions. The first one is additional moisture separation, to reduce the amount of moisture going to the air dryers. As the air flows through the wet air receiver the velocity of the air is reduced. Any moisture not removed in the upstream separator will drop out in this receiver. The second function is to stabilize the flow through the air dryers on system load changes. This vessel acts like a demand reservoir. The third function is providing storage capacity to prevent rapid compressor cycling on sudden load changes.

Dry Air Receivers

The dry air receiver serves several functions. The first one is to stabilize the system pressure as it acts as a demand reservoir. And because this vessel acts like a demand reservoir it helps to avoid overloading the air purification system with surges in air demand. The third one is it dampens out the dew point and temperature spikes that follow regeneration. In a system that uses a heated regeneration cycle for the air dryers, when the regenerated dryer tower comes on line, the initial air flow from the regenerated tower will be warmer than the air in the system. The dew point will be higher also. The cooler and dryer air in the dry air receiver helps to dampen out the temperature and dew point increases. The air supply to the system will be fairly constant in regards to temperature and dew point.

Filters

The removal of particulates, liquids and oil vapours from the air is key to ensuring the instrument air system functions efficiently. The two types of filters used in an instrument air system are prefilters and afterfilters. The prefilters are coalescing filters if the compressor is not an oil free design. The coalescing filters are located upstream of the air dryers. The purpose of these filters is to remove moisture and oil vapours from the air stream, so the dryers do not become overloaded. It also protects the dryer desiccant from becoming contaminated with oil vapour, and other contaminants.

A coalescing filter contains a filtering media that gathers together (coalesces) tiny moisture droplets from the air stream as the air passes through the filter media. The air stream enters the top opening of the filter element and moves through the filter media from the inside to the outside. As the air passes through the media, the moisture droplets become caught on the media fibers and begin to cling to each other. Once the moisture droplets have moved through the media, the larger, heavier droplets drain away to the bottom of the filter casing by gravity. The moisture can be drained from the filter casing manually or by means of a drain trap.

| Figure 15 | Instrument Air Filter |

(Courtesy of Atlas Copco)

An after filter is a particulate filter that is located downstream of the air dryers. Its purpose (Fig. 15) is to remove any particles that may carry over with the air stream from the air dryers. The airflow is from the outside of the filter media to the inside of the filter media. The outer layer removes the large particles, while the media removes the smaller particles. It has a differential pressure gauge to indicate when the filter media needs changing.

Air Dryers

The purpose of the air dryers is to lower the dew point of the air, so that there will be no water contamination of air operated instruments. Freezing problems with the air system in cold weather will also be avoided.

There are two main types of dryers used in the industry, refrigerated dryers and desiccant dryers.

- The refrigerated dryer uses a separate refrigeration system to cool the air. Adjusting the flow of refrigerant through a heat exchanger controls the cooling.
- The desiccant dryer removes the moisture from the air by adsorption in which a hydroscopic material such as alumina or silica gel is used. The dryer may be heated or heatless. The heatless type of dryer uses air that has been dried to regenerate the bed. The heated type of dryer uses a heater (internal or external) and a low-rate air purge to regenerate the moisture-laden bed.

INSTRUMENT AIR SYSTEM OPERATING PARAMETERS

The instrument air system illustrated in Figure 13 is typical of systems found in many types of industrial and power plants.

- The operating range of the dry air receiver fluctuates between 720 kPa and 780 kPa.

- The compressor discharge pressure fluctuates between 750 kPa and 810 kPa. The difference is due to the pressure drop though the system components such as the air dryers.

- The discharge air temperature varies widely (40°C to 5°C) since the air intake for the compressor is outside air, which can vary between 30°C in the summer and -30°C in the winter.

- It is important to ensure that the aftercooler discharge temperature does not get too high, since this can very quickly overload the air dryers with moisture. If the aftercooler is air-cooled, be sure to keep the finned tubes free of dust and fluff.

- The air dryer dew point is usually between -60° and -80°C. This range provides a safe operating margin during cold weather.

- The differential pressures at the coalescing prefilter and the particulate afterfilter should not be allowed to go over 70 kPa. Once the differential pressure reaches 70 kPa the filter element should be replaced.

- If there is a failure of the air purification system, all the low point drains on the entire air system should be blown down immediately, as well as air pressure regulators.

OBJECTIVE 5

Describe the components and operating principles and sequences of instrument air dryers. Explain dewpoint monitoring of air systems.

AIR DRYER COMPONENTS

Air dryers are critical components of the instrument air system. If the dryers fail to reduce the dew point of the air adequately, moisture will be carried into the air system. There will be water contamination of the air operated instruments and freezing problems with the air system in cold weather. There are several different types of dryers in use, the refrigerant type of air dryer, the heated regeneration type, and the heatless regenerating type.

The components of an air dryer system are:

- Prefilters
- Dryers
- Afterfilters
- Heater
- Switching valves

The components of a typical air dryer package are shown in Figure 16. The package has two towers so that one is adsorbing while the other is either regenerating or on standby. A pair of three-way switching valves is attached to each dryer to direct flow for the appropriate cycle, adsorption or regeneration.

| Figure 16 | Adsorbent Air Dryer Package |

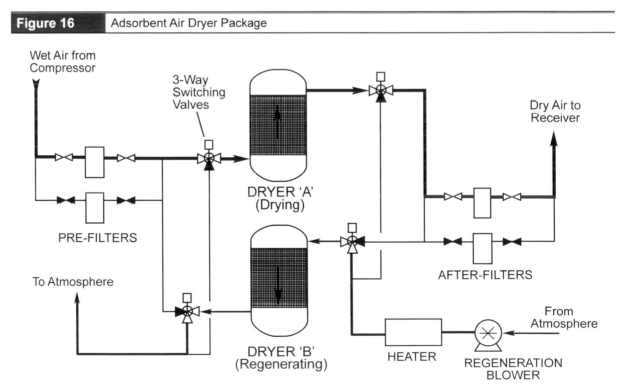

The diagram shows Dryer 'A' in adsorption, with the wet air from the compressor flowing up through the bed and the dry air leaving through the top valve. The dry air passes through a set of cartridge-type after filters to ensure no desiccant particles enter the air system.

Dryer 'B' is in regeneration. In this cycle a small air blower draws in atmospheric air and blows it through a heater, down through the bed, then out to atmosphere. The steam or electric heater increases the regeneration air temperature to about 80°C, which heats the bed and vaporizes the water from the desiccant. Normally, automatic timers are used to control the cycling of the dryers between adsorption and regeneration. Moisture sensors may also be used to continuously monitor the system.

Figure 17 shows a common variation of this package, in which a slipstream of the outlet airflow, rather than a blower, is used to produce the regeneration flow. This arrangement also has an external heater, and uses dried heated air to regenerate the off stream drier.

In this system a restriction orifice in the air supply line creates a pressure drop that allows flow through the regenerating dryer. After passing through the heater and the desiccant, the regeneration air, laden with water, is cooled condensing the removed water. The water is dropped out in a separator and then the regeneration air rejoins the flow entering the adsorbing dryer.

Figure 17	Regenerative Air Dryer System

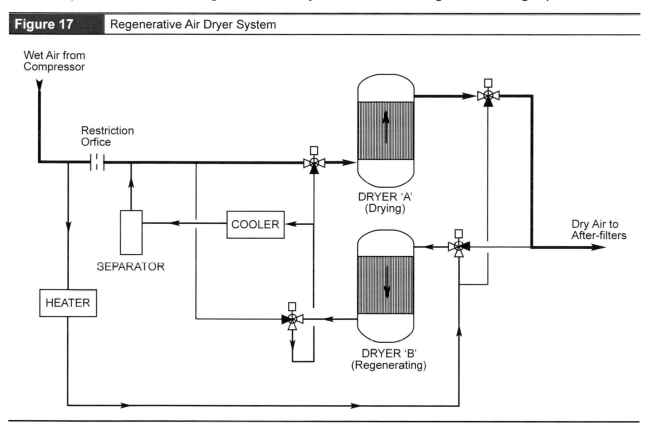

DRYER OPERATING PRINCIPLE

Desiccant dryers normally consist of two chambers, or tanks filled with desiccant like the ones in Figure 18. The desiccant is the material that actually performs the drying function. The standard desiccant used is silica gel or activated alumina. For lower dewpoints, -60°C and lower, a molecular sieve desiccant is used. The desiccant takes the form of small, spherical pellets that are approximately 2 to 5 mm in diameter. Each pellet contains thousands of microscopic pores, which are in the size range of water vapour molecules.

Figure 18 Air Dryer Package

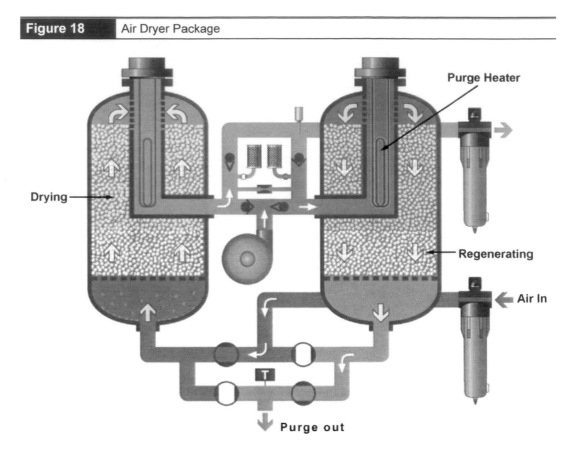

(Courtesy of Atlas Copco)

- For the tower in the **drying cycle**, as the moisture laden air passes over the pores, the water vapour molecules are attracted, adsorbed, into the tiny pores of the desiccant pellets. Once these pores become fully loaded with condensate, the bed is saturated or exhausted, since it cannot adsorb any more water vapour from the air. Prior to the desiccant bed becoming completely saturated, it must be removed from service, to prevent moisture from carrying over into the system.

- This bed is now put into the **regeneration cycle**. In the heatless dryer, regeneration of the bed is accomplished by depressurizing the bed to atmospheric pressure, which puts the condensate into the vapour state. Then a flow of very dry, low vapour pressure air is used to remove the water vapour from the desiccant bed. This dry air is referred to as purge air.

The dryer package in Figure 18 uses a blower and internal electric heaters to heat the purge air. The chamber to be regenerated is depressured to atmosphere before the purge airflow is started. The purpose of reducing the pressure to atmospheric pressure is to reduce its dewpoint and vapour pressure. For example, if the system pressure is 690 kPa gauge and the dewpoint of the air is minus 40°C, at 0 kPa gauge the dewpoint of the air is approximately minus 57°C. As the purge air flows through the desiccant bed the condensate is desorbed, or evaporated, into the low vapour pressure heated purge air, which carries it away, and vents it to atmosphere.

The cycling of the two towers between the drying cycle and the regeneration cycle is carried out by a timer system or PLC (programmable logic controller), which controls the various regeneration valves, and the timing sequence.

DEWPOINT MONITORING

'Dewpoint' is defined as the temperature at which the water vapour in the air will begin to condense (form dew) at the specified pressure. If the air temperature drops below the dewpoint temperature at any time, liquid water can form. In compressed air applications you will hear references to Atmospheric Dewpoint and Pressure Dewpoint.

- **Atmospheric Dewpoint** is the temperature of the air at which moisture will condense at ambient air conditions.

- **Pressure Dewpoint** is the air temperature which moisture will condense at system pressure conditions. The pressure dewpoint of the air is something that the operator must check on a regular basis. If the dewpoint begins to rise (-60°C to -40°C), the operator must take immediate action to rectify the situation, before moisture accumulates in the instrument air lines.

There are several ways that the operator can check the dewpoint of the compressed air. One of the easiest is to monitor the read-out on the front of the dewpoint analyzer, as shown in Figure 19. In some cases this reading is transferred from the analyzer to a read-out on the front of the air dryer control panel.

The dewpoint analyzer receives an electrical signal from a moisture-sensing probe like the one shown in Figure 20. It is situated in the air line downstream of the air dryers. The analyzer measures the signal and converts it to a numeric value, which indicates the pressure dewpoint of the compressed air.

If there were an afterfilter downstream of the air dryers, this sensing probe would be placed downstream of the afterfilter. This protects the probe from becoming contaminated with desiccant dust.

The moisture-sensing probe consists of a stainless steel housing with several holes, to allow the flow of air through the housing. Inside this casing are two electrodes, and between the two electrodes is a moisture-sensing element, which is composed of porous aluminum oxide. A small current of electricity is established between the two electrodes. As the air from the dryer flows through the sensing element, the moisture content in the air will create a resistance to the electrical current flowing between the two electrodes. This resistance is sent as an electrical signal to the analyzer. The analyzer measures the signal, and converts the reading to a numeric value, in °C, which corresponds to the pressure dewpoint of the compressed air.

| Figure 19 | Instrument Air Dewpoint Analyzer |

(Joslyn Sunbank Company, LLC)

| Figure 20 | Moisture Sensing Probe – ADC |

(Joslyn Sunbank Company, LLC)

Many air dryer systems have a small glass bulb that is filled with desiccant and has a slip stream of the outlet air from the dryer flowing through it. When the air is dry, the desiccant is blue. If the air is wet, the desiccant changes colour.

Another method is to attach a portable analyzer to a sample point downstream of the air dryers. The portable unit functions like the analyzer in Figure 19, with the moisture sensor housed in the analyzer case. There are several different types of portable dew point monitors available.

OBJECTIVE 6

Describe the design, fittings, and operating consideration for air receivers.

AIR RECEIVERS

An air receiver is a pressure vessel, which is used as a reservoir in a compressed air system. In addition to acting as a reservoir, it acts to dampen pulsations in the discharge pressure of a reciprocating compressor. Another function of the receiver is to allow dust, moisture, and oil droplets to settle out from the air. The settled material collects at the bottom of the receiver and is drained periodically.

Air receivers are usually of welded construction and may be horizontal or vertical. A vertical air receiver is shown Figure 21. Their specifications must conform to the ASME Code, Section VIII, Pressure Vessels. They must be fitted with a safety valve, pressure gauge, drain valve, openings for inspection and cleaning, and a regulator connection.

Figure 21	Vertical Air Receiver

The size of the receiver is important. If too small, the pressure in the receiver will fluctuate more rapidly, causing the air compressor to cycle more often and increasing power consumption. The air receiver should be placed as near the compressor as possible. A shut off valve should never be placed in this line unless a safety valve is installed between the valve and the compressor. By following this guideline the discharge line cannot be over pressured by running the compressor with the shut-off valve closed.

A similar safeguard must be provided in cases where the compressor discharge is connected to a large air main also served by other compressors. A safety valve must be fitted between the compressor and the first shut-off valve in the main. This will safeguard the compressor if it is started up before the shut-off valve is opened. All safety valves should be serviced on a regular basis to ensure that they will open and reset at the correct pressures. A typical air receiver installation is shown in Figure 22. The air receiver is mounted outdoors to aid in cooling the compressed air.

Figure 22	Air Receiver Installation

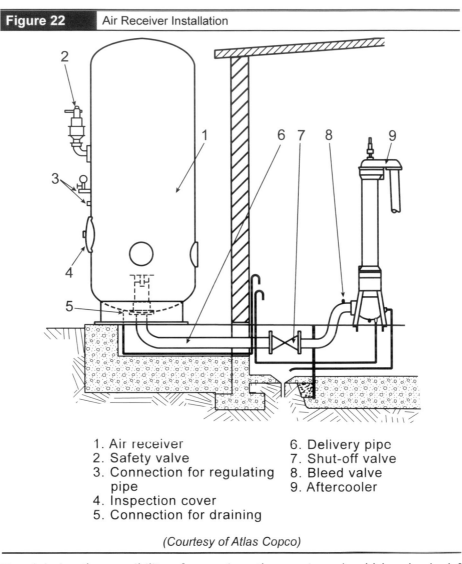

1. Air receiver
2. Safety valve
3. Connection for regulating pipe
4. Inspection cover
5. Connection for draining
6. Delivery pipe
7. Shut-off valve
8. Bleed valve
9. Aftercooler

(Courtesy of Atlas Copco)

To minimize the possibility of corrosion, the receiver should be checked for moisture on a regular basis. If moisture is collecting in the wet receiver then the upstream moisture separator should be checked to ensure that it is draining properly. If the dry air receiver has a lot of moisture in it then the operation of the air dryers should be checked. The air receivers should also be inspected on a regular basis and hydrostatically tested as required by the local pressure vessel authorities.

Explain the start-up procedure for a positive displacement compressor.

STARTING A POSITIVE DISPLACEMENT COMPRESSOR

1. Ensure that no one is working on the compressor. Ensure that all maintenance personnel have completed their work on the unit, and that the compressor has been properly turned back to operations, in accordance with safe operating procedures. Do an inspection to ensure that all flanges are tight, and that all tools have been removed from the compressor unit. Be sure that all required safety guards have been put back into place to prevent personal injury.

2. Ensure that all blinds have been removed from the compressor inlet and outlet and from the cooling water supply and return lines.

3. Turn on the cooling water for the compressor cylinders. The purpose of the cooling water is to protect the compressor cylinders from damage due to over heating. Check for leaks on the cooling water system. If leaks are found, they must be repaired before the compressor can be started.

4. Open the suction and discharge valves. Listen for leaks on flanges that were taken apart when the compressor was down for repair work. Be sure that all leaks are tightened up prior to starting the compressor.

5. Ensure that the compressor is in the unloaded position, to avoid overloading the motor when starting the compressor, and perhaps damaging the motor.

6. Close the breaker for the compressor motor. Before closing the motor breaker, be sure that the local start/stop switch is in the stop position. This will prevent the motor from starting as the breaker is being closed, and may also prevent the creation of sparks between the breaker connections as the breaker is being closed.

7. Check the crankcase/gearbox oil level. Ensure that the crankcase/gearbox oil levels are at the required levels, so that the compressor will have adequate lubrication when in service. Lack of adequate lubrication can result in damage to the compressor crankshaft, bearings or gears. If the levels are low, add additional lube oil as required.

8. Ensure the cylinder lubricator is full, so that the compressor cylinders will get the proper lubrication when the compressor is started.

9. Start the compressor.

10. Slowly load the compressor. As the compressor load increases, check the suction and discharge pressures as well as the lube oil pressures. If any of the pressures are abnormally low or high, shut down the compressor, and have the problem rectified, before restarting the compressor.

11. Check around the compressor for leaks, and listen for any unusual noises. If any leaks are found, tighten them up and if there are any unusual noises, find the cause of the noise, and have it corrected. You may need maintenance support to tighten the leaks or to remedy the cause of the noise.

12. Ensure that the cylinder lubricator is working. If the lubricator is not working, the result will be excessive wear of the cylinder walls and pistons.

OBJECTIVE 8

Explain the start-up procedure for a dynamic compressor/blower.

STARTING A DYNAMIC COMPRESSOR/BLOWER

1. Ensure no one is working on the compressor. Ensure that all maintenance personnel have completed their work on the unit, and that the compressor has been properly turned back to operations, in accordance with your safe operating procedures. Do an inspection to ensure that all flanges are tight, and that all tools have been removed from the compressor unit. Be sure all required safety guards have been put back to prevent personal injury.

2. Ensure that the compressor lube oil system is ready for service. Be sure that the lube oil reservoir has an adequate level in it.

3. Ensure that the surge valves are wide open, and that the suction flow control valve/ variable inlet vanes are in the closed position, so the compressor can be started in the unloaded position. With some compressors, the permissive to start the compressor will not be granted unless the surge valves and the inlet flow control valve/variable vanes are in the correct "start-up" position.

4. Ensure that any manual block valves in the suction or discharge lines are open. This is very important, so that the system will not shut down due to low suction pressure, or high discharge pressure. In either case, damage could be done to the system or the compressor.

5. Close the motor breaker. With some of the larger motors, the breaker may have to be closed by an electrician. Be sure to follow your safe operating procedures for the closing of electrical breakers.

6. Start the lube oil system, and check the system for leaks, and for any unusual noises. If any leaks are found, shut down the system and have the leak repaired. If any unusual noises are observed, find the cause of the noise before proceeding with the start-up of the compressor. Ensure that the lube oil pressures are within the normal operating range, and that there is adequate flow of lube oil to all the bearings.

7. Start the compressor and operate it unloaded, while checking for abnormal conditions such as oil leaks.

8. Slowly load up the compressor, or ensure that the compressor microprocessor brings the compressor on line properly.

9. Check around the compressor for leaks, and listen for any unusual noises. If you observe any leaks or hear any unusual noises check the cause of the leak or the noise, and shut down the compressor if required.

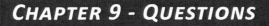
CHAPTER 9 - QUESTIONS

1. Would an operator start a positive displacement compressor with the discharge valve closed? Explain.

2. State three purposes of a receiver in a compressed air system.

3. What are three methods used to control the load on a positive displacement air compressor? Briefly describe each method.

4. Explain why some air systems have a wet air receiver and a dry air receiver.

5. Describe surging in dynamic compressors. What is one strategy used to stop surging in a dynamic compressor?

6. Using a single line sketch, describe an automatic condensate drain or trap that is attached to a compressor aftercooler.

7. Define dewpoint, pressure dewpoint, and atmospheric dewpoint in relation to compressed air systems.

8. Name the major components found in an adsorption type of instrument air-drying system.

ANSWERS: All answers are found within the content of the chapter.

Refrigeration Principles & Systems

LEARNING OUTCOME

When you complete this chapter you should be able to:

Explain the classification and properties of refrigerants and describe the operating principles and components of compression and absorption systems.

LEARNING OBJECTIVES

Here is what you should be able to do when you complete each objective:

1. *Explain the required properties of a refrigerant and describe the six group classifications for refrigerants. Identify the properties of common refrigerants.*

2. *Explain the ammonia compression refrigeration cycle, explaining the purpose of each major component and stating typical pressures and temperatures in the system.*

3. *Explain direct and indirect refrigeration. Describe a centrifugal compression system, using chilled water.*

4. *Describe and explain the operation of a two-stage, duplex compressor system with a brine cooler.*

5. *Describe and explain the operation of a two-stage refrigeration system with a rotary booster compressor.*

6. *Describe and explain the operation of a low-temperature multi-stage refrigeration system.*

7. *Explain the components and operating principle of an ammonia absorption system.*

OBJECTIVE 1

Explain the required properties of a refrigerant and describe the six group classifications for refrigerants. Identify the properties of common refrigerants.

REFRIGERANT PROPERTIES

Fluids used as refrigerants should possess the following properties:

- Environmentally safe in that it should not contribute to the destruction of the earth's ozone layer or to an increase in the earth's warming potential (greenhouse effect)
- Non-poisonous
- Non-explosive
- Non-flammable
- Stable as a gas
- Non-toxic in the pure state and when mixed with air
- Non-corrosive
- Leaks should be easily detected
- Not react unfavourably with lubricating oil or any other material normally used in the construction of refrigerating equipment
- Not contaminate foodstuffs or other products in the event of a system leak
- High latent heat of evaporation to change from a liquid to a gas
- Low boiling point at atmospheric pressure
- Relatively inexpensive
- Detectable, but non-offensive odour

Refrigerant Group Classifications

The Canadian Standards Association (CSA) Mechanical Refrigeration Code B52 and the American Society of Heating, Refrigeration, and Air Conditioning Engineers (ASHRAE) Standard 34 define the refrigerant group classifications according to their toxicity and flammability. These classifications yield six groups, A1, A2, A3, B1, B2 and B3, shown in Figure 1.

Figure 1	Refrigerants Group Classifications	
High Flammability	A3	B3
Low Flammability	A2	B2
Non-Flammable	A1	B1
	Lower Toxicity	Higher Toxicity

Toxicity

Toxicity refers to the relative poisonous characteristic of a substance. The capital letters 'A' and 'B' are used to identify the relative toxicity of the refrigerant.

- Class "A" refrigerants have lower toxicity. More specifically, they are refrigerants that have no evidence of toxicity at 400 ppm (or less) concentration.
- Class "B" have higher toxicity, which means they do show evidence of toxicity at concentrations less than 400 ppm.

Flammability

Flammability is an indication of the refrigerant's ability to support combustion. The numerical part of the classification (1, 2 or 3) identifies the relative flammability of the refrigerant. The following is taken from the ASHRAE Handbook.

- Class 1 refrigerants are not flammable in air at 21°C and 101 kPa.
- Class 2 refrigerants have a lower flammability limit (LFL) greater than 0.10 kg/m^3, at 21°C and 101 kPa, and a heat of combustion less than 19 000 kJ/kg.
- Class 3 refrigerants are highly flammable. These refrigerants have an LFL of less than or equal to 0.10 kg/m^3, at 21°C and 101 kPa, or a heat of combustion greater than or equal to 19 000 kJ/kg.

Note: The lower flammability limit (LFL) is the lowest concentration (ie. grams of refrigerant per cubic meter of air) at which the refrigerant burns in air under the listed test conditions. The heat of combustion (HOC) is an indicator of how much energy the refrigerant releases when it burns in air.

COMMON REFRIGERANTS

Some of the common refrigerants that are currently in use are:

- Refrigerant R-12
- Refrigerant R-22
- Refrigerant R-134a
- Ammonia

Refrigerant R-12

Refrigerant R-12 (CCl_2F_2) is a member of the CFC (chlorofluorocarbon) group of refrigerants and has been the most widely used of all of the refrigerants. It is non-toxic, non-flammable and non-explosive. It is a highly stable compound that is difficult to break down even under adverse operating conditions. However, when brought into contact with an open flame or with an electrical heating element, it will decompose into highly toxic products, which cause harmful effects to humans in small concentrations and on short exposure.

R-12 has a boiling point of -29.8°C, at atmospheric pressure, which makes it suitable for high, medium and low temperature applications. It is oil miscible, meaning it will dissolve in oil under operating conditions. This tends to increase the efficiency and capacity of the system in that the solvent action of the refrigerant keeps the evaporator and condenser tubes relatively free of oil films, which otherwise would tend to reduce the heat transfer capacity of these units.

R-12 contains chlorine molecules, which are destructive to the environment. This is due to the fact that they have exceptionally long life (up to 100 years or more) in the atmosphere. They have been proven to cause depletion of the earth's ozone layer and to contribute to the greenhouse effect (ie. global warming). For this reason, R-12 is being gradually replaced by other, less harmful refrigerants, such as R-134a.

R-12 was widely used in automotive air conditioning systems, home freezers and refrigerators, water fountains and transport refrigerators.

Refrigerant R-22

Refrigerant R-22 ($CHClF_2$) is a member of the HCFC (hydro chlorofluorocarbon) group of refrigerants and has a boiling point, at atmospheric pressure, of -40.8°C. It was originally developed as a low temperature refrigerant and has been used in the past in domestic and farm freezers and commercial and industrial low temperature systems, down to temperatures as low as -87°C. Its primary use today is in packaged air conditioners, where, because of space limitations, the relatively small compressor displacement required is an advantage.

Although R-22 is miscible with oil at temperatures found in the condensing section, it will often separate from the oil in the evaporator. The use of synthetic oils, with R-22, alleviates the problem of oil separation.

HCFC compounds generally have fewer chlorine atoms and a much shorter atmospheric life than CFC's. However, since the HCFC's are not completely environmentally safe, they are being phased out.

Refrigerant R-134a

Refrigerant R-134a (CH_2FCF_3) is an HFC (hydroflourocarbon) and has zero ozone depletion potential. It is non-flammable and non-explosive, with a boiling point, at atmospheric pressure, of -26.2°C. R-134a has a miscibility problem with mineral oil lubricants. This problem is eliminated through the use of ester-based synthetic lubricants.

Since HFC compounds contain no chlorine atoms, they do not deplete the ozone. Most have a relatively short atmospheric life and a minimal greenhouse effect. R-134a is being used to replace R-12 in automotive air conditioning systems.

Ammonia

Refrigerant R-717 (NH_3) is the only refrigerant outside of the fluorocarbon group that is used to any great extent. Although ammonia is toxic and somewhat flammable and explosive under certain conditions, its excellent thermal properties makes it the most widely used refrigerant in the food industry. Dairies, meat packing plants, cold storage warehouses, are all major users of ammonia refrigeration. Ammonia is an environmentally safe refrigerant.

Ammonia has a boiling point, at atmospheric pressure, of -33.3°C. Pure anhydrous ammonia is non-corrosive to all metals in a refrigeration system. However, in the presence of moisture, ammonia becomes corrosive to nonferrous metals, such as copper and brass, which should not be used in ammonia systems.

Ammonia is not miscible in oil, so will not dilute the oil in the compressor crankcase. Provisions must be made for the removal of oil from the evaporator. Ammonia is readily available and the least expensive of the commonly used refrigerants.

OBJECTIVE 2

Explain the ammonia compression refrigeration cycle, explaining the purpose of each major component and stating typical pressures and temperatures in the system.

AMMONIA COMPRESSION CYCLE

Figure 2 shows the main components of an ammonia compression cycle, which operates as follows. (Note: pressures quoted are gauge pressure)

- Liquid ammonia, at 28°C and 1065 kPa, flows from the Receiver, and passes through the Expansion Valve to the low-pressure side of the system, where the pressure is 135 kPa. The boiling temperature for ammonia at 135 kPa is -15°C. Therefore, when the 30°C liquid enters the low-pressure section some of it immediately begins to boil and vaporize. The heat of vaporization is absorbed from the remaining liquid and the temperature of the vapour-liquid mixture drops to -15°C.

Figure 2   Ammonia Refrigeration System

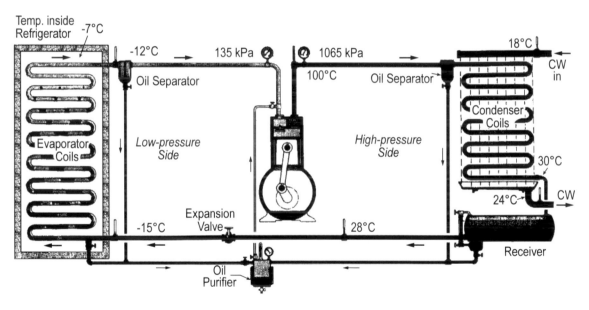

- The mixture now enters the Evaporating Coils of the refrigerator, where it absorbs heat from the air surrounding the coils. The remaining liquid refrigerant vaporizes at a temperature of -15°C and the air temperature in the refrigerator drops.
- If insufficient ammonia passes through the expansion valve, vaporization will complete (ie. no more liquid) before the refrigerant reaches the upper section of the evaporating coils. Then, as the refrigerant vapour continues passing through the upper section, it will absorb more heat from the air and its temperature will increase above the boiling point, thus becoming superheated. In Figure 2, the refrigerant vapour is leaving the evaporator at -12°C, which is 3° above its boiling temperature. Therefore, it has 3° of superheat.
- Leaving the evaporator, the refrigerant vapour passes through an Oil Separator to remove entrained oil and prevent it reaching the compressor. The refrigerant enters the compressor at 135 kPa, where it is compressed to 1065 kPa. Heat of compression increases the temperature to 100°C.

- At 1065 kPa the boiling point (or condensing point) of ammonia is 30°C. The refrigerant enters the condenser and is cooled by the cooling water, causing it to condense when it reaches 30°C. In the system shown in Figure 2, the cooling water enters at 18°C and leaves at 24°C. The refrigerant vapour completely condenses and becomes sub-cooled (ie. below the condensing temperature) to 28°C before entering the receiver.

Figure 2 shows four locations from which oil can be drained from the system. There are oil separators on the suction and discharge lines of the compressor, plus drains from the bottom of the evaporator and receiver. The oil drains lead to an Oil Purifier, where any ammonia in the oil is boiled off and drawn into the compressor suction. The oil can then be drawn off and reused.

Ammonia Refrigeration Components

An ammonia refrigeration system has a high-pressure side and a low-pressure side. The high-pressure side includes the discharge of the compressor, the condenser, the liquid receiver and up to the expansion valve. The low-pressure side contains the discharge of the expansion valve, the evaporator and up to the inlet of the compressor.

The major components of the ammonia refrigeration system are:

- Compressor
- Condenser
- Liquid receiver
- Expansion valve
- Evaporator

COMPRESSORS

The function of the compressor is to remove the low pressure refrigerant vapour from the evaporator and to increase the pressure and temperature to a point at which the condensing temperature is higher than the temperature of the available cooling water. The compressor supplies the necessary energy input to circulate the refrigerant and to compensate for the heat energy lost in the evaporator.

The three most common designs of refrigeration compressors are:

- Reciprocating
- Rotary
- Centrifugal

Reciprocating Compressors

Reciprocating refrigeration compressors may be single or double acting. Generally, the single acting type has vertical cylinders, while the double acting has horizontal cylinders.

Two-stage compressors are often used in some applications, but single stage compression is usually sufficient to provide the necessary pressure differential. The single stage compressor often has two or more cylinders arranged in parallel.

Figure 3 shows a partial cutaway, end view of an eight-cylinder compressor.

| **Figure 3** | Single Acting, Single Stage, Eight-Cylinder Compressor |

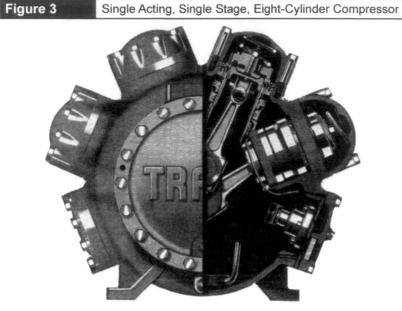

(Courtesy of Trane)

Figure 4 is a side view of the same compressor. This design has two cylinders at each of four radial locations around the compressor casing. The cylinders are fitted with safety heads to prevent damage from slugs of liquid refrigerant. Other features include cylinder unloaders, which allow the compressor to start in an unloaded condition. The compressor usually contains a magnetic plug that attracts and holds small metal particles present in the oil. An oil foam breaker reduces oil foaming, caused by refrigerant in the oil.

| **Figure 4** | Eight Cylinder Compressor |

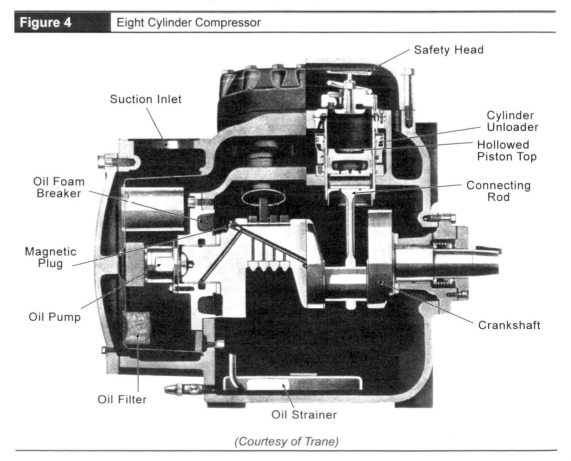

(Courtesy of Trane)

Rotary Compressors

Rotary compressors are frequently used in household refrigerators and for other low capacity installations. Two different designs of rotary compressors are:

- Vane type
- Roller type

Vane Type

The principle of operation of a vane type is shown in Figure 5. As the rotor turns, the vanes are forced out against the casing by centrifugal force. The refrigerant, entering at the suction connection, is trapped between the vanes and the casing and is carried around and forced out the discharge connection. Compression of the refrigerant is achieved due to the steadily reducing space between the rotor and the casing as the refrigerant moves to the discharge.

Figure 5	Rotary Vane Compressor

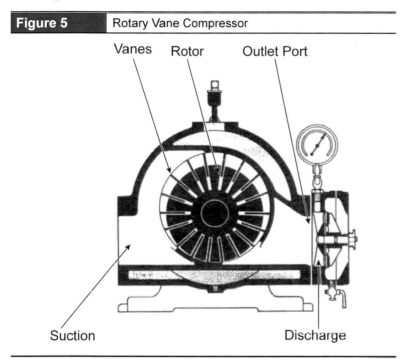

Roller Type

In the roller type shown in Figure 6, the roller is eccentric to the casing so that, as it revolves, one point on the roller circumference is always in contact with the casing. The suction and discharge openings are separated from each other by a spring-loaded blade, which bears against the roller. As the roller turns, the refrigerant gas that enters at the suction is forced by the roller into a continually decreasing space and is thus compressed.

Figure 6 shows the roller in four different positions during one revolution as it pushes the refrigerant gas toward the discharge.

Rotary compressors produce a smooth flow, are comparatively free from vibration and are quiet in operation. They are, however, expensive to manufacture because of the precision machining required and lubrication must be supplied to prevent metal-to-metal contact between casing and vanes or rollers.

Figure 6	Rotary Roller Compressor

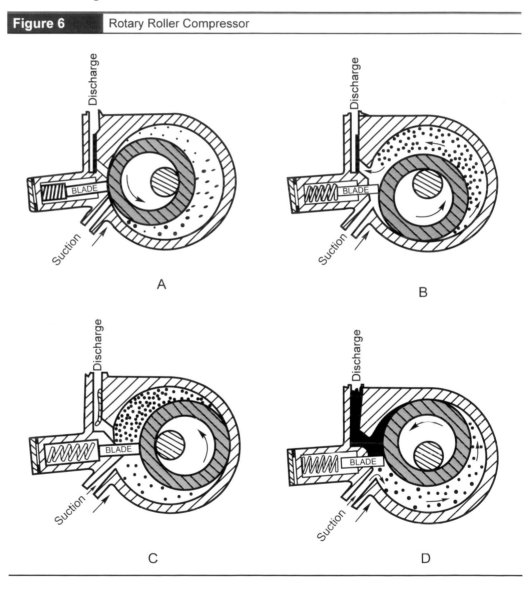

Centrifugal Compressors

Centrifugal compressors are particularly suited for refrigeration systems where the volume of refrigerant is large and the pressure difference required is small or moderate. They are used extensively in large air conditioning installations.

The operating speed of the centrifugal compressor is high. Therefore, direct connected electric motors or steam turbines are often used as drivers. The compressor itself is usually the multistage type.

Figure 7 shows a cutaway view of a two stage centrifugal refrigeration compressor.

The refrigerant gas is drawn into the eye of the first stage impeller and, due to centrifugal force, travels at high velocity to the periphery of the impeller. It then passes through a diffuser section where the velocity is converted to pressure. The refrigerant gas then enters the eye of the second stage impeller where its velocity is again increased and then converted to pressure.

A gear type oil pump provides pressure lubrication to the shaft bearings and shaft seal. The bearings are also equipped with rings to ensure lubrication during starting up and shutting down.

Centrifugal compressors require less maintenance than reciprocating and rotary compressors. There is no contamination of the refrigerant with lubricating oil since only external lubrication is required.

The main disadvantage of the centrifugal compressor is its lower efficiency and lower pressure range.

Figure 7	Two Stage Centrifugal Compressor

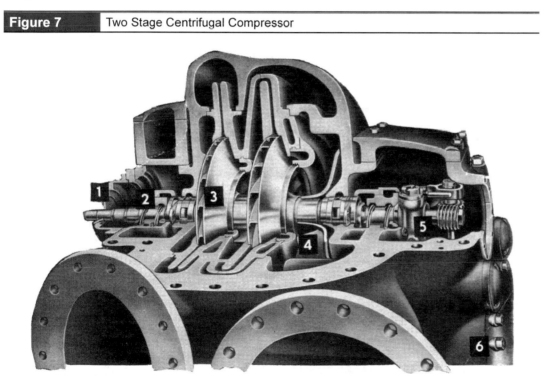

1. Shaft seal
2. Ring-oiled bearing, pressure lubricated
3. Second stage impeller
4. Inlet vanes for capacity control
5. Oil pump drive
6. Location of gear type oil pump within casing

CONDENSERS

The function of the condenser is to cool the hot compressed refrigerant vapour until it condenses to a liquid. There are three basic types of condensers, based on the cooling medium used:

- Air-cooled
- Water-cooled
- Air and water-cooled

Air-Cooled Condensers

Air cooled condensers have the advantages of simplicity and low installation costs and are frequently used in domestic units and some commercial plants. They employ finned tubes through which the refrigerant passes. Fans usually blow the cooling air across the outside surface of the finned tubes.

Figure 8 illustrates a small air cooled condenser.

Figure 8	Air Cooled Condenser (Copeland)

Water Cooled Condensers

There are two types of water-cooled condensers:

- Shell and tube
- Double type

Shell & Tube

The shell and tube condenser, illustrated in Figure 9, is the most common. It consists of a welded steel shell containing a number of tubes. The cooling water makes two passes, flowing first through the lower set of tubes and then back through the upper set of tubes. The hot refrigerant gas enters at the top of the shell and condenses by coming in contact with the outer surface of the tubes. As it condenses, it drains down and collects as a liquid on the bottom of the shell.

Figure 9 | Shell and Tube Condenser

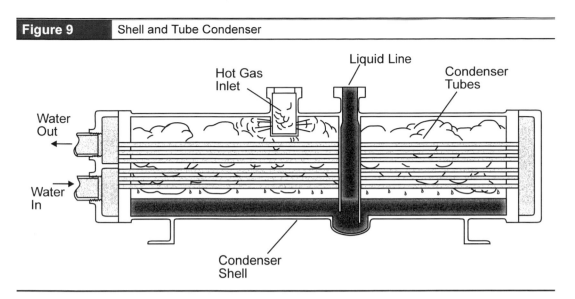

Double Pipe Condensers

This type, shown in Figure 10, consists of small pipes or tubes contained concentrically within larger tubes or pipes. The cooling water circulates within the smaller inner tubes while the hot refrigerant gas passes through the space between the inner and the outer tubes. Additional cooling is produced by the air that surrounds the outer tubes.

Figure 10 | Double Tube Condenser

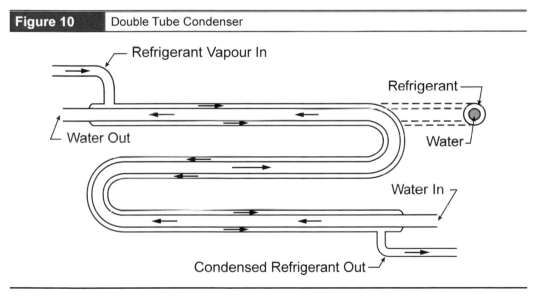

Air & Water-Cooled (Evaporative Condenser)

In the evaporative condenser shown in Figure 11, both air and water provide the cooling. The refrigerant vapour flows through a set of coils over which water is sprayed from overhead nozzles. A current of air is drawn in by a fan, counter flow to the water flow. This causes evaporation of a portion of the water, producing a cooling effect on the remaining water. A pump continuously circulates the water from a sump at the bottom of the condenser back to the spray nozzles. The fan may be the induced draft type (as shown in Fig. 11) or it may be the forced draft type, which forces the air up through the condenser.

Figure 11	Evaporative Condenser

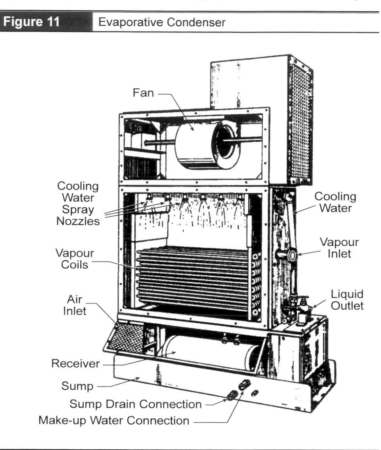

Fan

Cooling Water Spray Nozzles

Cooling Water

Vapour Coils

Vapour Inlet

Air Inlet

Liquid Outlet

Receiver

Sump

Sump Drain Connection

Make-up Water Connection

LIQUID RECEIVER

Since the volume of refrigerant in the evaporator and condenser varies with the system load, a liquid receiver is required. In addition to accommodating changes in the refrigerant charge, the receiver keeps the condenser drained of liquid. This prevents a liquid level from building up in the condenser, which ensures the maximum surface area is available in the condenser to cool the ammonia vapours. The receiver serves as a draw down storage tank for the liquid refrigerant.

Figure 12 is an example of an ammonia system liquid receiver.

Figure 12	Liquid Receiver

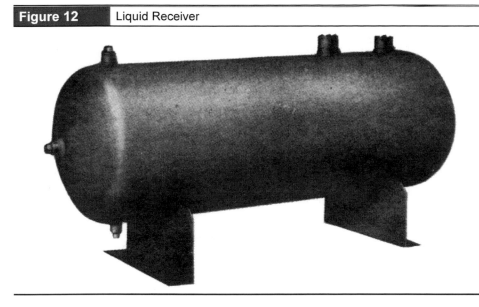

EXPANSION VALVE

The function of the expansion valve is to meter the liquid refrigerant from the liquid line into the evaporator, at a rate equal with the rate at which vaporization of the liquid is occurring in the evaporator. It also creates a pressure differential between the high and low pressure sides of the system.

Figure 13 is a manual type of expansion valve, which is basically a needle-type valve, providing a narrow restriction in the liquid line.

Figure 13	Hand Expansion Valve

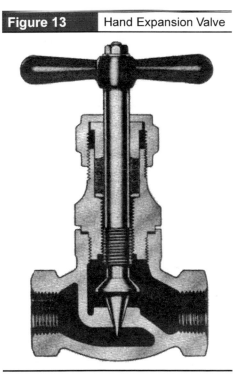

EVAPORATORS

The evaporator is the space where the liquid refrigerant absorbs heat from the surroundings and evaporates.

Three common types of evaporator construction are:

- Bare tube
- Finned tube
- Plate surface

Bare Tube Evaporator

The bare tube type, shown in Figure 14, consists of pipe or tubing that is either bent or connected to form a continuous coil. Several of these coils are used in parallel, connected to common inlet and outlet headers.

| **Figure 14** | Bare Tube Coil Evaporator |

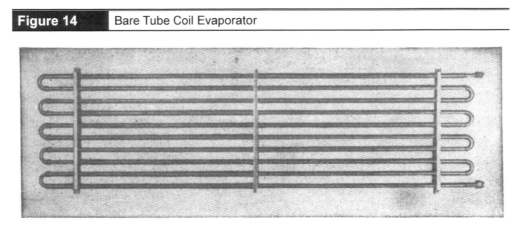

Figure 15 shows another bare tube design in which straight tubes are connected to tubesheets within a shell. This is typical of an evaporator used to cool water for an air conditioning system. The refrigerant evaporates within the tubes by absorbing heat from the water to be cooled, which circulates around the outside of the tubes. In some cases the refrigerant is contained in the shell, while the medium to be cooled flows through the tubes.

| **Figure 15** | Straight Bare Tube Evaporator |

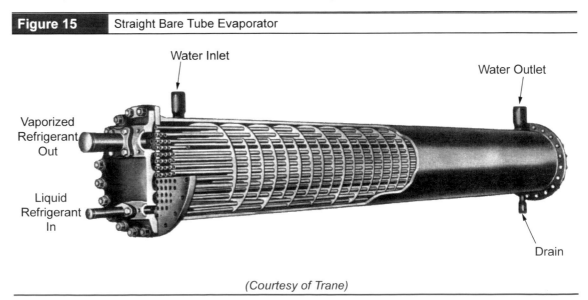

(Courtesy of Trane)

Finned Tube Evaporator

A finned tube evaporator appears in Figure 16.

In this type, the fins serve to increase the heat transfer surface as they conduct heat to the tubes to which they are attached and through which the refrigerant passes.

Figure 16	Finned Tube Evaporator Coil

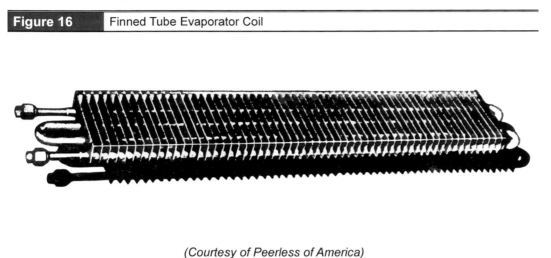

(Courtesy of Peerless of America)

Plate Surface Evaporator

The construction of a plate surface evaporator is illustrated in Figure 17.

This design consists of a continuous coil of tubing contained between two metal plates, which are welded together at their edges. A vacuum is then produced between the plates and atmospheric pressure holds the plates tightly against the tubing.

Figure 17	Plate Surface Evaporator

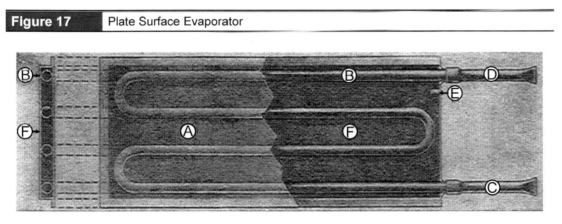

(Courtesy of Dole Refrigerating Company)

The lettered parts in the sketch are as follows:

A – outside plate	D – vapour outlet
B – tubing	E – vacuum fitting
C – liquid inlet	F – vacuum space

OBJECTIVE 3

Explain direct and indirect refrigeration. Describe a centrifugal compression system, using chilled water.

DIRECT & INDIRECT REFRIGERATION

A refrigeration plant may use either a direct system or an indirect system. A direct system is one in which the evaporator is in direct contact with the material or space being refrigerated (see Fig. 2). An indirect system is one in which a liquid, such as brine or water, is cooled by the refrigerant and then this liquid is circulated to the material or space being refrigerated.

Figure 18 illustrates an indirect system.

- The evaporating coils are located within a tank of brine and, as the refrigerant is evaporating within the coils, the brine is cooled.

- The cold brine is then pumped through coils located within the refrigerated space. The cold brine absorbs the heat from this space and then returns to the brine tank to be cooled again.

Figure 18	Indirect Refrigeration

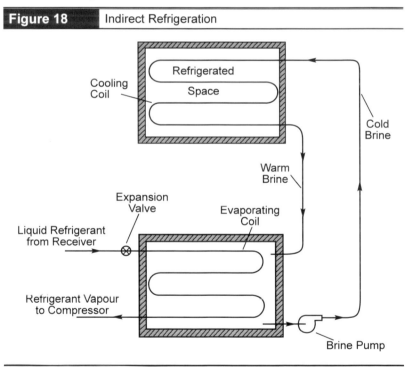

This method is common for skating and hockey rinks, with the brine cooled to about -11°C and then circulated below the floor to provide the freezing effect for the ice surface. The brine is usually a solution of calcium chloride, which can be subjected to temperatures as low as -51°C without freezing. Other types of brines for indirect refrigeration systems are alcohol, glycerine, and ethylene glycol, which are all suitable for low temperatures.

Air conditioning systems frequently use indirect refrigeration with water as the brine. In this case, the water is cooled by the evaporator coils and then is circulated through air-cooling coils over which the air to be cooled, is passed. Water is suitable in this case since cooling below 4°C is not required and, therefore, the water will not freeze.

CENTRIFUGAL COMPRESSION SYSTEM

Figure 19 is a diagrammatic representation of an air conditioning system using a centrifugal compressor.

- The compressed refrigerant gas is discharged from the compressor into a condenser.
- In the condenser, the cooling water flowing through the tubes condenses the refrigerant gas surrounding the tubes.
- The resulting refrigerant liquid collects in a sump at the bottom of the condenser and flows down to the evaporator float chamber.
- The evaporator float valve maintains a constant level of liquid refrigerant in the evaporator. In the evaporator (or cooler as it is called), the refrigerant evaporates by absorbing heat from water, which is flowing through the chilled water tubes.
- The vaporized refrigerant is withdrawn from the evaporator by the compressor and compressed, once again.
- The chilled water, after leaving the evaporator or cooler, is used to reduce the temperature of the air used for the building air conditioning.

The centrifugal compressor used is a two stage machine with a crossover pipe leading from the first stage to the second stage.

Figure 19	Centrifugal Compressor System

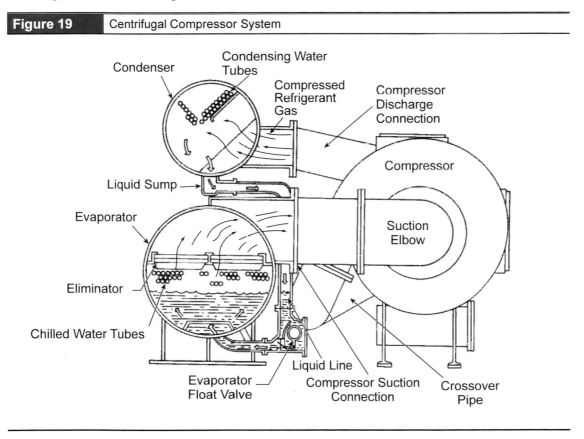

Figure 20 is a cutaway view of a similar centrifugal compression system. The arrangement is quite compact with all components mounted on the same base.

Figure 20	Centrifugal Compressor System

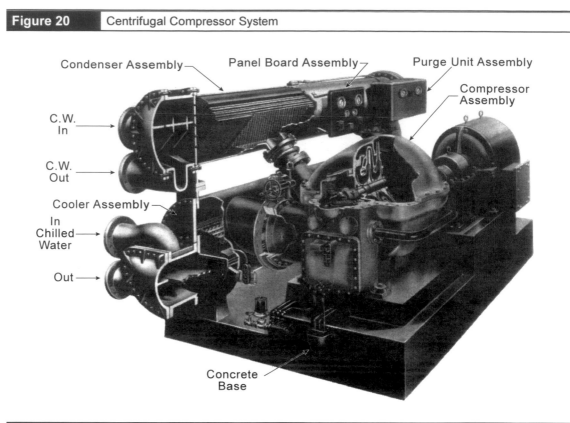

OBJECTIVE 4

Describe and explain the operation of a two-stage, duplex compressor system with a brine cooler.

Figure 21 shows an indirect refrigeration system, which incorporates a duplex compressor to accomplish two-stage compression, resulting in low temperature operation. Compression of refrigerant vapour is accomplished in the two cylinders of a single machine, with one cylinder serving as the low-pressure stage and the other as the high-pressure stage.

The superheated vapour leaving the low-pressure cylinder mixes with high-pressure saturated liquid (from the intercooler expansion valve) just before entering the intercooler. The liquid absorbs the superheat from the vapour, then drains from the bottom of the intercooler and goes to the economizer (aka, liquid cooler). The economizer is maintained at the pressure of the second stage suction (see the line from top of economizer to the 2nd stage suction line). This allows the liquid in the shell of the economizer to evaporate, which, in turn, cools the high-pressure liquid that is going to the evaporator (brine cooler).

The drains from separators, traps and coils are piped to a central oil-recovery drum and still. A connection from the top of the still to the low-pressure suction allows any liquid refrigerant that drains into this receiver with the oil to boil off.

Figure 21	Two-Stage Plant with Duplex Compressor

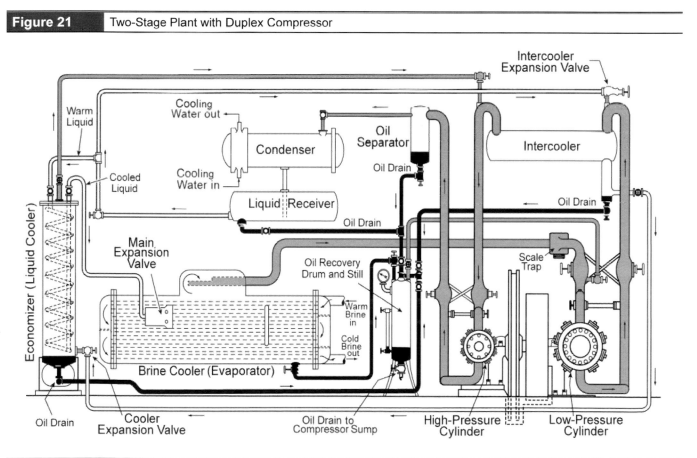

The above system is somewhat obsolete in design, although there are many still in service. Two-stage reciprocating compressors have been largely replaced by rotary compressors. Also, the method shown for intercooling (mixing liquid with vapour to absorb superheat) has been replaced by intercoolers that have an internal cooling coil.

OBJECTIVE 5

Describe and explain the operation of a two-stage refrigeration system with a rotary booster compressor.

TWO-STAGE REFRIGERATION SYSTEM

Since low-suction pressure is required for low refrigeration temperatures, a kilogram of vapour coming from the evaporator has a very large volume. To handle the large volumes, multi-stage plants usually employ a rotary compressor for the first (low-pressure) stage. The rotary compressor operates at high speed and a relatively small compressor will handle a large amount of low-density vapour. It has good efficiency at the low to moderate first-stage pressures. In this application, the compressor is also called a "booster" compressor.

Figure 22 shows a refrigeration plant with two cold rooms, each maintained at a different temperature. Suction of the booster machine is taken from the evaporator in the low-temperature room. The intermediate pressure vapour passes through an oil separator and into the intercooler where it is cooled by liquid from the receiver. It then joins the suction of the 2nd stage compressor.

The second-stage compressor also takes suction from the evaporator in the high-temperature room. It then discharges to the condenser, where the refrigerant vapour is condensed before draining into the receiver. The liquid provides cooling in the intercooler before expanding through separate expansion valves to the two evaporators.

Figure 22	Two Stage Plant with Rotary Booster Compressor

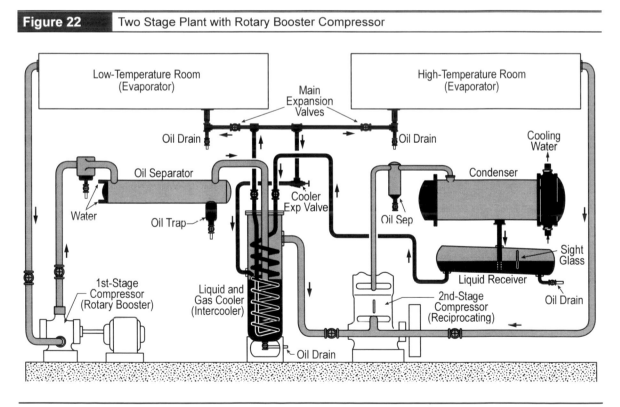

OBJECTIVE 6

Describe and explain the operation of a low-temperature multi-stage refrigeration system.

MULTI-STAGE REFRIGERATION SYSTEM

The system, in Figure 23, shows the five basic elements common to all compression refrigeration systems:

- Compressor
- Condenser
- Receiver
- Regulator or expansion valve
- Evaporator

However, because of the greater range between suction and discharge pressures, the necessary compression has been divided between two single-stage compressors. An accessory piece of equipment, a water-cooled intercooler, is provided between the discharge of the low-pressure compressor and the suction of the high-pressure compressor to remove some of the heat added as a result of the work done on the vapour in the low-pressure stage. This intercooler reduces the temperature of the vapour, increases its density and permits a corresponding decrease in the size and power consumption of the high-pressure compressor.

The pressures and temperatures indicated at various points in the system are typical of those that might be present when using ammonia as the refrigerant.

Figure 23	Low Temperature Multi-Stage Plant

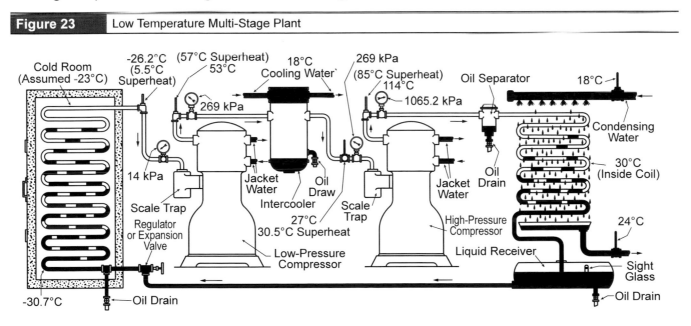

OBJECTIVE 7

Explain the components and operating principle of an ammonia absorption system.

AMMONIA ABSORPTION SYSTEM

Figure 24 shows an ammonia absorption refrigeration system, which operates as follows.

- A solution of water and ammonia, called strong liquor or strong aqua, is heated in the generator using steam coils. The heating causes ammonia vapour, at a pressure of about 1200 kPa, to be driven off from the solution along with some water vapour. The vapour enters the analyzer where strong liquor, pumped from the absorber, through a heat exchanger, flows downward over trays and comes in contact with the rising vapours. This causes most of the water vapour to condense, while the ammonia vapour, together with a small amount of water vapour, passes into the rectifier.

- The rectifier contains cooling water tubes, which further cool the ammonia vapour. This cooling condenses the remaining water vapour, leaving dry, high-pressure ammonia vapour to continue on to the condenser. The condensed water vapour flows from the rectifier back to the generator, via the analyzer.

- In the condenser, the ammonia vapour is condensed to liquid by heat exchange with cooling water and the liquid ammonia flows to the evaporator through a control or expansion valve.

- As the ammonia passes through the control valve, its pressure is reduced from 1200 kPa to about 240 kPa. At this low pressure, the ammonia will boil at a temperature of about -15°C, which it does in the evaporator by absorbing heat from the medium to be cooled.

- The low-pressure ammonia vapour produced in the evaporator enters the absorber, where it is absorbed by the weak liquor flowing from the bottom of the generator. The absorbing process produces a certain amount of heat, which is removed by cooling water coils in the absorber. When the weak liquor absorbs the ammonia vapour it becomes strong liquor.

- The strong liquor is drawn off by the strong liquor pump and pumped at a pressure of about 1200 kPa through a heat exchanger to the analyzer and then to the generator. As the strong liquor passes through the heat exchanger it is heated by the weak liquor flowing from the generator to the absorber. The level of weak liquor in the absorber is maintained by the weak liquor control valve.

Figure 24 Ammonia Absorption System

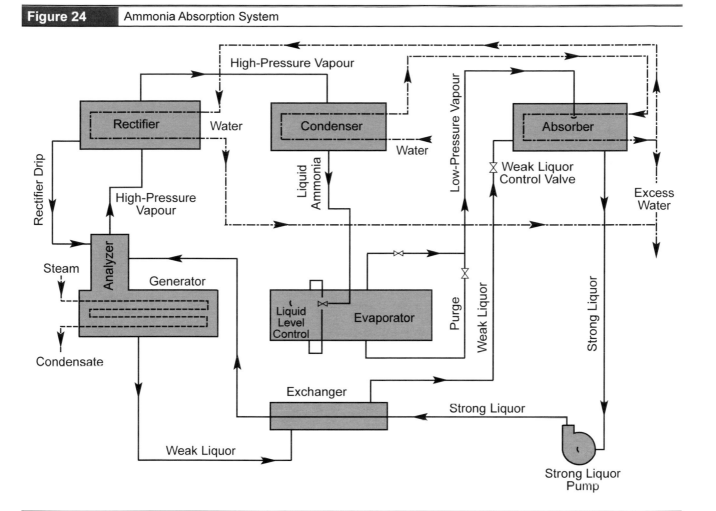

CHAPTER 10 - QUESTIONS

1. State the properties of the following refrigerants:
   a) Ammonia
   b) R-22
   c) R-134a

2. Use a simple sketch, explain the ammonia compression refrigeration cycle. Include typical pressures and temperatures around the cycle.

3. Describe the following rotary compressors. State their advantages and disadvantages.
   a) Vane Type
   b) Roller Type

4. Explain the differences between direct and indirect refrigeration systems.

5. Explain the operation of a two-stage, duplex compressor system with a brine cooler.

6. Explain the operation of a low-temperature multi-stage refrigeration system.

7. With the use of a simple sketch, explain the components and operating principle of an ammonia absorption system.

ANSWERS: All answers are found within the content of the chapter.

CHAPTER 11

Refrigeration Auxiliaries & Operation

LEARNING OUTCOME

When you complete this chapter you should be able to:

Explain control and safety devices on a compression refrigeration system and explain procedures and equipment to control oil, non-condensables, moisture, refrigerant, and brine.

LEARNING OBJECTIVES

Here is what you should be able to do when you complete each objective:

1. Explain the purpose, design and operation of the following controls on a compression refrigeration system: expansion valve, low-side float, high-side float, compressor controls (temperature and pressure-actuated), and condenser cooling water control.

2. Explain the purpose of the following refrigeration system safety devices: high-pressure cutout, oil pressure cutout and pressure relief devices.

3. Explain the effects of oil in ammonia and Freon systems and describe the location and operation of an oil separator and oil still. Explain how oil is manually drained from these systems.

4. Explain the effects and location of non-condensable gases. Describe the operation of manual and automatic purge devices.

5. Explain the effects of moisture in a refrigeration system and describe its removal.

6. Explain leak testing of a system and describe the procedure for adding refrigerant.

7. Explain the principles of brine control in an indirect system and explain the procedures for charging and controlling brine strength.

8. Explain refrigeration safety and environmental issues.

OBJECTIVE 1

Explain the purpose, design and operation of the following controls on a compression refrigeration system: expansion valve, low-side float, high-side float, compressor controls (temperature and pressure-actuated), and condenser cooling water control.

EXPANSION VALVES

Automatic Expansion Valve

The automatic expansion valve is actually a pressure controlled valve, which maintains a constant pressure within the evaporator when the compressor is operating and, in addition, closes when the compressor stops.

An automatic expansion valve is shown in Figure 1. The valve push rod is attached at the top to the diaphragm. Above the diaphragm is the opening spring, which acts downward on the diaphragm, pushing the valve open.

- Evaporator pressure enters the underside of the diaphragm, through the equalizer connection, and this pressure tends to push the diaphragm upwards and close the valve.

- The closing spring acts upwards on the valve, which assists the closing action.

- During operation, the opening spring may be adjusted to give the desired evaporator pressure.

- When the temperature in the refrigerated space drops below the desired temperature, the compressor is stopped by means of a thermostatic switch. The evaporator pressure will begin to rise as refrigerant is still entering and vaporizing in the evaporator and the compressor is no longer removing this vapour. This increased evaporator pressure acts upon the underside of the expansion valve diaphragm and causes the valve to close, thus stopping refrigerant flow to the evaporator.

Figure 1	Automatic Expansion Valve

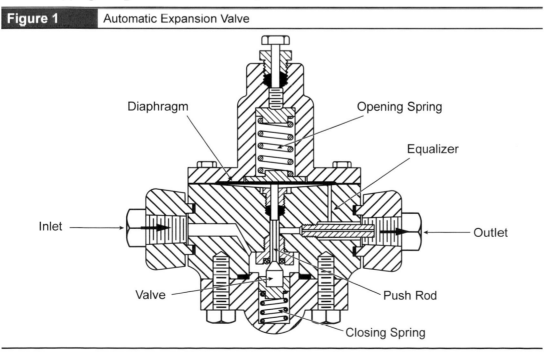

- When the temperature in the refrigerated space rises, the compressor is started by the thermostatic switch and immediately pumps out the evaporator, producing a low evaporator pressure. This results in less pressure acting upon the diaphragm of the expansion valve and the opening spring will now be able to force open the valve, allowing refrigerant to again flow to the evaporator.

Thermostatic Expansion Valve

The thermostatic expansion valve is the most widely used refrigerant control. It is similar in construction to the automatic expansion valve, but it also has a thermal power element. This element consists of a diaphragm chamber, connected to a bulb by a small diameter capillary tube. The element is usually charged with the same refrigerant that is being used in the system.

A diaphragm type thermostatic expansion valve, with capillary tube and bulb, is shown in Figure 2.

Referring to Figure 2:

The bulb is strapped to the evaporator piping at the evaporator outlet while the thermostatic valve itself is located at the evaporator inlet. The force tending to open the valve is the force due to the pressure of the refrigerant in the power element (bulb, tube and diaphragm chamber). The forces tending to close the valve are the evaporator pressure acting under the diaphragm via the external equalizer connection and the force of the spring.

- If insufficient refrigerant is flowing to the evaporator, the temperature of the vapour leaving the evaporator will be higher than saturation temperature (ie. the vapour will be superheated). This higher temperature will increase the pressure of the refrigerant in the power element to above the pressure in the evaporator and the diaphragm will be forced down, opening the valve further. This will allow more refrigerant to enter the evaporator.

- Conversely, if there is too much refrigerant flowing to the evaporator, then the superheat of the vapour will be reduced or eliminated. Therefore, the pressure within the power unit will be reduced and the combined action of the spring and the evaporator pressure acting under the diaphragm will tend to close the valve.

Figure 2	Thermostatic Expansion Valve (Diaphragm Type)

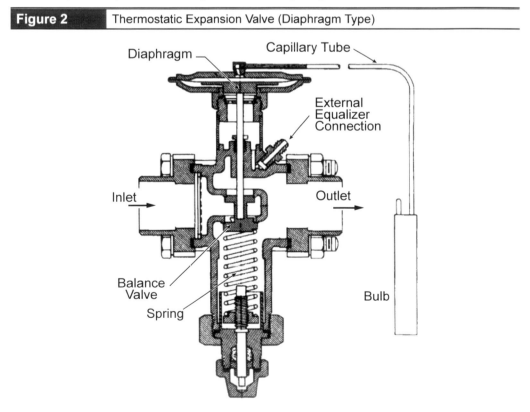

A bellows type thermostatic expansion valve is illustrated in Figure 3.

The operating principle is the same, but the diaphragm chamber is replaced by a bellows. The numbered parts in the sketch are, as follows:

1. Capillary tube
2. Power element
3. Bellows
4. Push rod
5. Feeler bulb
6. Valve yoke

Figure 3 | Thermostatic Expansion Valve (Bellows Type)

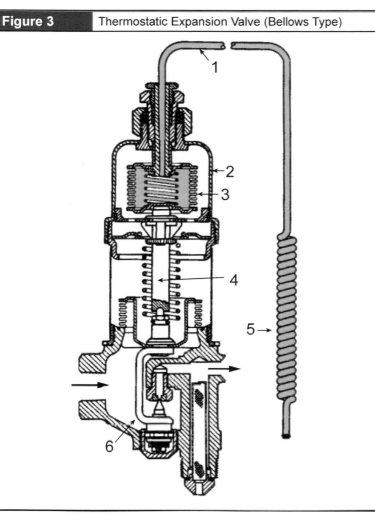

LIQUID LEVEL CONTROL

Low Side Float Valve

The low side float valve is used to maintain the liquid refrigerant level in a flooded evaporator. The term "low side" refers to the fact that the float is located in the low-pressure side of the system and is exposed to evaporator pressure. It is normally located in the surge drum or accumulator, of the flooded evaporator.

Figure 4 shows a low side float valve arrangement.

With this arrangement, the flow of refrigerant into the evaporator is regulated in accordance to the amount of refrigerant evaporated so that a constant level is maintained in the evaporator.

Figure 4	Low-Side Float Valve Arrangement

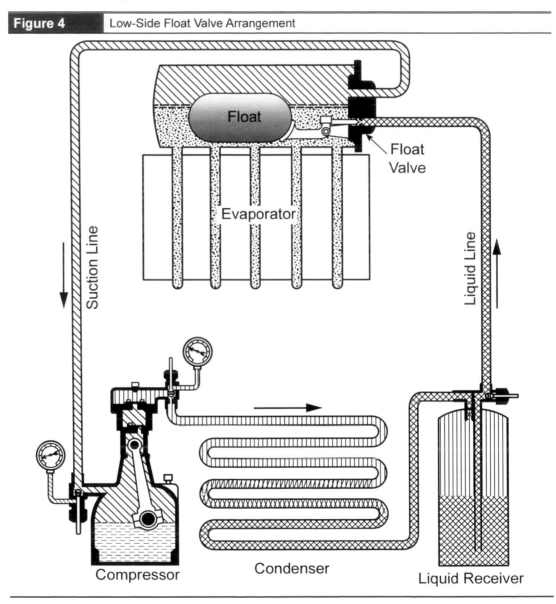

High Side Float Valve

The high side float valve is installed with the float in the high-pressure side of the system. The float may be installed in the liquid receiver or in its own float chamber, which acts as a receiver.

Figure 5 shows an arrangement with the liquid refrigerant from the condenser flowing directly into the float chamber, with no receiver.

The float maintains a constant level in the float chamber. If the rate of vaporization in the evaporator increases, a larger volume of vapour will be pumped by the compressor to the condenser. More liquid refrigerant will flow to the float chamber. The level in the chamber will rise and the float valve will open to allow more liquid to flow to the evaporator.

The heat exchanger in the sketch causes the liquid refrigerant to be cooled by heat exchange with the refrigerant vapour from the evaporator.

Figure 5	System with High-Side Float Valve

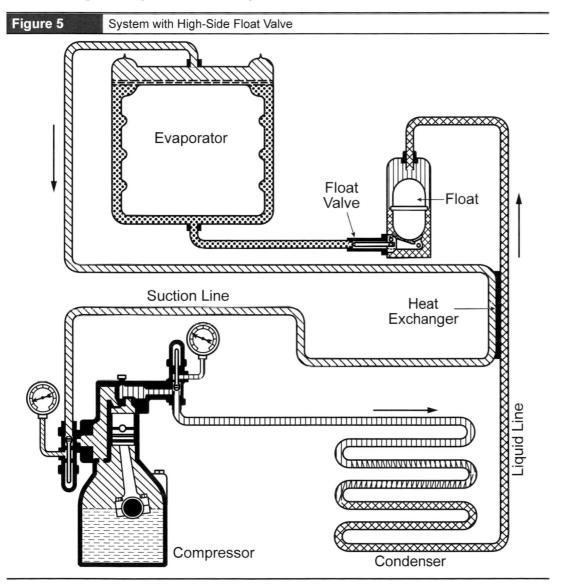

COMPRESSOR CONTROLS

Besides regulating the flow of refrigerant to the evaporator, refrigeration control can also be achieved by regulating the output of the compressor.

One method is to have the compressor run continuously, but vary the output by adjusting its speed or by using clearance pockets or inlet valve unloaders.

Another method is to operate the compressor at constant speed, but intermittently. This means that the compressor is stopped when the desired temperature in the refrigerated space is attained. Then, when the temperature of the space rises a certain amount, the compressor is started again. This starting and stopping is normally done automatically by a temperature-actuated or pressure-actuated control.

TEMPERATURE ACTUATED CONTROL (THERMOSTAT)

Direct Type

With direct temperature control, a thermostat is located directly in the space to be cooled and the temperature-sensing element is a bimetallic strip. The strip is made up of two dissimilar metals (usually Invar and brass or Invar and steel), which are bonded together into a flat strip. Invar is an alloy that has a very low coefficient of expansion, whereas brass and steel have relatively high coefficients of expansion. Since the change in the length of the Invar, per degree of temperature change, will always be less than that of the brass or steel, increasing the temperature of the bimetal element causes the bimetal to warp in the direction of the Invar (the inactive metal), as seen in Figure 6(a).

A decrease in temperature causes the bimetal to bend in the direction of the brass or steel (the active metal), as shown in Figure 6(c). This bending action can then be used to open or close an electric circuit, thus starting or stopping the compressor.

Figure 6	Bi-Metal Type Temperature Sensing Element

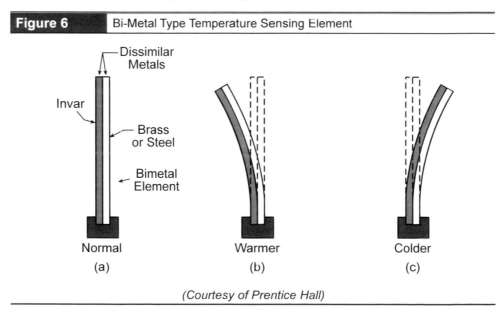

(Courtesy of Prentice Hall)

Indirect Type

The indirect temperature control uses a fluid-filled tube, or bulb, that is connected to a bellows or diaphragm chamber and filled with a gas, liquid or saturated mixture of the two.

Figure 7 shows the arrangement. The fluid-filled bulb is installed in the refrigerated space, while the remainder of the control is located outside the space. Changes in temperature will change the pressure exerted by the fluid in the bulb and this will cause the bellows or diaphragm to move and thus open or close an electric switch, thus stopping or starting the compressor, as shown in Figure 8.

Figure 7	Bulb Type Temperature Sensing Element

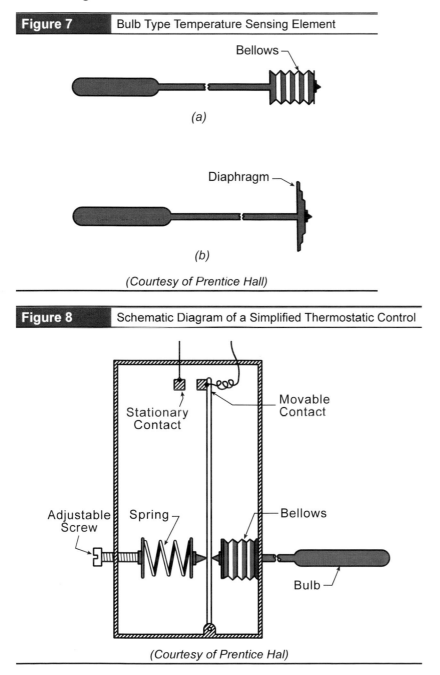

(Courtesy of Prentice Hall)

Figure 8	Schematic Diagram of a Simplified Thermostatic Control

(Courtesy of Prentice Hal)

PRESSURE ACTUATED CONTROL (PRESSURESTAT)

This device, also called a low-pressure control, consists essentially of a low-pressure bellows, which is connected by means of tubing to the evaporator outlet piping. The pressure in the evaporator outlet piping depends upon the refrigerant temperature in the evaporator. For example, when using the refrigerant R-12, if the refrigerant is boiling at a temperature of -18°C in the evaporator, then the evaporator pressure will be about 62 kPa. If the temperature was increased to -16°C, the pressure would increase to about 75 kPa. Similarly, if the evaporator temperature dropped to -20°C, the corresponding pressure would be about 48 kPa.

These pressure changes acting upon the bellows will cause it to expand or contract and this movement can be used to operate a switch to start or stop the compressor.

Note that a pressure actuated control for the compressor cannot be used in conjunction with an automatic expansion valve refrigerant control. This is because the automatic expansion valve maintains a constant evaporator pressure and, therefore, the pressure-actuated control would not operate.

Also, the pressure-actuated control is not suitable for use with a capillary tube. This is because with the capillary tube, the high and the low-pressure sections of the system equalize as soon as the compressor shuts down. The rising pressure in the evaporator would then restart the compressor immediately.

A pressure actuated control for compressor starting and stopping is illustrated in Figure 9.

Figure 9	Pressure Actuated Control

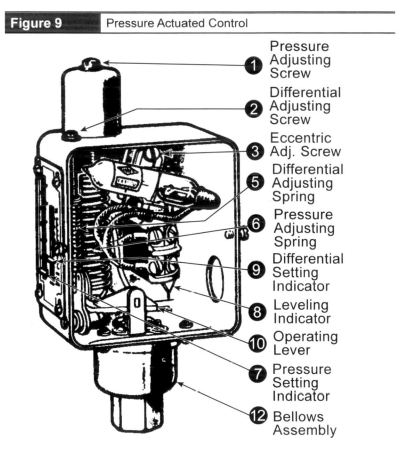

1. Pressure Adjusting Screw
2. Differential Adjusting Screw
3. Eccentric Adj. Screw
5. Differential Adjusting Spring
6. Pressure Adjusting Spring
9. Differential Setting Indicator
8. Leveling Indicator
10. Operating Lever
7. Pressure Setting Indicator
12. Bellows Assembly

CONDENSER COOLING WATER CONTROL

Most refrigerating systems use the more efficient water-cooled condensers rather than the air cooled type. To avoid wasting water, the flow of cooling water through the condenser should be controlled automatically. This control can be achieved by a solenoid operated shut off valve or a pressure operated throttling valve.

Figure 10 shows a cutaway of a solenoid valve.

- When the compressor starts, the solenoid coil is energized and acts as a magnet, drawing the valve plunger up into the center of the coil. This opens the valve and admits cooling water to the condenser.

- When the compressor stops, the power supply to the solenoid is also cut off and the coil no longer acts as a magnet. Therefore the valve plunger will drop and shutting the valve, stopping the flow of cooling water.

Figure 10	Solenoid Valve

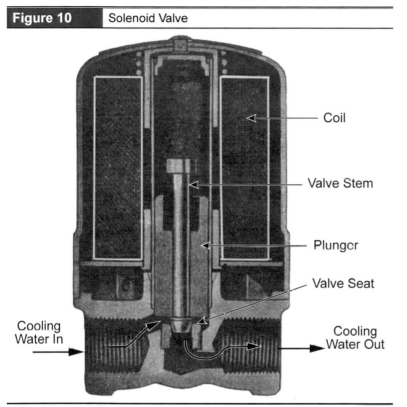

A pressure operated throttling valve is show in Figure 11.

The valve is operated by a bellows that acts to open the valve and by a spring that tends to close the valve. The bellows is connected by tubing to the high-pressure side of the system. When the compressor starts, the high side pressure begins to increase and this pressure, acting upon the bellows, will open the valve and allow cooling water to flow to the condenser. When the compressor stops, the condenser pressure will drop and the spring will close the valve, shutting off the cooling water supply.

Figure 11 | Pressure Operated Valve

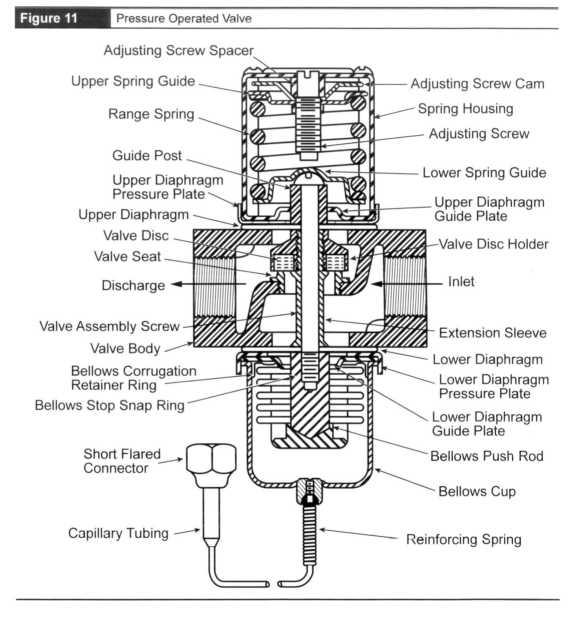

OBJECTIVE 2

Explain the purpose of the following refrigeration system safety devices: high-pressure cutout, oil pressure cutout, and pressure relief devices.

SAFETY DEVICES AND CONTROLS

High-Pressure Cutout

High-pressure controls are used only as safety controls. Connected to the discharge of the compressor, the purpose of the high-pressure control is to stop the compressor if the pressure on the high-pressure side of the system becomes excessive. This prevents possible damage to the equipment. When the pressure returns to normal, the high-pressure control closes the circuit and starts the compressor.

Some high-pressure controls are equipped with "lock-out" devices that require the control to be reset manually before the compressor can be started again. Although this type of control is not desirable on all systems, they are essential on systems using water-cooled condensers, due to the possibility of water supply failure.

CSA B52 states the following:

- Pressure limiting devices shall be provided on all systems containing more than 9 kg of refrigerant and operating above atmospheric pressure, and on all water cooled systems so constructed that the compressor or generator is capable of producing a pressure in excess of the high side design pressure.
- Pressure limiting devices shall be designed to stop the action of the compressor or generator at a pressure less than 90% of the pressure relief valve setting.
- Pressure limiting devices shall be connected between the compressor and the stop valve on the discharge side.

Since the condensing pressures of the various refrigerants are different, the cutout and cut-in settings of the high-pressure control depend on the refrigerant used.

Figure 12 is a type of high pressure cutout that also incorporates a low-pressure control.

Figure 12	L-P Control and H-P Cutout Combined

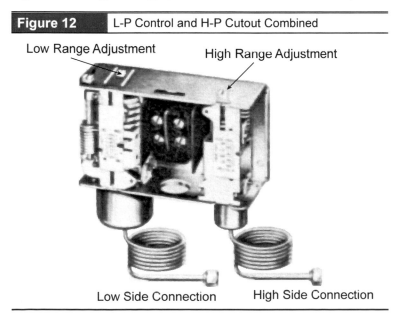

Low Range Adjustment   High Range Adjustment

Low Side Connection   High Side Connection

Oil Pressure Cutout

Failure of the forced lubrication system could cause extensive damage to a refrigeration compressor. It is therefore necessary to equip the compressor with an oil pressure failure switch that shuts down the compressor when the oil pressure drops below the safe minimum limit, for longer than a predetermined period.

Since the crankcase or housing of a compressor is subjected to suction pressure, the oil pressure should be related to this pressure and be measured as the pressure difference between the oil pump discharge pressure and the suction pressure.

Figure 13 shows a typical oil pressure failure switch.

The switch has two opposed pressure bellows, which operate a timed switch controlling the power supply to the compressor motor. The pressure of the oil pump discharge is exerted on one bellow while the suction pressure is exerted on the other. As long as the oil pressure is a specific amount higher than the suction pressure, the timed switch is kept in the closed position allowing operation of the compressor.

When the compressor is started the differential pressure switch and the timer switch are closed. The time delay allows the compressor to operate for about two minutes to establish the required oil pressure differential. If this pressure differential is not established within the preset time, the compressor motor shuts off. Also, when the oil pump discharge pressure drops below the differential pressure switch cut-in point, the differential pressure switch closes and the time delay relay shuts down the compressor in a given time.

Figure 13	Oil Pressure Failure Switch

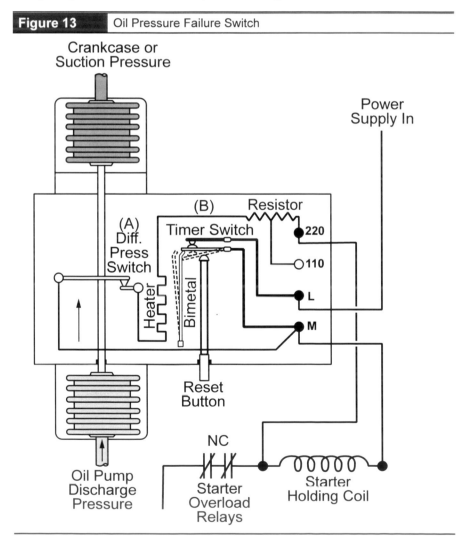

In Figure 13, the contacts of the differential pressure switch (A) and timer switch (B) are both closed when the compressor is started. After the pressure differential increases to the cut-in point within the required time, the differential pressure switch will open and de-energize the heater circuit of the time delay before the bimetal strip can open the timer switch contacts. The compressor continues to operate normally.

If the oil pressure differential does not build to the cut-in point within a preset time, the energized heater causes the bimetal strip to bend. The timer switch contacts open and the compressor stops. The compressor cannot be started again until the heater and the bimetal strip have cooled and the timer switch is manually reset.

If the oil pump discharge pressure drops below the cut-in point during compressor operation, the crankcase or suction pressure closes the differential pressure switch. The heater circuit is energized causing the timer switch to stop the compressor in a given time.

PRESSURE RELIEF DEVICES

According to CSA B52:

- Every refrigerating system shall be protected by a pressure relief device or some other means designed to safely relieve pressure due to fire or other abnormal conditions.
- All pressure-relief devices shall be directly pressure actuated. A pressure-relief device shall protect each part of a refrigerating system that can be valved off and contains one or more pressure vessels having internal diameters greater than 152 mm and containing liquid refrigerant.
- Stop valves shall not be located between the means of pressure relief and the part or parts of the system protected.
- All pressure relief devices and fusible plugs shall be connected as nearly as practicable directly to the pressure vessel or other parts of the system protected thereby, above the liquid refrigerant level, and installed so that they are readily accessible for inspection and repair and so that they cannot be readily rendered inoperative. Fusible plugs may be located above or below the liquid refrigerant level, except on the low side.
- All refrigerating systems must be protected by one or more pressure relief devices. These pressure relief devices may be relief valves, fusible plugs, or rupture members.
- All pressure-relief valves shall be set to start to function at a pressure not exceeding the design pressure of the parts of the system, being protected.
- All rupture members used in lieu of, or in series with, a relief valve shall have a nominal rated rupture pressure not to exceed the design pressure of the parts of the system protected.

The relief valve is a spring-loaded valve, which is set to open and discharge refrigerant if the pressure exceeds the set value. The spring-loaded safety valve has the advantage of resealing itself, or closing, when the pressure drops to a safe limit.

A typical relief valve is shown in Figure 14.

Figure 14	Spring Loaded Pressure Relief Valve

Installation Date Tag

Neoprene O-Ring Helps Seal Valve from Moisture

Accurately Factory Set and Sealed

Stainless Steel Spring

Ductile Iron Body for Added Strength

Stainless Steel Piston

Stainless Steel Seat Insert

Premium Grade Virgin Teflon Seat Disc

(Courtesy of Hansen Technologies)

Figure 15 shows a cross-section of a fusible plug.

The fusible plug contains a metal alloy that will melt at a design temperature. This temperature will be reached if the saturation pressure of the refrigerant reaches a certain value. The fusible plug has a pipe thread for connection to the liquid receiver plus a connection to the discharge line, which carries the released refrigerant outdoors.

Figure 15	Fusible Plugs

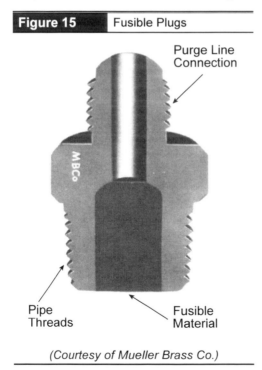

Purge Line Connection

Pipe Threads

Fusible Material

(Courtesy of Mueller Brass Co.)

Figure 16 is a cross-section of a rupture disc.

The rupture disc looks similar on the outside to the fusible plug, but it has a thin metal disc inside, which will burst before the pressure in the system reaches a dangerous level. It is also threaded into the liquid receiver and is connected to a purge line to carry away the released refrigerant.

Figure 16	Rupture Disc

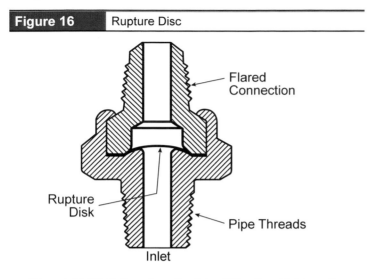

(Copyright 1998, American Society of Heating, Refrigerating and Air-Conditioning Engineers, Inc. www.ashrae.org. Reprinted by permission from ASHRAE 199 Handbook-Refrigeration)

OBJECTIVE 3

Explain the effects of oil in ammonia and Freon systems and describe the location and operation of an oil separator and oil still. Explain how oil is manually drained from these systems.

EFFECT OF OIL IN THE SYSTEM

Any oil circulating through the system with the refrigerant will have an adverse effect on efficiency and capacity. This is because the oil tends to form a film on the surface of the condenser and evaporator tubes, thereby lowering the heat transfer capacity of these two exchangers. Since the oil thickens as the temperature is reduced, the oil problem is greatest in the evaporator and worsens as the evaporator temperature drops. The result is higher discharge pressure and increased power consumption by the compressor.

OIL SEPARATORS

To prevent oil from carrying over to the condenser, an oil separator is usually installed between the compressor and the condenser.

Figure 17 illustrates one type of cyclone oil separator used in a refrigeration system. The compressed gas from the compressor enters the separator and is given a cyclonic motion, which causes centrifugal force to throw the oil out of the stream. The oil will run down the wall and collect at the bottom, from which it is drained and recovered for reuse.

Figure 17	Cyclone Oil Separator

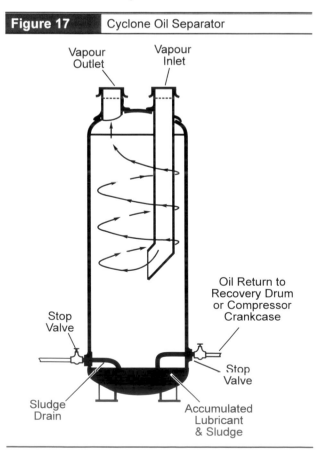

Figure 18 shows another type of oil separator, which uses an impingement principle.

Figure 18   Impingement Type Oil Separator

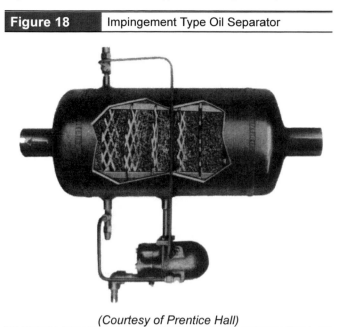

(Courtesy of Prentice Hall)

The separator has a series of baffles (or screens) through which the oil-laden refrigerant must pass. The velocity of the refrigerant vapour is considerably reduced, due to the larger area of the separator in relation to the inlet line. The oil particles, having a greater momentum than the refrigerant vapour, impinge on the baffle surfaces. The oil runs by gravity down the baffles and into the bottom of the separator, from where it returns, through a float valve, to the compressor inlet or crankcase, as shown in Figure 19.

Figure 19   Oil Return Piping to Compressor Crankcase

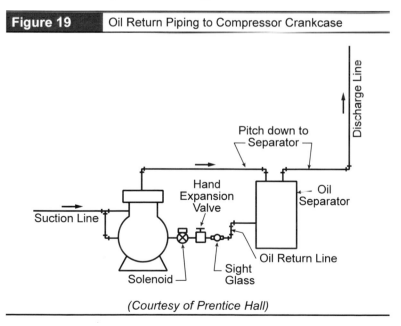

(Courtesy of Prentice Hall)

OIL STILL

Figure 20 shows an oil still incorporated into a refrigeration system. The still drives off any refrigerant that might be entrained with the oil that is drained from the oil separators, liquid receiver, coolers and evaporator. Refrigerant losses are reduced and the drained oil is more agreeable to handle.

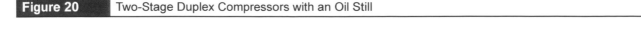

Figure 20   Two-Stage Duplex Compressors with an Oil Still

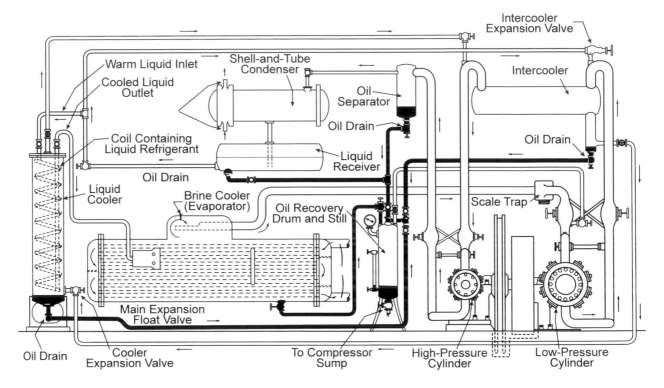

Figure 21 shows one form of still in which waste heat from condenser water or other convenient source is used to distil the vapour from the oil-refrigerant mixture. The vapour is led away to the compressor suction. The remaining oil is returned to the compressor sump.

In an oil still of this type, the oil and refrigerant mixture is made to boil very slowly, under compressor suction pressure, in a small diameter vessel of considerable height. Refrigerant vaporizes and rises to the top of the still. Some oil droplets will be entrained with the refrigerant, but these are separated at the top of the still and fall back into the oil at the bottom. The bottom oil is drained to a recovery drum or directly to the compressor sump.

Figure 21   Oil Still

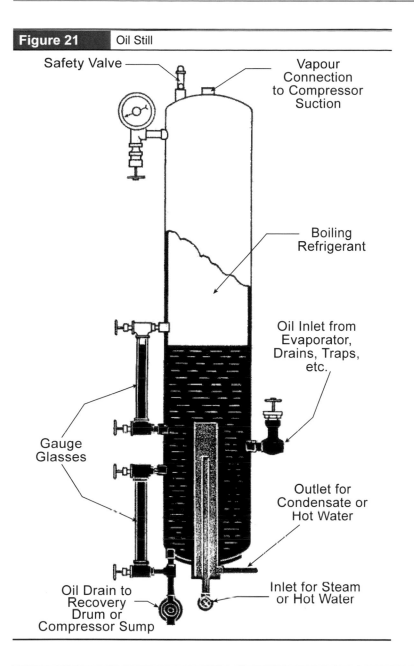

Safety Valve

Vapour Connection to Compressor Suction

Boiling Refrigerant

Oil Inlet from Evaporator, Drains, Traps, etc.

Gauge Glasses

Outlet for Condensate or Hot Water

Oil Drain to Recovery Drum or Compressor Sump

Inlet for Steam or Hot Water

REMOVING OIL FROM THE SYSTEM

All points at which lubricating oil accumulates in the refrigeration system must be drained at frequent intervals, to maintain efficient operation. A system of piping, as shown in Figure 20, is normally installed to connect all these points to a common oil receiver or recovery drum. This vessel must be designed to withstand the pressure in the high-pressure side of the system.

Before draining the oil, make sure that the drain valve on the recovery drum or still is closed, and then slightly open the line from the drum to the compressor suction. Each oil drain may now be separately drained to the drum. When all oil has been removed from a particular point, that valve should be closed before starting to drain another point.

Any refrigerant in the oil will boil off in the recovery drum and will return to the compressor suction. If the drum has a heating element, the refrigerant will boil off faster. This boiling action will be indicated by frost accumulation on the outside of the drum or still. When frosting ceases, close the vapour valve between the drum and the compressor suction and allow the oil to settle for about an hour. Then open the oil drain valve in the line to the compressor sump.

To drain the oil from an ammonia system that does not have an integral oil recovery arrangement is a fairly simple operation. The drain pipe from each point should be extended (using a rubber hose) into a pail of water. The water will absorb any ammonia that might escape with the oil and will minimize the pungent odour. Crack the drain valve and allow the accumulated oil to blow into the water. When a crackling sound occurs, it is an indication that the oil has been drawn off completely and that ammonia vapour is condensing in the water. When this happens, shut the valve.

The oil may appear as milky foam in the pail. After standing for a short time, clear oil should float on the surface. If this oil appears discoloured, it may not be suitable for re-use. A laboratory analysis should be done and if the oil has experienced little deterioration it should filtered (to remove dirt and scale) then re-used.

If the drained oil, after standing in the pail, floats on top of the water but remains milky looking, it is most likely that water or brine has leaked into the system. Steps should be taken to locate and stop this leak.

The frequency at which oil is drained will depend upon the size of the trap and the amount of oil that usually enters the system. The amount and rate at which oil level is lost from the compressor crankcase is a good indication of how often the oil drains should receive attention.

OBJECTIVE 4

Explain the effects and location of non-condensable gases. Describe the operation of manual and automatic purge devices.

NON-CONDENSABLE GASES

One cause of high discharge pressure at the compressor is the presence of non-condensable gases in the system. This is primarily air that has leaked into the system, plus other gases that result from impurities in the refrigerant or the breakdown of lubricating oil.

The high discharge pressure caused by the non-condensable gases results in higher power consumption by the compressor and a reduction in compressor capacity. Also, compressor parts will be stressed more and the higher temperatures that accompany the higher pressures will be detrimental to the compressor valves and lubricating oil.

Most of the gases tend to collect at the highest point of the condenser, but some of the heavier gases will accumulate at the bottom of the condenser and find their way into the receiver. Here they will separate from the liquid refrigerant and collect at the top of the receiver.

Non-condensable gases may be removed from the system by purging, either manually or automatically. Some form of purge should be fitted to the condenser, the receiver, and located in a system where experience has shown that non-condensable gases are prone to accumulate.

MANUAL PURGING

The simplest purge is a manual blow-off valve, which may be opened by the operator as required. The purged gases may go directly to the atmosphere or, since the process may also incur loss of refrigerant, it is more usual to purge a system in a manner that will reduce or eliminate refrigerant loss while purging.

There is a variety of purging devices that use refrigeration to condense the refrigerant vapour and separate it from the non-condensable gases. The condensed refrigerant returns to the receiver, while the non-condensable gases are vented to the atmosphere.

Figure 22 shows a manually operated purger that must receive regular attention from the operator.

The purger is connected to the condenser and the receiver, with a separate purge valve for each since each should be purged separately. The purge operation (for each location) is as follows, starting with all valves closed.

- Open the suction valve and the vapour inlet valve. Refrigerant vapour, containing the non-condensable elements, will then enter the purge housing.

- Partially open the expansion valve to admit liquid refrigerant into the coil. Since the purger is open to the compressor suction, the liquid will evaporate and cool the surrounding gases to a temperature that corresponds to the compressor suction pressure. The refrigerant vapour in the purger will now condense.

- When a liquid level appears in the upper sight glass, close the hand expansion valve and open the liquid drain valve to permit the refrigerant condensate to pass through the coil to the compressor suction.

- When a liquid level is seen at the lower sight glass, close the liquid drain and vapour inlet valves and then open the purge valve to vent the gases to atmosphere, through the water beaker. The water enables purged gas to be seen and also seals the system to prevent air entering.

- When no more purge gas is evident, close the purge valve.

- Repeat the procedure until the temperature on the thermometer matches the saturation temperature for the pressure shown on the pressure gauge.

- Repeat the entire procedure for each of the purge points.

Figure 22   Non-Condensable Gas Purge

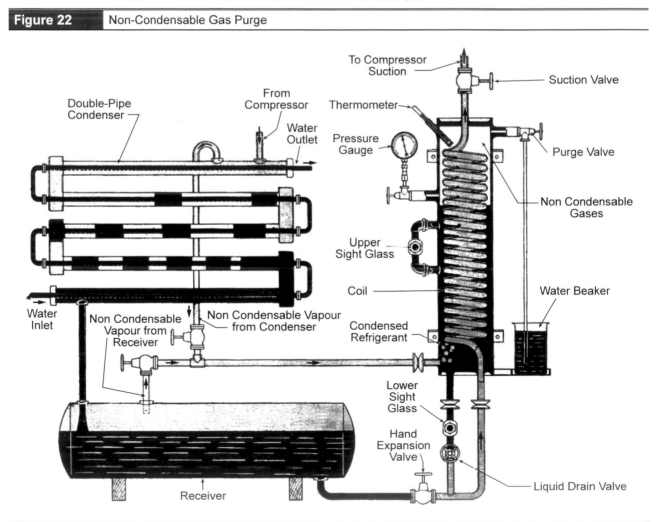

AUTOMATIC PURGING

Most systems use automatic purging rather than manual purging. Figure 23 shows the basics of a simple automatic purger.

- Non-condensable gases from the top of the condenser or receiver, together with some refrigerant vapour, enter the purger and collect under the inverted bucket trap, holding the bucket up. This closes the liquid supply valve attached to the bucket.

- The gases and vapour then slowly escape through a vent hole in the top of the bucket, causing the bucket to lose buoyancy and sink, which opens the liquid supply valve.

- Liquid fills the purger, causing the air relief trap valve to be closed by the float.

- The non-condensable gases displace the liquid at the top of the purger and the liquid level drops. This causes the air relief trap float to fall and open the air relief trap valve.

- The non-condensable gases then leave the top of the purger.

- When more air and gases enter the purger they will raise the inverted bucket, thus closing the liquid valve and the process repeats itself.

- Any refrigerant vapour entrained with the gases is condensed by the cooling action of refrigerant passing through the refrigeration coil and thus prevented from escaping with the gases.

Figure 23	Automatic Purger

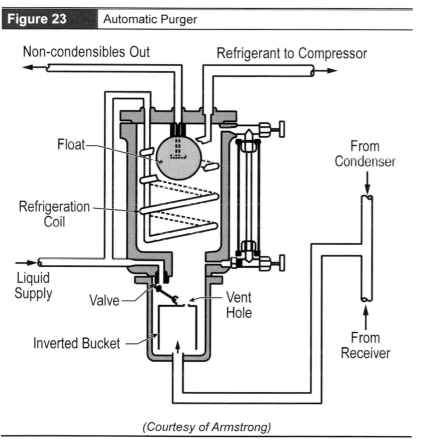

(Courtesy of Armstrong)

OBJECTIVE 5

Explain the effects of moisture in a refrigeration system and describe its removal.

MOISTURE IN SYSTEM

Moisture will combine with most of the common refrigerants, forming highly corrosive compounds (usually acids) that will react adversely with the lubricating oil and with other materials in the system, including metals. This may cause pitting and other damage to valves, seals, bearing journals, cylinder walls, and other polished surfaces. It may deteriorate the lubricating oil and form sludges that tend to clog valves and oil passages, score bearing surfaces, and generally reduce equipment life. Moisture corrosion also contributes to compressor valve failure.

The moisture content must be maintained below a harmful level. The minimum level that will produce harmful effects is not clearly defined and will vary considerably with the nature of the refrigerant, the quality of the lubricating oil, and the operating temperature of the system.

Moisture may exist as "free water" or it may be in solution with the refrigerant. Free water will freeze in the refrigeration control (expansion valve) and/or the evaporator, if the evaporator is below the freezing point of water. Ice in the expansion valve will prevent the flow of refrigerant and render the system inoperable until the ice melts and flow is restored. In fact, refrigeration is usually intermittent as the flow of liquid starts and stops due to the alternate melting and freezing in the expansion valve.

Refrigerants differ greatly in the amount of moisture they can hold in solution and in the effect the moisture has on them. For example, the straight hydrocarbon refrigerants, such as propane, ethane, and butane, absorb little if any moisture. Therefore, any moisture in these systems will be free water and will freeze in the refrigerant control. This moisture must be removed immediately to keep the system operative, so moisture corrosion is not usually a problem with these refrigerants.

Ammonia, on the other hand, has an affinity for water and is capable of absorbing moisture in such large quantities that free water is seldom a problem. However, the combination of water and ammonia produces aqueous ammonia, a strong alkali that attacks nonferrous metals (such as brass and copper) but has little effect on iron, steel or other system materials.

Corrosion will not occur in systems using halocarbon refrigerants when the moisture content is maintained below the level that will cause freezing, providing that high quality lubricating oils are used and that discharge temperature are reasonably low.

Despite the care taken at the factory and during installation, there is always some moisture present in a new system. To combat this it is common to install a dehydrator (dryer) in the system, usually in the liquid line immediately upstream of the expansion valve. The dryer is a container filled with a drying agent, such as silica gel or activated alumina, which must be compatible with the refrigerant. It has a strainer or screen at each end. As the liquid refrigerant passes through the dryer, the drying agent absorbs any moisture and acid that may be present. The drying agent must be replaced when it can hold no more moisture.

Figure 24 shows a dehydrator with a replaceable cartridge containing the drying agent.

Figure 24	Refrigerant Dehydrator

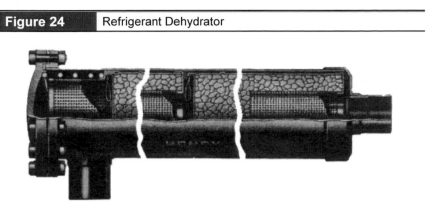

(Courtesy of Henry Valve Co.)

OBJECTIVE 6

Explain leak testing of a system and describe the procedure for adding refrigerant.

SYSTEM LEAK TESTING

A new refrigeration installation must be thoroughly tested, to locate and repair any refrigerant leaks to atmosphere. There are several methods of leak testing.

Inert Gas Testing

Testing with an inert gas is done before the system is charged with refrigerant. An inert gas is charged into the system and all joints and possible leak sources are checked.

One recommended inert gas is oil-pumped dry nitrogen, which is nitrogen gas that has been pumped through oil to remove any moisture present. The nitrogen gas is supplied in pressurized cylinders. Another common test gas is dry carbon dioxide, which is also supplied in cylinders.

⚠ WARNING

Do not use oxygen or any flammable gas, such as acetylene, for pressure testing, as explosions may result.

Assuming the testing medium to be used is dry nitrogen, then proceed as follows:

- Remove control and relief valves that may be damaged by the test pressure and isolate the compressor, by shutting the discharge and suction valves.
- Open the liquid line valve (king valve) and expansion valve, so that both the high and low-pressure sides of the system may be tested together, initially.
- Connect the nitrogen cylinder to the system at a point between the compressor discharge valve and the liquid line valve. The nitrogen cylinder should be equipped with a shut off valve, a pressure-reducing valve or regulator, a cylinder pressure gauge, a line pressure gauge and a bleed valve. The arrangement is shown in Figure 25.
- Set the pressure reducing valve for the required low side pressure, as given in Table 4 of CSA B52. For example, if the refrigerant to be used is ammonia R-717, the low side pressure would be 951 kPa; if the refrigerant is R-12, the low side pressure would be 579 kPa.
- Open the cylinder valve and feed nitrogen into the system. When the line pressure reaches the required low side pressure, then shut off the cylinder. The compressor suction line gauge should also read this pressure since the high and low sides of the system are interconnected via the liquid line and expansion valves.
- The high side of the system must now be tested at the required high side pressure, as given in Table 4 of CSA B52. This pressure is 1473 kPa for R-717 and 875 kPa for R-12. To test the high side, first shut the expansion valve, thus separating the high and the low sides. Then, set the cylinder pressure-reducing valve for the required high side pressure and open the cylinder shut-off valve. When the line pressure gauge reads the required pressure, close the cylinder shut-off valve, again.
- Now the high and low sides of the system are both at their required test pressures.
- Test all pipe joints in the system for leaks by brushing a soap solution around each joint. Leaks will be indicated by the presence of bubbles.

- After the testing, bleed off the nitrogen from the high side using the bleed valve at the cylinder. When the high side pressure equals the low side pressure, open the expansion valve and let the nitrogen bleed off from both the high and the low sides.

- When the system is totally depressurized, repair any leaks that were discovered during the test.

Figure 25	Nitrogen Cylinder Hook-Up

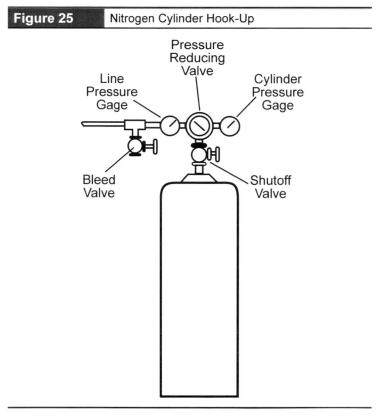

Halide Torch Leak Detecting

If the refrigerant used is a halogen refrigerant (Freon) such as R 12 or R 22, a halide torch test may be used. The leak detector consists of a torch that burns acetylene, propane, or alcohol. At the tip (flame area) of the torch is a copper reactor plate, which becomes heated by the flame. Normally the flame will burn blue, but if there is any halogen refrigerant present the reaction with copper will turn the flame green. The general test procedure is as follows:

- Admit a small amount of refrigerant into the system.

- Using dry nitrogen, pressurize the low and high sides to their required test pressures.

- Check all joints with the halide leak detector. Hold the free end of the rubber tube at the joint, allowing any leakage to flow up the tube and into the flame area. Observe the flame closely for any change in color.

- If no leaks are discovered with the halide torch, leave the system pressurized for 24 hours. Disconnect the nitrogen cylinder when leaving the system unattended. If this is not done the system could become over-pressurized if nitrogen leaks into the system.

- If after the 24-hour period there is no change in the system pressure, then the system can be considered tight. Bleed the nitrogen/refrigerant mixture from both sides of the system and re-install any controls or valves that were removed for the test.

- The system is now ready for charging.

Figure 26 shows a halide torch leak detector.

Figure 26	Halide Torch

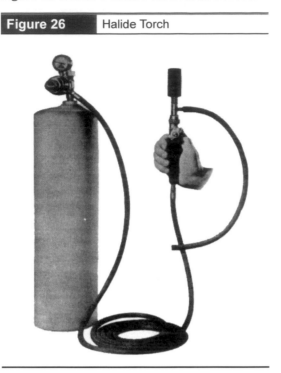

Electronic Leak Detector

The most sensitive of all leak detector types is the electronic detector, as shown in Figure 27.

Figure 27	Electronic Leak Detector

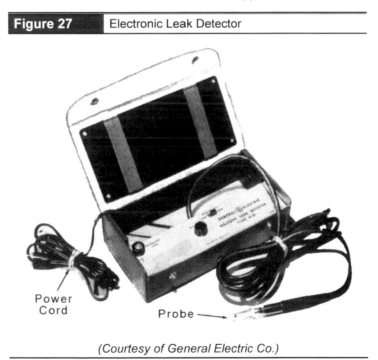

Power
Cord

Probe

(Courtesy of General Electric Co.)

This instrument is of the dielectric type, which samples the surrounding air and only responds to halogen gas.

Referring to Figure 28:

- The instrument is turned on and calibrated in a normal atmosphere.
- The leak-detecting probe is then passed over the joint being tested. If there is a leak the halogenated refrigerant is drawn into the leak sample intake side. The instrument will alarm, since the new gas changes the resistance in the circuit.

Figure 28	Schematic of Electronic Leak Detector

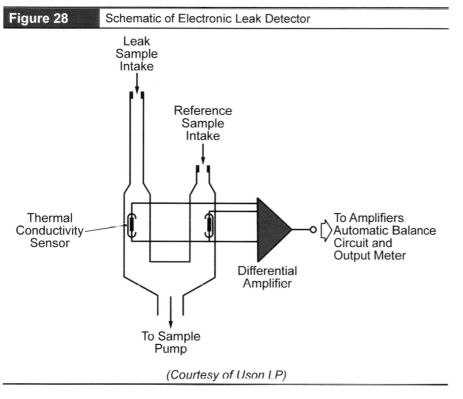

(Courtesy of Uson LP)

ADDING REFRIGERANT

The steps for adding refrigerant to a new system or after major maintenance are as follows:

- Before admitting any refrigerant, the entire system is put under a very high vacuum. This is to remove any moisture in the system. The vacuum will cause the moisture to evaporate and it can then be removed in vapour form. A special vacuum pump should be used to produce the high vacuum. The system compressor should not be used; the moisture and foreign materials in the system could damage compressor valves.

- After the high vacuum is established, break the vacuum by admitting dry nitrogen gas. Then use the vacuum pump to evacuate the nitrogen gas from the system, again producing a high vacuum. This second evacuation removes the last traces of moisture, so the system is now ready for charging.

- Check the entire system, including the compressor and controls, to ensure it is ready, for operation.

- Connect the refrigerant drum to the liquid charging valve, which is located in the liquid line between the liquid shut-off valve and the expansion valve.

- With the connection at the liquid charging valve left loose, crack open the drum valve and allow refrigerant gas to blow through the charging line and out the loose connection. This purges any air from the charging line.

- Tighten the connection at the charging valve and invert the refrigerant drum. This arrangement is shown in Figure 29.

- Close liquid shut-off valve and open the expansion valve; the drum valve will act as an expansion valve.

- Turn on the condenser water supply; if the evaporator is used to cool brine (an indirect system), start brine circulation.

- Open the liquid charging valve.

- Open the drum valve sufficiently to allow the refrigerant to slowly flow into the system.

- Start the compressor and let the refrigerant feed steadily to the system until the correct amount has been added. The correct amount may be determined by weighing the refrigerant drum during the charging period. If the receiver has a sight glass, check the level.

- When the correct amount of refrigerant has been added, close the drum valve and the liquid charging valve.

- Open the liquid shut-off valve. The expansion valve should now be controlling the flow of refrigerant to the evaporator.

- Check the entire system for normal operation. If everything is satisfactory, disconnect the charging line, taking precautions, as the line will contain some refrigerant under pressure.

After the system has been operating for some time, it may be necessary to add small amounts of refrigerant periodically. In this case, the refrigerant is usually added in its gaseous state by connecting the drum, in an upright position, to the suction line of the compressor. When using this method, care must be taken that no liquid refrigerant is carried over from the drum to the compressor.

Note: When handling refrigerants, WEAR GOGGLES. Even the "safe" refrigerants can cause serious injury by freezing the moisture in the eyes.

Figure 29 Charging Hook-Up

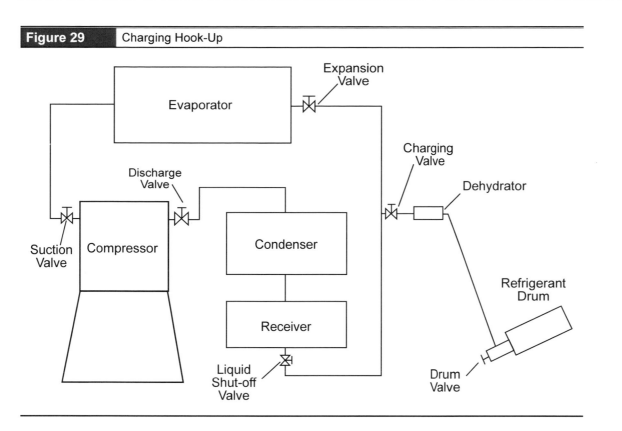

OBJECTIVE 7

Explain the principles of brine control in an indirect system and explain the procedures for charging and controlling brine strength.

BRINE CONTROL

Brine is the solution that results when various salts are dissolved in water. The freezing temperature of the brine is lower than that of water alone. In general, the greater the salt concentration, the lower will be the freezing point of the brine. However, if the salt concentration goes beyond a certain point, the freezing point of the brine will actually increase, rather than decrease.

Therefore, a solution of any salt in water has a certain concentration at which the freezing point is the lowest. A concentrated solution at this critical point is called a **eutectic** solution. At any mixture above and below this critical concentration, the freezing temperature of the solution will be higher, that is above the eutectic temperature.

- If the brine is too weak (ie. too much water), the excess water will begin to precipitate from the solution in the form of ice crystals.
- Conversely, if the brine is too strong (ie. the salt concentration is in excess of the amount required for a eutectic solution) the excess salt will begin to precipitate from the solution in the form of salt crystals

Figure 30 shows the relationship between the freezing point and salt concentration for sodium chloride (NaCl) brine. A Salometer is a type of hydrometer that is used to indicate the percentage of salt in a solution.

Figure 30	Freezing Point of Salt Brine Mixtures

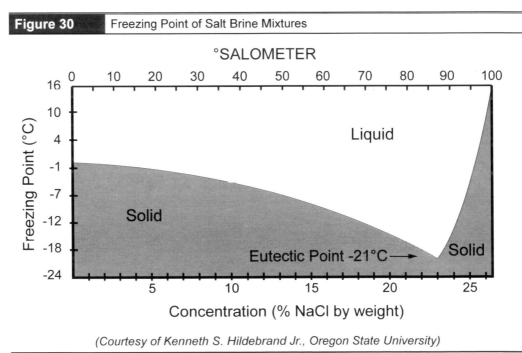

(Courtesy of Kenneth S. Hildebrand Jr., Oregon State University)

As Figure 30 shows, the lowest freezing point obtainable for sodium chloride brine is -21°C. This occurs at a concentration of 23%, by weight.

If the brine is calcium chloride and water, the lowest freezing point obtainable is -51°C, at a concentration of 29.87%, by weight.

SYSTEM CHARGING & CONTROLLING BRINE STRENGTH

If it becomes necessary to strengthen the brine or to add brine to the system after the initial charge, the brine charging valve, located between the brine shutoff valves and the system is used. A brine-mixing tank is used and a connection is made from the bottom of the tank to the brine charging valve adjacent to the pump suction. This outlet connection should be protected by a suitable screen to prevent solids being drawn into the system. Another line from the brine-charging valve, adjacent to the outlet of the chiller, feeds back into the top of the mixing tank.

To add new brine to the system:

- Fill the mixing tank with fresh water
- Add flaked calcium chloride and stir until the calcium chloride is completely dissolved.
- Use a hydrometer to determine the specific gravity of the brine. If necessary add more calcium chloride until the specific gravity is at least 1.2.
- Start the brine pump and open the charging valve on the pump suction. This will allow brine to be drawn into the system.
- When the mixing tank is drawn down, close the charging valve open the main line valve to allow adequate mixing of the new brine with the old.
- If the brine requires further strengthening, open the brine charging valve on the pump discharge, with the pump operating, allowing the mixing tank to fill with weak brine from the system. Add more calcium chloride and then draw it back into the system as new brine.

OBJECTIVE 8

Explain refrigeration safety and environmental issues.

REFRIGERATION SAFETY

Regulations

There are special regulations in every Province dealing with refrigerating plants and every engineer in charge of such a plant should be familiar with these regulations. A few of the most important Regulations are outlined in the following paragraphs as taken from Canadian Standards Association B 52, which is recognized as law in most Provinces.

Emergency Discharge

All systems designed for operation over 103 kPa and containing 182 kg or more of Group A1 or 91 kg or more of all other refrigerants shall be constructed so that in case of emergency the refrigerant can be discharged by a manually operated valve into the atmosphere.

The emergency discharge line shall be connected directly to the top of the receiver or other vessel used for storing the refrigerant. There shall be no other valve between the emergency valve and the vessel.

The emergency valve shall be installed in a glass fronted box painted bright red, outside of the building and so placed that it cannot be tampered with by any other than the person called upon to open the valve in an emergency.

The emergency line shall be provided with a diffuser at its upper end which shall be placed above the roof and set back from the roof edge and also not less than a radius of 7.6 m from any windows or other openings.

The manually operated emergency valve shall be installed on a horizontal pipe outside the building.

Design & Construction

Every refrigerant containing part of every item that is erected on the premises, except compressors, condensers, evaporators, safety devices, pressure gauges, control mechanisms and systems that are factory tested, shall be tested and proved tight after complete installation and before operation.

The high or low side of each system shall be tested and proved tight at not less than the lower of the design pressure (see Table 4 of the CSA B52-05 Mechanical Refrigeration Code) or the setting of the pressure relief device protecting the high or low side of the system, respectively.

Pressure Limiting Devices

Pressure limiting devices shall be provided on all systems operating above atmospheric pressure, except that a pressure-limiting device may be omitted on any factory-sealed system that contains less than 10 kg of Group A1 refrigerant and has been listed by an approved testing laboratory.

On systems with no pressure relieving device, the setting of the pressure-limiting device shall not exceed the high-side design pressure; on systems with a pressure relieving device, the setting of the pressure-limiting device shall not exceed 90% of the high-side design pressure.

Figure 31   Pressure Limiting Devices

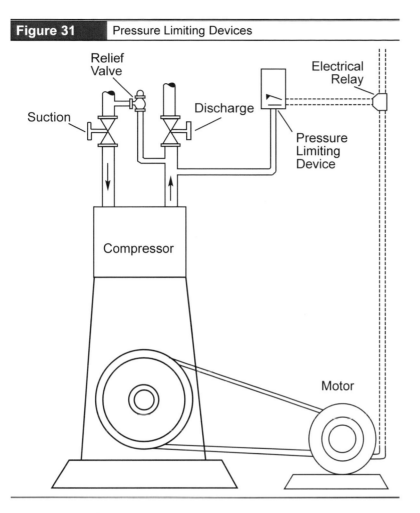

Pressure Gauges

Pressure gauges shall be checked for accuracy prior to testing and immediately after every occasion of unusually high pressure, by comparison with master gauges or by using a dead weight tester.

When the gauge is permanently installed on the high side of a system, the dial of the gauge must be graduated up to double the operating pressure, but in no case less than 1.2 times the design working pressure.

Pressure Relief Devices

(also see page 11-15)

Every refrigerating system shall be protected by a pressure relief device or some other means designed to safely relieve pressure due to fire or other abnormal conditions.

All pressure relief devices shall be directly pressure actuated. A pressure relief device shall protect each part of a refrigerating system, which can be valved off and contains one or more pressure vessels having internal diameters greater than 152 mm and containing liquid refrigerant.

Stop valves shall not be located between the means of pressure relief and the part or parts of the system protected thereby.

All pressure relief devices and fusible plugs shall be connected, as nearly as practicable, directly to the pressure vessel or other parts of the system being protected, above the liquid refrigerant level. They must be installed so that they are readily accessible for inspection and repair and so that they cannot be readily rendered inoperative. Fusible plugs may be located above or below the liquid refrigerant level, except on the low side.

The seats and discs of pressure relief devices shall be constructed of suitable material to resist refrigerant corrosion or other chemical action caused by the refrigerant. Seats or discs of cast iron shall not be used.

All pressure relief valves shall be set to start to function at a pressure not to exceed the design pressure of the parts of the system, being protected.

All rupture members used in lieu of, or in series with a relief valve, shall have a nominal rated rupture pressure not to exceed the design pressure of the parts of the system being protected.

Discharge of Pressure Relief Devices

Discharge of pressure relief devices shall be to the outside of the building in an approved manner, as shown in Figure 32. Figure 32 also illustrates a method that can be used to empty the contents, of a refrigeration system, in the case of an emergency.

Figure 32	Pressure Relief Devices Discharge

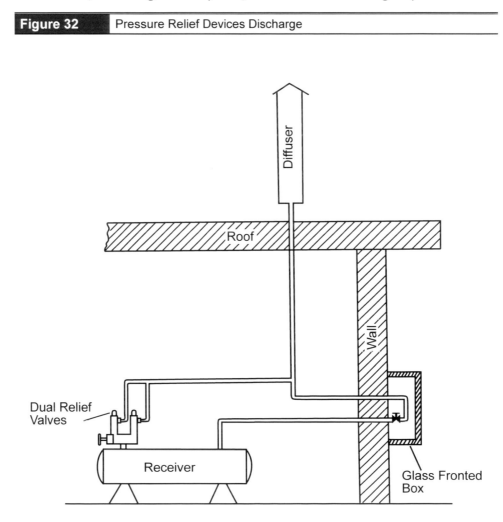

Pressure relief valves may also discharge into the low side of the system, provided the pressure relief devices are of a type not appreciably affected by back pressures and provided the low side of the system is equipped with pressure relief devices. The relief devices on the low side of the system shall have sufficient capacity to protect the pressure vessels that are relieving into the low side of the system, or to protect all pressure vessels on the low side of the system, whichever relieving capacity is the largest.

Figure 33 shows an alternate arrangement for the discharge of pressure relief valves, which is permissible if the refrigerant is ammonia. With this system, the water in a tank, which shall be used for no other purpose, absorbs the discharged ammonia. This method can be used as an alternative to discharging directly into the atmosphere.

At least 10 litres of fresh water must be provided for every 1 kg of ammonia, in the system, and this water shall be prevented from freezing without the use of salt or other chemicals. The tank must be vented or have a hinged cover and all pipe connections shall be through the top of the tank, only. The discharge valve shall discharge the ammonia into the center of the tank near the bottom.

Figure 33	Ammonia System Relief Valves Discharge

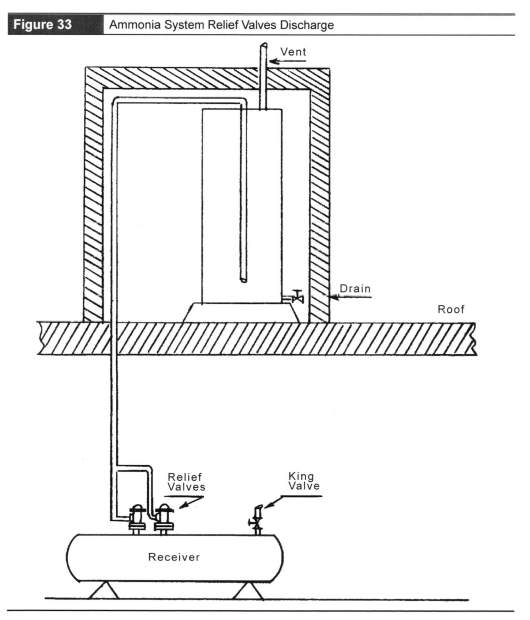

Protective Equipment

CSA B52, Clause 9.1.1, states that "The owner of a refrigeration system shall apply and maintain for its employees, the personal protective equipment required by the jurisdiction where the system is located."

In Clause 9.1.2 it further states that "Installation and service personnel working on a refrigeration system shall be equipped, on arrival at the premises, with the personal protective equipment required by the jurisdiction where the system is located."

NOTE: In the practical handbook, B52HB-05, the CSA qualifies the above clauses by saying that the details of protective equipment are left to each jurisdiction and that persons should contact their own provincial or territorial jurisdictional for those details.

Enclosed Spaces

CSA B52, Clause 9.2, requires that any enclosed space (cold storage room) that provides a means for entry and has a refrigeration system at temperatures detrimental to health shall have a door that can be readily opened from the inside and at least one of the following protective measures:

a) a suitable alarm system operable from within the refrigerated room

b) a second door or knockout panel readily opened from within the refrigerated room"

NOTE: If other personnel are not available at all time to respond to an alarm, then b) must be provided.

Posting of Instructions

CSA B52, Clause 5.11.5, states that, "The owner of a refrigeration system or systems with a prime mover or movers having a capacity exceeding 125 kW must place in a conspicuous location, as near as practical to the refrigerant compressor, a card giving directions for operating the system, including precautions in case of breakdown or leakage, as follows:

a) phone number of first response organization for an emergency situation;

b) instructions for shutting down in case of emergency;

c) name, address, and phone numbers for obtaining service, and

d) name. address, and phone number of nearest regulatory authority, and instructions to notify this authority in case of emergency."

CHAPTER 11 - QUESTIONS

1. Explain the differences between the two types of refrigeration thermostats.

2. With the aid of a simple sketch, describe the use of a fusible plug.

3. Using a simple sketch, explain the principal of operation of a cyclone separator that is used to remove oil from the refrigeration gas.

4. Using a simple sketch, explain the principal of operation of an oil still.

5. Discuss the following, pertaining to the buildup of noncondensable gases, in the refrigeration system:
   a) Sources of these gases
   b) Different means used to remove these gases
   c) Results of allowing these gases to stay in the system

6. How will the accumulation of moisture affect the refrigeration system and what means are used to remove this moisture?

7. With the aid of a sketch, describe a method that can be used to complete a pressure test of the entire system.

8. What is meant by the term "eutectic temperature" of a brine solution?

9. With the aid of a sketch, describe a method of safely removing the contents of an ammonia refrigeration system.

ANSWERS: All answers are found within the content of the chapter.

Heat Exchangers & Cooling Towers

LEARNING OUTCOME

When you complete this chapter you should be able to:

Describe the design, operation, and applications of various types of industrial heat exchangers.

LEARNING OBJECTIVES

Here is what you should be able to do when you complete each objective:

1. Describe double pipe heat exchangers, including jacketed pipe, U-tube, and concentric pipe designs.

2. Describe shell-and-tube heat exchangers including fixed straight tube and U-tube designs. Describe common front and rear head designs, shell flow configurations, and explain the purpose of baffles.

3. Explain the operation and the typical fittings/equipment on the steam/condensate side of a reboiler and a feed water heater.

4. Describe the design and operation of a plate-and-frame exchanger.

5. Describe the design and components of overhead, aerial coolers, including fan and cooler arrangements. Explain cooler control.

6. Describe the design and components, including controls, of an overhead, aerial condenser. Explain condenser operation, control and precautions when used to condense excess steam.

7. Describe the design and explain the operation of natural draft cooling towers, including atmospheric and hyperbolic styles.

8. Describe the design and operation of mechanical draft cooling towers, including forced draft, induced draft counterflow, and induced draft crossflow.

OBJECTIVE 1

Describe double pipe heat exchangers, including jacketed pipe, U-tube, and concentric pipe designs.

DOUBLE PIPE HEAT EXCHANGERS

A double-pipe exchanger is basically a pipe (or bundle of pipes) within a larger pipe. The hot and cold fluids do not come into direct contact with each other. The heat exchanged flows from one fluid to the outer surface of the pipe, through the pipe wall, and then from the inside surface of the pipe to the second fluid. The fluid flows may be co-current (both flowing in the same direction) or counter-current (flowing in opposite directions).

Figure 1 shows a jacketed pipe, which is the simplest arrangement of a double pipe exchanger. It consists of an inner pipe surrounded by another larger diameter pipe, which forms an annulus space around the inner pipe. The outer pipe is often welded directly to the inner pipe, with caps at each end. An inlet and outlet connection is then welded to the outer pipe. Figure 1 is a counter-current design. One example of this design is a steam-jacketed line, where steam fills the outer pipe and is used to heat a process fluid in the inner pipe.

Figure 1	Basic Double Pipe Heat Exchanger

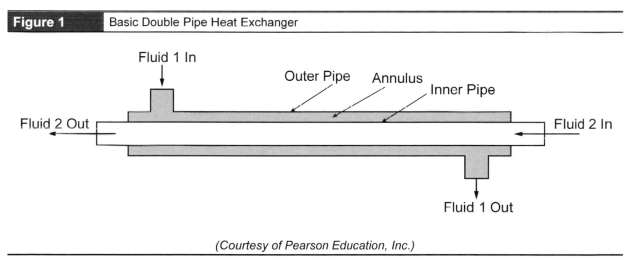

(Courtesy of Pearson Education, Inc.)

Concentric Pipe Heat Exchanger

Figure 1 could be called a concentric pipe heat exchanger, which implies a single inner pipe located concentrically inside a larger outer pipe. There are more complicated versions of this arrangement. The inner pipe may be plain or it may have fins or studs attached. These increase the efficiency of the exchanger by increasing the heat transfer surface.

Figure 2 shows typical fin and stud attachments.

Figure 2	Fin Construction Details

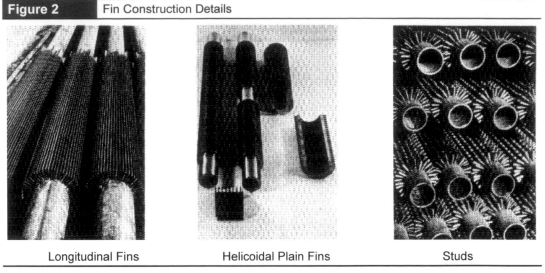

Longitudinal Fins	Helicoidal Plain Fins	Studs

Rather than a single inner pipe, there may be several smaller pipes (tubes), connected by tubesheets at each end. This also increases efficiency since several tubes provide greater total heat transfer surface than a single tube. This is illustrated in Figure 3, which shows a cross-sections of a bundle with seven bare tubes, and a bundle with seven fin tubes.

Figure 3	Double Pipe Exchanger with Inner Tube Bundle

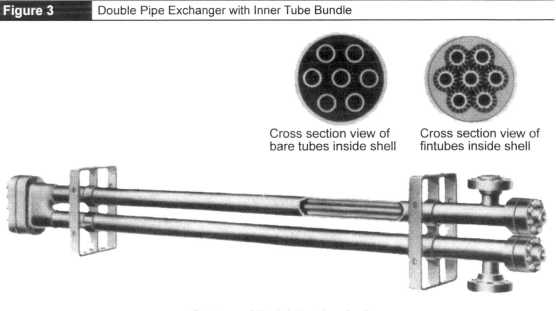

Cross section view of bare tubes inside shell   Cross section view of fintubes inside shell

(Courtesy of Koch Industries, Inc.)

Hairpin (Serpentine) Exchangers

The term "hairpin exchanger" refers to an arrangement of double pipe exchangers, which takes the appearance of a hairpin or several hairpins joined together. These arrangements are often referred to as "serpentine" because of their snake-like configuration. Several double pipe exchangers are joined together in such a way that the length of the flow path for both the inner and outer flows is much longer. This provides the opportunity for longer retention time and, therefore, greater overall heat transfer between the two fluids.

Figure 4(a) shows a single hairpin arrangement. In this case the inner fluid is water, which is used to cool oil in the outer pipe. The inner pipes (or tube bundles) are connected by return bends at each end. The outer pipes are connected by return bends and flanged tees.

Figure 4(b) shows how several hairpins may be joined together to form a much larger exchanger.

Figure 4   a) Hairpin Joined in Series

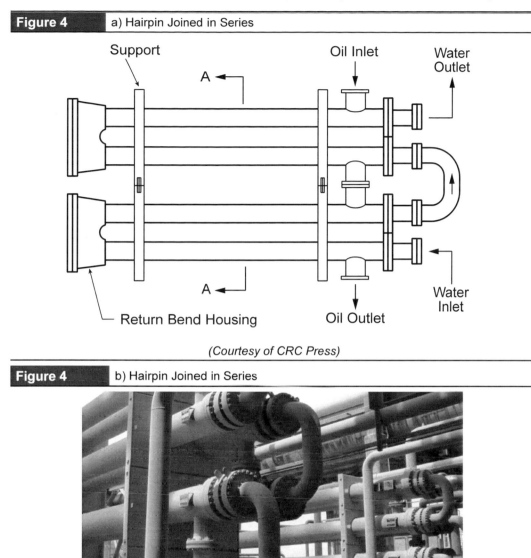

(Courtesy of CRC Press)

Figure 4   b) Hairpin Joined in Series

The advantages of double pipe exchangers include:

- Relatively simple construction compared to other designs
- Suitability for high pressures. The small diameters allow for stronger construction.
- Flexibility of configuration. Units can be added or removed to meet the design heat transfers, particularly in the hairpin designs. They are also flexible in connecting for co-current or counter-flow.
- Simple maintenance and replacement of sections, tube bundles, etc., compared to other designs.
- Compactness. The flexibility of arrangement allows for less floor space.
- Are very suited to situations where both fluids require a temperature change; one fluid to be heated and the other to be cooled.

The biggest disadvantage is the high number of joints, which increases the possibility of leaks.

OBJECTIVE 2

Describe shell-and-tube heat exchangers including fixed straight tube and U-tube designs. Describe common front and rear head designs, shell flow configurations, and explain the purpose of baffles.

SHELL-AND-TUBE HEAT EXCHANGERS

Shell-and-tube is the most common heat exchanger design. Its versatility allows designs to meet most applications. Shell and tube heat exchangers have large surface areas for heat transfer and can be constructed for high temperatures and pressures.

The shell-and-tube heat exchanger has an outer shell surrounding a bank or bundle of tubes, which are parallel to the longitudinal axis of the shell. Two principal types are:

- U-tube
- Fixed tube sheet

U-Tube Exchanger

The tubes in this shell and tube exchanger are U-shaped. Both ends of the U-shaped tubes are fixed to a single tubesheet. The construction of U-tube exchangers requires only one tube sheet joint to the shell. This is a great advantage since it eliminates the problems of differential thermal expansion. The shell and tubes can expand at different rates. This design is well suited to high temperature and high pressure applications.

Figure 5 shows the construction of a small U-tube exchanger, with threaded connection, much like would be used on an oil cooler.

Figure 5	U-Tube Heat Exchanger

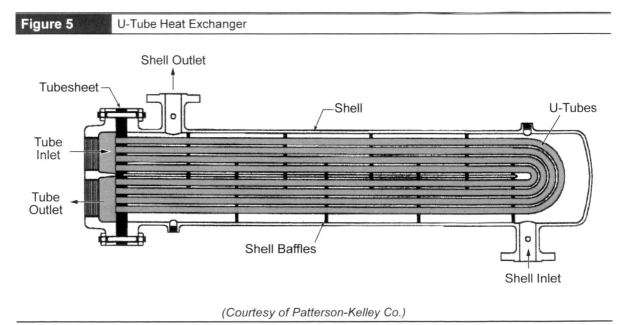

(Courtesy of Patterson-Kelley Co.)

Figure 6 illustrates a larger U-tube exchanger. In this case, a head is bolted to the open end of the shell and the tubesheet is held in place between the flanges. The head has inlet and outlet nozzles for the tubeside fluid and a horizontal partition, which directs the inlet flow into the tubes and separates it from the outlet flow. A cover is bolted to the head and can be removed for inspection and tube cleaning.

Figure 6	U-Tube Shell and Tube Heat Exchanger

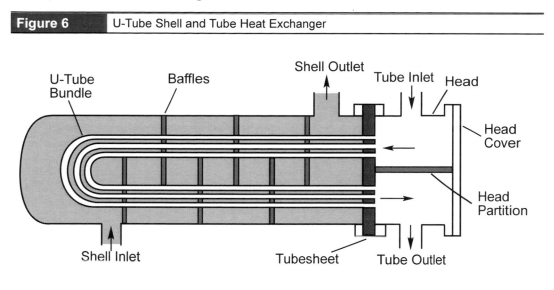

Another advantage of U-tube exchangers is that the tube bundle can be separated from the shell, giving access for inspection and cleaning of the shell interior. When the head is unbolted and removed the tubesheet can be slid out of the shell. The baffles, being attached to the tubes will slide out with the bundle.

Figure 7 shows a U-tube bundle partly removed from the shell.

Figure 7	U-Tube Bundle Removal

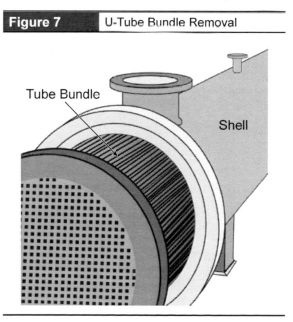

Figure 8 shows a stainless steel U-tube bundle and baffles, which have been totally removed from the shell.

Figure 8	U-Tube Bundle

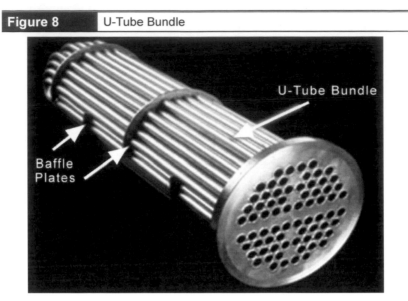

(Courtesy of Edmonton Exchanger)

A disadvantage of the U-Tube design, compared to a straight-tube design, is a reduction in heating surface. This is because when a straight tube is bent into a "U", the outer wall of the bend becomes thinner. To prevent excessive thinning and maintain design strength, a minimum bend radius must be adhered to and this creates larger spaces between tubes, limiting the number of tubes that can be fitted into a particular shell size.

U-Tube exchangers should always have the fouling (deposit forming) fluid on the shell side. Even thin deposits reduce the heat transfer so it is better to foul the shell than the inside of the tubes. A disadvantage of this is that the outside surface of the tubes cannot be easily cleaned and tube repair is restricted to only the outside rows. Damaged tubes are usually plugged off.

Floating Head Exchangers

The floating head shell-and-tube exchanger, shown in Figure 9, has an external fixed head and tubesheet plus an internal head and tubesheet that are free to slide (float) horizontally within the shell. Straight tubes connect the two tubesheets. This design allows the tubes to expand at different rates than the shell without applying stresses to the shell or tubes.

Figure 9	Floating Head Exchanger

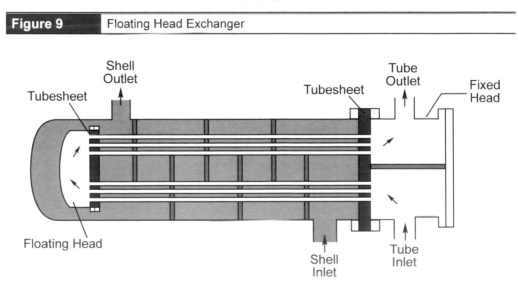

The floating head design allows the tube bundle to be removed for convenient inspection, cleaning and repair of the shell. It also allows for easier inspection and cleaning of the tubes by removing the floating head. Leaking tubes can be replaced, rather than just plugged. The biggest disadvantage is the possibility of leaks at the floating head flange.

Fixed Tube Sheet Exchangers

In this exchanger, the tubesheets are welded to the shell at both ends. The tubes are straight and either welded or expanded into the tubesheets. Access to the tubesheets is through flanged covers and/or heads at each end.

Figure 10 shows two common designs. Figure 10(a) is an exchanger that would be suitable for lower pressures on the tube side, allowing the end covers to be flat. The design in Figure 10(b) is suited for higher pressures on the tube side, with a dished head at each end.

Figure 10	Fixed Tubesheet Exchangers

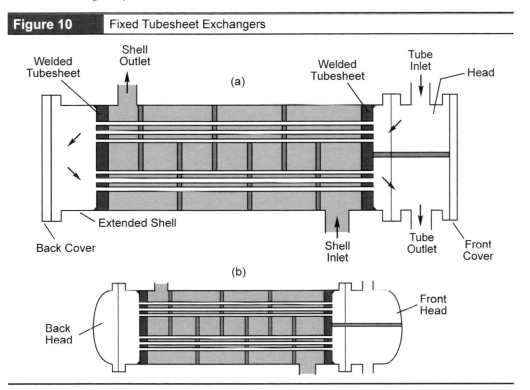

The advantages of the fixed tubesheet shell-and-tube exchanger include:

- Simplicity of design, which makes fabrication relatively simple and less costly.
- Tube maintenance, whether cleaning, plugging or replacing is relatively easy, due to the easy access and the straight-through design. Removing both end covers allows for easy inspection and cleaning. Brushes or high-pressure water jets can easily be run through the tubes. Individual tubes can be easily replaced.
- There is considerable flexibility in designing the number of passes through the tubes and the number and sizes of tubes that are fitted into the available shell space. Maximum heating surface can be created with minimal design restrictions.

There are some significant disadvantages to the design:

- If the temperature difference between the two fluids is very large, there will be unacceptable stresses in the tubes and the shell unless steps are taken to account for the unequal expansion and contraction. This often requires installing an expansion joint in the shell.
- Inspection, cleaning and repairs on the shell side are very difficult. Without removing the tube bundle, cleaning can only be done by chemical means. For full inspection and repairs the welds must be ground off to remove the tubesheets and tubes.
- Because of the difficult access to the shell side, this design is somewhat restricted to fouling fluids being only on the tubeside.

Head & Shell Designs

Figure 11 shows many of the head and shell designs available for shell-and-tube exchangers. The left column shows typical arrangements for front heads and the right column shows arrangements for rear heads. Some of the designs, particularly of floating heads, are somewhat intricate, but should be understandable from the brief captions given. The middle column shows various ways (and the corresponding terminology) that inlet and outlet nozzles can be attached to the shell. These, together with internal baffles, determine the flow pattern through the shell.

Figure 11   Types of Shell and Tube Heat Exchangers

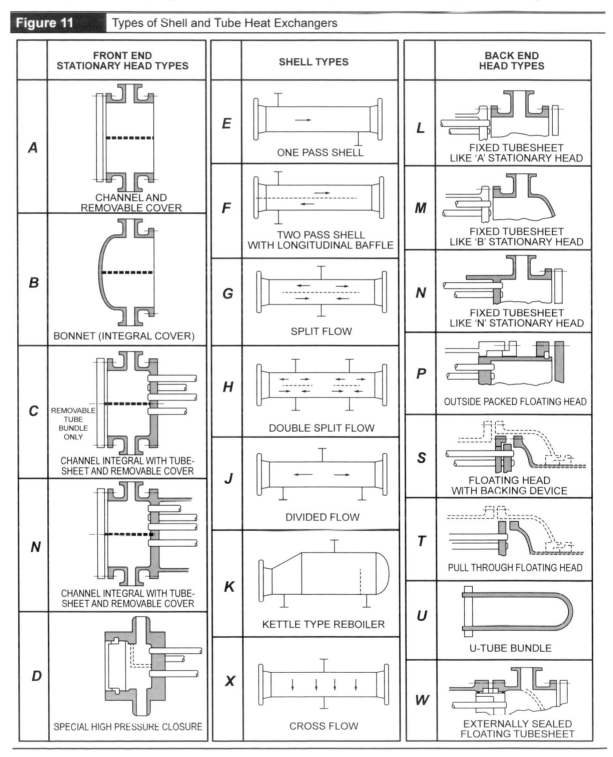

FRONT END STATIONARY HEAD TYPES	SHELL TYPES	BACK END HEAD TYPES
A — CHANNEL AND REMOVABLE COVER	**E** — ONE PASS SHELL	**L** — FIXED TUBESHEET LIKE 'A' STATIONARY HEAD
B — BONNET (INTEGRAL COVER)	**F** — TWO PASS SHELL WITH LONGITUDINAL BAFFLE	**M** — FIXED TUBESHEET LIKE 'B' STATIONARY HEAD
C — REMOVABLE TUBE BUNDLE ONLY — CHANNEL INTEGRAL WITH TUBE-SHEET AND REMOVABLE COVER	**G** — SPLIT FLOW	**N** — FIXED TUBESHEET LIKE 'N' STATIONARY HEAD
N — CHANNEL INTEGRAL WITH TUBE-SHEET AND REMOVABLE COVER	**H** — DOUBLE SPLIT FLOW	**P** — OUTSIDE PACKED FLOATING HEAD
	J — DIVIDED FLOW	**S** — FLOATING HEAD WITH BACKING DEVICE
D — SPECIAL HIGH PRESSURE CLOSURE	**K** — KETTLE TYPE REBOILER	**T** — PULL THROUGH FLOATING HEAD
		U — U-TUBE BUNDLE
	X — CROSS FLOW	**W** — EXTERNALLY SEALED FLOATING TUBESHEET

Baffles

Unless directed otherwise, the fluid in the shell would take the shortest path between the inlet and outlet connection of the shell, reducing the use of the available heating surface. Baffles are used to direct the shell fluid flow over tube surface to ensure heat transfer occurs in all parts of the shell. The baffles also increase the velocity and the turbulence of the flow, both of which improve heat transfer.

The most common baffles are flat plates, which are welded to the shell and drilled with holes through which the tubes are installed. An added benefit of this design is the support they provide for the tubes along their length.

Figure 12(a) shows one design, called segmental baffles because they are in the shape of segments of a circle. The flow is forced up and down as it alternately flows over and under adjacent baffles.

Figure 12(b) shows another baffle arrangement, called annular ring baffles. Alternating annular rings and central discs cause the flow to flow outwards and inwards as it progresses through the shell.

Figure 12	Shell Baffles

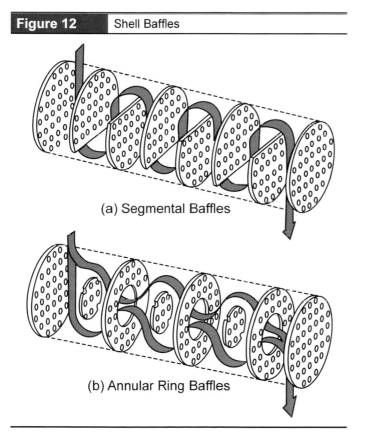

(a) Segmental Baffles

(b) Annular Ring Baffles

The horizontal distance or spacing between baffles is called the baffle pitch. It is a design consideration, since it affects the pressured drop between the inlet and outlet of the shell. The pitch is designed to maximize heat transfer without significantly increasing the pressure drop.

OBJECTIVE 3

Explain the operation and the typical fittings/equipment on the steam/condensate side of a reboiler and a feedwater heater.

REBOILERS

Reboilers are shell and tube heat exchangers found in gas processing and petrochemical plants. They consist of a shell with a tube bundle inside. Steam (or a heating liquid such as hot oil) flows through the tubes and vaporizes a process liquid that flows through the shell. The produced vapour collects in a vapour space above the tube bundle. Excess liquids that do not vaporize overflow a vertical weir plate, which ensures the tubes remain covered with liquid. The liquid leaves the bottom of the shell, while the vapours leave from the top.

There are three types of reboilers:

- kettle
- thermosyphon horizontal
- thermosyphon vertical

Kettle Type Reboiler

The kettle type reboiler (Fig. 13) provides flexibility and ease of control. It has a large liquid volume and is easily accessible for maintenance. This type of reboiler depends on gravity for circulation of the liquid through the unit, as shown in Figure 14. Liquid flows from the attached vessel into the bottom of the reboiler. The tubes remain flooded, while the level downstream of the weir is controlled by a level control valve. The reboiler vapours are returned to the attached vessel (in this case a fractionating tower) where it is used for heating and stripping vapour.

Figure 13	Kettle Type Reboiler

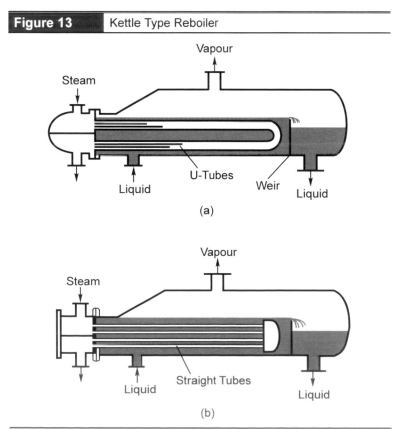

(a)

(b)

| Figure 14 | Kettle Reboiler Arrangement |

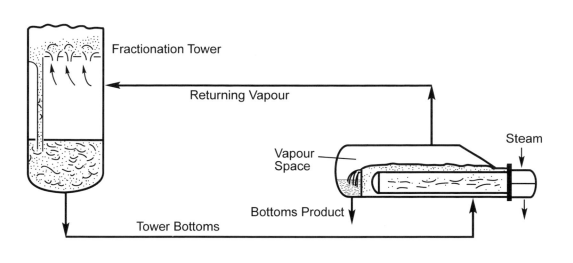

Horizontal Thermosyphon Reboiler

The horizontal thermosyphon reboiler (Fig. 15) has no vapour space above the tubes. The top of the exchanger is at a lower elevation than the liquid level in the bottom of the tower. This ensures that the entire shell is flooded completely, submerging all the tubes and a part of the return line in liquid hydrocarbon. When steam is supplied to the unit some of the liquid boils and the vapours return to the tower. The density of the liquid and vapours in the reboiler is less than the density of liquid in the tower, which causes continuous circulation (thermosyphon) to occur through the reboiler.

| Figure 15 | Horizontal Thermosyphon Reboiler |

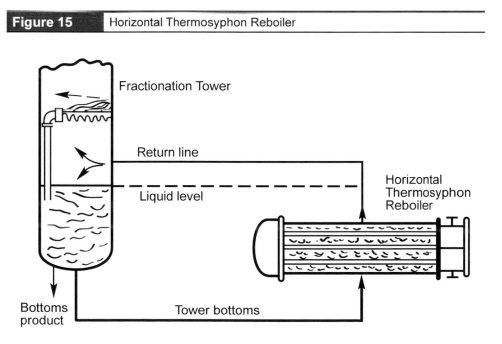

Vertical Thermosyphon Reboiler

The vertical thermosyphon reboiler is positioned vertically and attached closely to the side of the tower. Often vertical reboilers have the heated liquid on the tube side and the steam or heating medium on the shell side.

Reboiler Steam Side Operation

Figure 16 shows a horizontal, thermosyphon, U-Tube reboiler. The process liquid being heated flows into the bottom of the shell side and the vapour exits at the top of the shell. Steam enters the top of the channel head and flows into the tubes where it transfers heat to the process liquid. The steam condenses and condensate collects in the bottom of the lower channel end.

A level transmitter on the steam/condensate side is connected to a level controller, which operates a level control valve. The condensate flows through the level control valve and into a condensate return header.

Varying the level controller setpoint will vary the level of condensate in the tube side of the exchanger. This will expose more or less heating surface to the steam. In this way the amount of solution passing through the shell side can be varied. The level controller may be a local controller or it may reside in the control room. The hand/auto station enables the field operator to control the valve manually in the field.

Figure 16	Horizontal Thermosyphon Reboiler

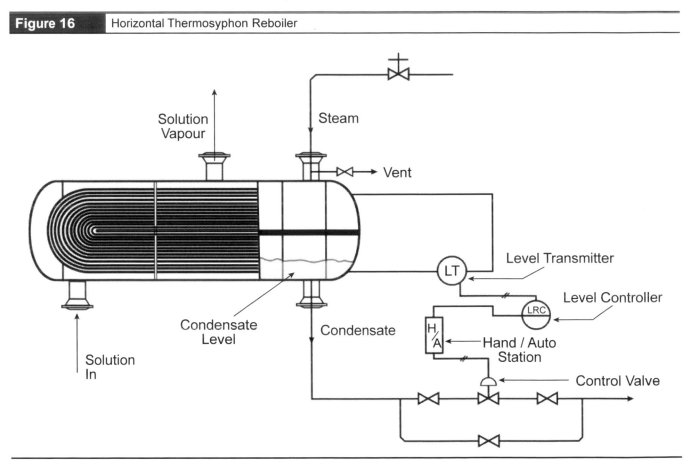

Feedwater Heaters

Feedwater heaters are utilized in many steam generating systems to heat the boiler feedwater before it goes to the economizer section of the steam generator. Low-pressure feedwater heaters are located between the hot well or extraction pumps and the dearator, while high-pressure feedwater heaters are located between the boiler feedwater pumps and the boiler. Steam, which is extracted at different pressures from the turbine, is used to heat the feedwater as it passes through the heaters.

Industrial plants use feedwater heating to improve the efficiency of a steam cycle. There are usually less feedwater-heating stages than in larger power plant cycles. It is common to have one feedwater heater upstream of the deaerator and one or two downstream of the deaerator. The heating medium may be low-pressure steam or any process fluid.

Figure 17 shows a typical low-pressure feedwater heater from a power plant cycle. It is the first heater downstream of the hot well pumps. The heater is a vertical, U-tube design with the water on the tube side and low-pressure steam on the shell side.

The steam is bled off the L.P. turbine, condenses in the shell side and heats the feedwater passing through the tubes. A vent line from the shell carries non-condensable gases to the vent condenser.

The condensate exits the bottom of the shell and goes to the surface condenser. First it flows through a liquid seal leg that has a water level of sufficient height to stop any steam from passing out of the shell bottom. Next the condensate passes through the flash box. Since the condensate from the heater is hotter than the hot well, the flash box allows some of the condensate to vaporize before it enters the hot well. The flash steam enters the surface condenser to be condensed and the liquid drains to the hot well through a second seal leg.

The shell side of the heater has a float-operated trip gear, which trips the heater if the condensate level becomes too high. A trip causes the motor-operated inlet and outlet valves to close and the bypass valve to open. This prevents the shell from being over-pressured by water if a tube leak occurs, since a tube leak would cause high-pressure water to enter the shell. The level would soon reach the float-operated trip gear, causing the heater to trip off-line. High-pressure heaters are often arranged in pairs and a trip of one heater will cause both to trip.

Figure 17	U-Tube Feedwater Heater

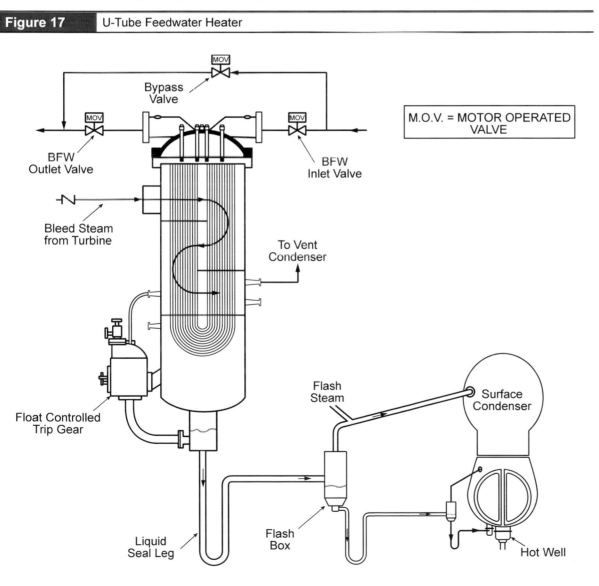

OBJECTIVE 4

Describe the design and operation of a plate-and-frame exchanger.

PLATE-AND-FRAME EXCHANGERS

A plate-and-frame heat exchanger (PHE) consists of many thin metal plates, supported and aligned on a sturdy frame, and pressed tightly together with gaskets between them. Each plate is corrugated, with alternating ridges and grooves in a pattern that produces a turbulent and lengthened flow path between the plates. The inlet and outlet ports are located in the corners of each plate. Gaskets are installed in grooves on the periphery of each plate, plus around the inlet and outlet holes. The gaskets direct the flow, prevent leakage between plates, and prevent leakage to the outside of the exchanger.

The "hot" and "cold" exchange fluids flow between alternating plates. One flows upward and the other flows downward. The flow distribution is directed by the circumferential gaskets to the inlet and outlet ports. The nominal spacing between adjacent plates is usually two to five millimetres.

Figure 18 illustrates the general flow through a plate-and-frame exchanger. A few plates only are shown and in an expanded view. The inlet and outlet channels appear to be actual pipes, but they are not. They are simply channels created by the alignment of the holes in the plates.

Figure 18	Flows Through a Plate Heat Exchanger

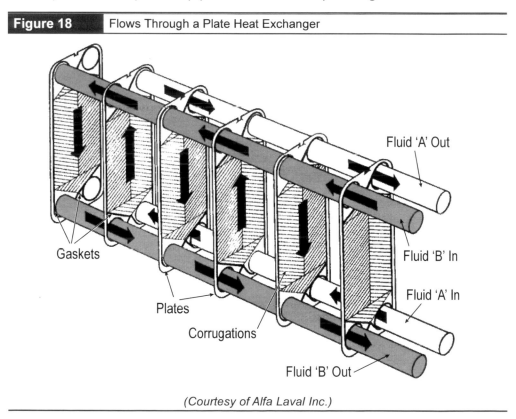

(Courtesy of Alfa Laval Inc.)

Figure 19 shows a partially disassembled view of a plate-and-frame exchanger. The main components are listed and described as follows:

Plates: Thin, pressed metal plates with corrugations to provide turbulence and surface area for heat transfer.

Ports: Inlet and outlets ports for fluids. Ports are formed by holes in the end covers and in each plate.

Gaskets: Made of rubber or synthetic material (eg. neoprene); fit in groves in the plates to prevent leakage between plates and to atmosphere.

End Plates: Heavy, metal, pressure plates that do not contact fluid, but provide strength against internal pressure and keep the plates tight and flat.

Compression Bolts: Long bolts between end plates, used to tighten plat assembly.

Carrying Bars: Heavy bars that carry and align the plates. The upper bar carries the weight of the plates. Plates are installed by sliding them, in notches, along the bars.

Figure 19	Parts of a Heat Plate Heat Exchanger

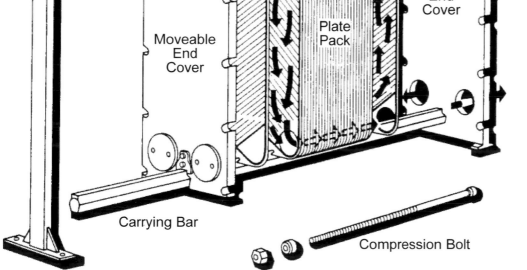

Figure 20 illustrates more clearly the gasket positions between the plates. It also shows the flows of the two process fluids. Normally the plates are tightened and the gaskets are compressed until there is no external leakage from the exchanger.

Figure 21 shows a plate exchanger that has been spread apart for cleaning.

Figure 20   Plate-and-Frame Exchanger Gaskets

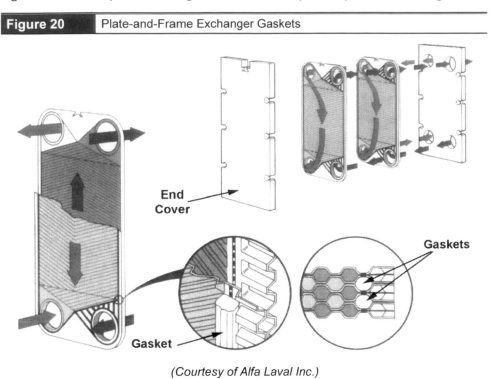

(Courtesy of Alfa Laval Inc.)

Figure 21   Plate Cleaning

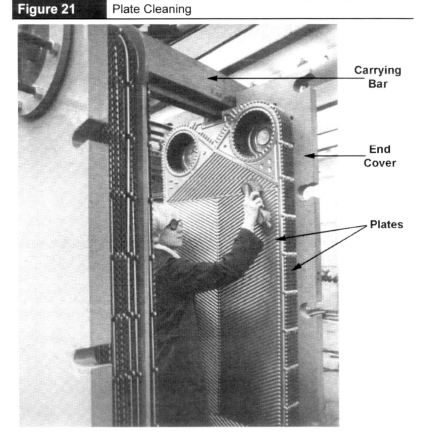

(Courtesy of Alfa Laval Inc.)

Advantages of Plate-and-Frame Exchangers

1. Low fouling characteristics due to high turbulence, high velocity, few stagnant regions and low residence times.

2. High heat transfer rates and efficiency, due to the thin transfer surfaces and the turbulence. This reduces the surface area required for a given heat exchange duty to one third or one half of that required for a shell-and-tube exchanger.

3. Leakage is detected immediately, since any gasket or plate leaks result in fluid being seen on the outside of the exchanger and on the floor.

4. Floor space required is relatively small, since the exchanger is compact. They also require relatively small space for dismantling, repair or cleaning.

5. The number of plates can be easily changed to modify the rating of the exchanger.

6. Capable of rapid start-up and quick response to process changes.

7. No insulation is required, since heat loss is minimal.

8. Vibration free.

Disadvantages of Plate-and-Frame Exchangers

1. Limited to applications where pressure doesn't exceed 2.07 MPa and temperature doesn't exceed 175°C. Pressure affects plates, frames and gasket sealing. Temperature affects gasket material.

2. Not suitable for viscous (thick) fluids, as the small spacing would restrict flow.

3. Not suitable for very dirty fluids, since the small clearance between plates will prevent larger particles from passing through.

4. At low flows, velocities between plates will be low, which can create poor flow distribution. Less than 3.94 in/sec is considered poor.

5. High pressure drops between inlets and outlets, since the friction factor is high and the entry port diameters are small. This makes them not suitable for air coolers and gas-to-gas services.

6. Not suitable for toxic fluids that may form explosive mixtures with air, since any leakage would be to the surrounding atmosphere.

7. Can only be disassembled a certain number of times before new gaskets are required. New gaskets often have to be bonded to the plates.

OBJECTIVE 5

Describe the design and components of overhead, aerial coolers, including fan and cooler arrangements. Explain cooler control.

AERIAL COOLERS

Aerial coolers use air as the cooling medium. The fluid to be cooled or condensed passes through the inside of bundles of tubes while atmospheric air flows across the outside. This is basically a non-contact, convection heat exchanger in which the air flow may be induced or forced.

Air-cooled exchangers are often called finned-tube exchangers because fins are attached to the outside of the tubes to improve the efficiency of heat exchange. The fins may be welded to the tubes, wrapped mechanically or expanded to fit the tubes. The size and number of fins on each tube is based on the heat transfer required.

The aerial cooler is preferred in processes where the fluids being cooled are at least 130°F. They are also preferred where fouling of the tubes on the cooling waterside of a water-cooled exchanger is a concern. If a fluid stream must be cooled below ambient temperature, a combination of aerial cooling followed by water-cooling often proves to be efficient and economical, since a large portion of the cooling is done by the air, before the water is used.

Forced & Induced Draft Coolers

Induced draft air coolers use a top-mounted motor driven fan, which induces airflow across a horizontal bank of tubes and then discharges the air upwards. The tubes carry the fluid in a closed circuit, with the tube ends enclosed in box headers at both the inlet and outlet ends. Baffles inside the headers direct the fluid through the tubes in two or more passes. In a forced draft cooler the fans are located below the tubes and force the air vertically upwards around the tubes.

Figure 22 shows the general layout of forced draft and induced draft aerial coolers.

Figure 22	Forced Draft and Induced Draft Aerial Coolers

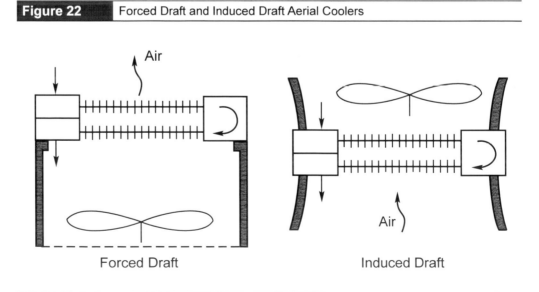

Forced Draft   Induced Draft

Figure 23 shows slightly more detail of forced draft and induced draft aerial coolers, with the main components of each. The driving motor and its connection to the fan is shown. The plenum is the shrouding or ducting, which directs the airflow through the fan and cooler coils.

Figure 23	Forced Draft and Induced Draft Aerial Coolers

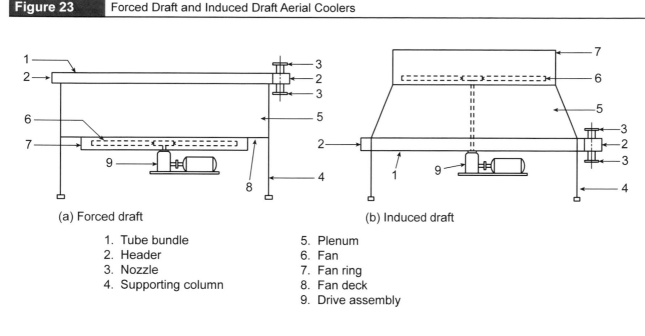

(a) Forced draft   (b) Induced draft

1. Tube bundle
2. Header
3. Nozzle
4. Supporting column
5. Plenum
6. Fan
7. Fan ring
8. Fan deck
9. Drive assembly

(Courtesy of Pearson Education)

Aerial Cooler Arrangements

Figure 24 shows a forced draft cooler with a single tube bundle and two fans. This is a simple arrangement, but there are many possible arrangements for aerial coolers, some with many bundles, banks and fans.

Figure 24	Forced Draft Aerial Cooler

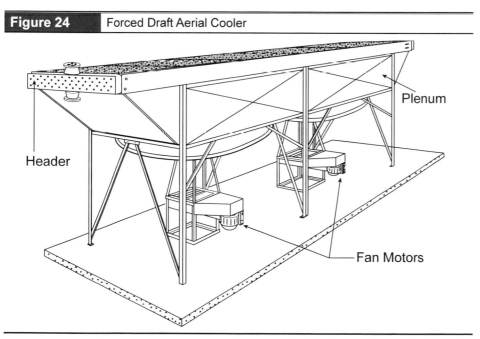

Plenum

Header

Fan Motors

Figure 25 shows an overhead schematic of a cooler with several fans and tube bundles. The common terminology used to describe the major tube layouts are as follows.

- A Bundle is a single set of tubes that are attached to a common header at each end. Figure 25 shows seven bundles.

- A Bay is a section of the cooler (containing one or more tube bundles) with one or more cooling fans dedicated solely to those tube bundles. Usually bays are separated by dividing walls that prevent interaction of the air flow between them. Each bay may be controlled separately from the others. Figure 25 shows 3 bays.

- A bank is a group of bays, arranged in a single or continuous structure and serving the same purpose. There may be air flow interaction between the bays for control purposes.

Figure 25	Coolers Arranged in Bays

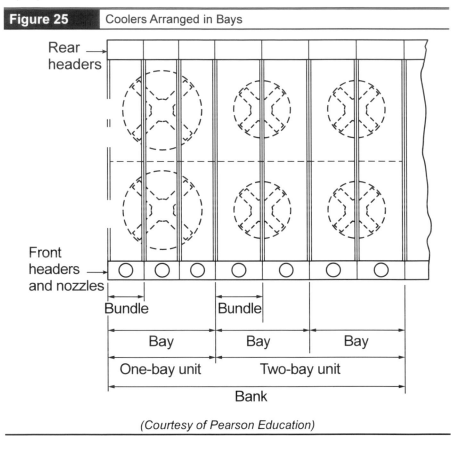

(Courtesy of Pearson Education)

Aerial Cooler Control

The primary concern with an aerial cooler is to control and maintain a steady outlet temperature for the cooled fluid. The easiest and most common control methods include changing the speed of the fans or by starting and stopping fans. An alternate method is to use adjustable louvres to change the volume of air flow.

Fan speeds are adjusted by variable frequency motor drives. A temperature transmitter on the outlet flow will automatically change the frequency to the motor and, thereby, the fan speed and resultant air flow. This method is common when the temperature must be keep very steady for process reasons.

When there is room for the temperature to vary within an acceptable range, the start-stop method is most common. If there are two fans in a bay, one is usually kept running on manual, while the other is on automatic and will start and stop as required.

Louvre control involves adjustable louvres at the inlet to a bank. The fluid outlet temperature controller may directly adjust the position of the louvres, changing the mass of air through the fan(s). In some cases there may also be recirculation louvres, which direct some of the warm discharge air back to the fan inlet. This would most likely be in locations where ambient temperatures may be very low (Winter) and subcooling would occur without recirculating some of the warm air.

In very warm ambient conditions, it is not uncommon for coolers to be undersized and fail to achieve the required outlet temperature. In this case, louvres are kept wide open and fans at full speed, with all available fans operating. If sufficient cooling cannot be attained, one trick is to spray or run water down onto the cooling coils. The water itself, plus the evaporative effect helps to lower the product temperature.

Figure 26 shows one arrangement of control louvres on an aerial cooler. There are MANY different arrangements possible.

The louvres at the entrance or exit to the cooler can be throttled to reduce the airflow. If the temperature of the controlled product is still too low, hot air can be recirculated back to the inlet of the cooler. In this design, control louvres allow hot air from above the fans to recirculate and mix with the cold inlet air.

The control louvres may be manually operated, controlled by field control loops, or connected to a control room or DCS (distributed control) system. The finer or more exact the temperature control required, the more elaborate the control scheme is. Usually the side, inlet louvres are controlled by the outlet fluid temperature controller. The recirculation louvres are then used to control the air temperature below the tube bundle (between the fans and the tubes).

Figure 26	Aerial Cooler Temperature Control

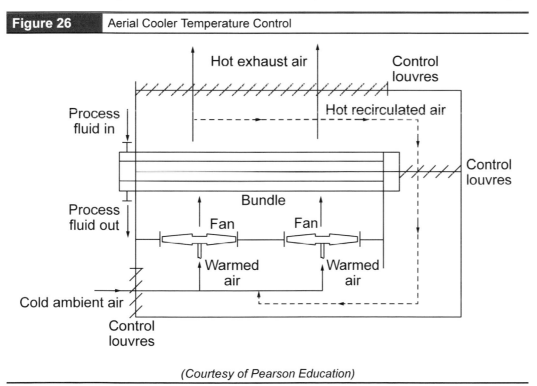

(Courtesy of Pearson Education)

Aerial Cooler Cleanliness

Aerial coolers must be cleaned from time to time. The external fins on the tubes create very small spaces, which tend to collect airborne particles. Over time the accumulation is enough to restrict the air flow to the point where sufficient cooling cannot be attained. The air that would normally pass through the cooler begins to recycle within the fan. If plugging is expected in certain environments, it is common to install screens over the fan inlet. These are much easier to clean than the tubes.

Figure 27 illustrates the effect of blocked coils.

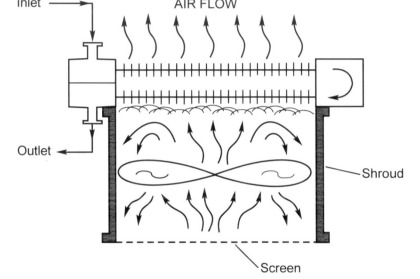

| Figure 27 | Coils Plugging with Airborne Debris |

OBJECTIVE 6

Describe the design and components, including controls, of an overhead, aerial condenser. Explain condenser operation, control and precautions when used to condense excess steam.

OVERHEAD AERIAL CONDENSERS

An aerial condenser is an aerial cooler that cools the process fluid below its condensing temperature and, therefore, causes the fluid to condense. Since this is a more demanding service, requiring the removal of latent heat and with two phases of fluid (liquid and vapour) within the tubes, aerial condenser designs are somewhat more complicated than aerial cooler designs.

Figure 28 shows four common configurations for the tube bundles of aerial condensers: horizontal, vertical, V-frame, and A-frame. The horizontal design is most common in smaller sizes and when liquid removal is less critical. The vertical arrangement is popular in smaller sizes where floor space is limited and liquid drainage is more critical. The performance of vertical units is affected by the wind direction.

The V-Frame and A-Frame bundle arrangements require less room than the horizontal types, and are less affected by wind than the vertical types. They are usually applied in larger designs, such as steam condensers, where condensate volumes are high and liquid removal is most critical. They provide a large exchange surface without excessive floor space.

| Figure 28 | Air-Cooled Exchanger Bundle Configurations |

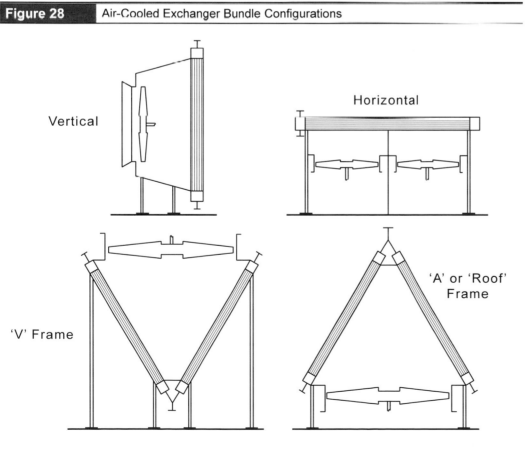

(Courtesy of Pearson Education)

Tube bundles are connected to header boxes at each end. The tubes are finned to create larger heat transfer surface. Plugs in the header boxes are aligned with each tube and allow the tubes to be cleaned by lancing or high-pressure water jet. The tubes may also be chemically cleaned.

Figure 29 shows the box header arrangement. It illustrates a two-pass bundle, with the vapour entering at the top of the header, flowing to the other end and then back, as liquid, to the bottom outlet.

Figure 29   Headers and Finned Tubes

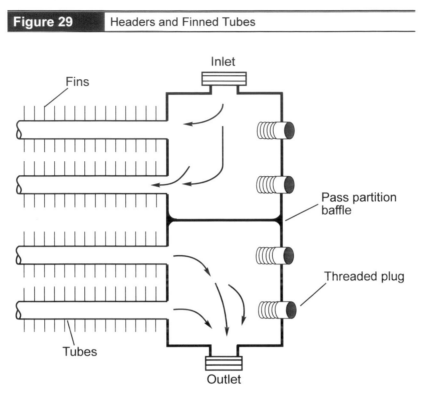

Figure 30 shows an external, end view of a box header.

The shaded dots represent the threaded cleaning plugs for the five rows of tubes. They are often a source of leaks, particularly if a large number of the plugs are removed to clean the tubes. The inlet is a larger diameter than the outlet, since the fluid occupies a larger volume in the inlet (vapour) state. Box headers are usually fitted with drains and vents for purging and depressuring, etc.

Figure 30   End View of Header Box

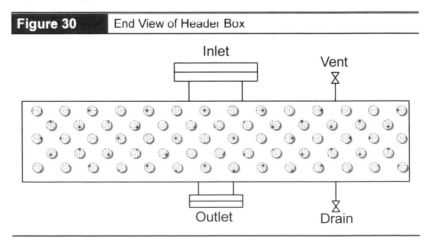

Figure 31 shows two A-Frame steam condensers, installed at a waste incineration plant and operating at a vacuum. The steam enters at the top of the condensers and condensate drains from the bottom. These are vacuum condensers installed at a waste incineration plant to condense turbine exhaust steam.

Figure 31	A-Frame Aerial Steam Condensers

(Courtesy of Jord Balcke-Duerr)

Aerial condensers, especially steam condensers, require careful control of the outlet condensate temperature. This is especially critical in freezing temperatures, since freezing will plug the tubes and could cause the tubes to break when the ice expands in them. Like aerial coolers, condensers may have variable speed fans, start-stop fans, and/or control louvres.

Figure 32 shows aerial condensers in a 680 mW combined cycle power station.

Figure 32	Power Plant with Aerial Condensing

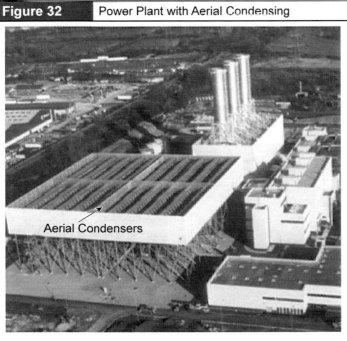

(Courtesy of Jord Balcke-Duerr)

OBJECTIVE 7

Describe the design and explain the operation of natural draft cooling towers, including atmospheric and hyperbolic styles.

NATURAL DRAFT COOLING TOWERS

There are two classes of natural draft cooling towers:

- Atmospheric cooling towers
- Hyperbolic cooling towers

Atmospheric Cooling Towers

Atmospheric towers, shown in Figures 33 and 34, are those in which the air movement through the tower is dependent solely on atmospheric conditions. They operate effectively only in locations where there are relatively constant winds and large open spaces away from obstructions. The sides of atmospheric towers have louvres, which direct airflow into the tower and help to contain the water inside the tower. Air flows across the tower by natural currents.

Figure 33	Atmospheric Spray-Filled Tower

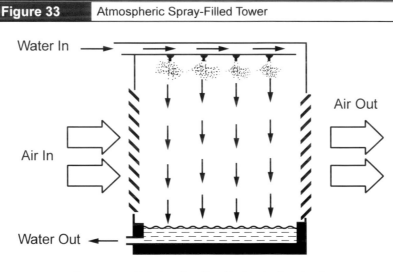

(Courtesy of Marley Cooling Technologies, Inc.)

The spray filled tower in Figure 33 has nozzles that spray the water downward. The water flow creates airflow by natural induction or aspiration of the spray nozzles. Wind currents add to the airflow inside the tower. There is no packing or fill material. These are inexpensive towers and used mostly in industrial applications.

Figure 34 shows an atmospheric tower that contains fill or packing made of wood or plastic slats. As the water falls from a perforated overhead flume or from spray nozzles, down through the packing, it strikes the faces of the packing and breaks into fine droplets. The fine water droplets contact the air currents, enhancing the process of evaporation and cooling. A basin at the bottom of the tower collects the cooled water.

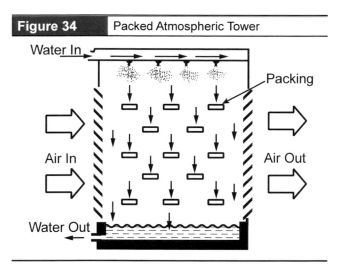

Figure 34 — Packed Atmospheric Tower

Hyperbolic Cooling Towers

Hyperbolic cooling towers such as the one in Figure 35 are large, round, chimney-like structures, up to 150 metres high. The term, hyperbolic, derives from their geometric shape. Made of a steel-reinforced concrete shell, the tower is mostly empty space. The bottom 10 to 15 metres contains packing material and water spray nozzles. The water is sprayed down from above the packing. Air flow is created upwards in the tower by the density differential between the heated air inside the tower and the cooler, denser air outside the tower.

Hyperbolic towers are used when there is a stable heat load, such as in large electrical generation plants. They function best in locations with high relative humidity. Their operation is extremely dependable and predictable. One advantage they have is the savings in power and maintenance costs, since there are no fans. Due to their size, hyperbolic towers are expensive to construct.

Hyperbolic towers may be counterflow or crossflow. In counterflow towers, the air flow is upward through the fill, counter to the falling water flow. In crossflow towers, the air flows across the fill and the water flow.

Figure 35 — Hyperbolic Cooling Tower-Counterflow

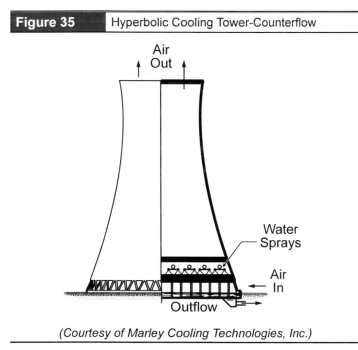

(Courtesy of Marley Cooling Technologies, Inc.)

Operation of Natural Draft Cooling Towers

The operator has minimal control over the airflow through natural draft cooling towers, since it is very dependent upon ambient conditions. Some of the operating variables that can be checked are:

- Water flow over the tower, making sure that no nozzles are plugged or obstructed
- Suction screens on cooling water to the pumps should be clean
- Cooling tower basin level. High level leads to overflowing and low level may cause a decrease in flow
- Cooling water loss or drift. This can be caused by high winds, or broken louvres
- Cooling water quality and chemical treatment should be monitored closely to ensure the packing stays clean.

OBJECTIVE 8

Describe the design and operation of mechanical draft cooling towers, including forced draft, induced draft counterflow, and induced draft crossflow.

MECHANICAL DRAFT COOLING TOWERS

Mechanical draft towers use one or more fans to move large quantities of air through the tower. They are divided into two classes:

- Forced draft
- Induced draft

Forced Draft Cooling Towers

The forced draft tower, shown in Figure 36, has the fan, basin, and piping located within the tower structure. There are no louvres in the exterior walls. Instead, the structural steel or wood framing is covered with paneling made of aluminum, galvanized steel, or fiberglass. Air can only enter the tower through the forced draft fan, which is located at the base.

Figure 36	Forced Draft Tower

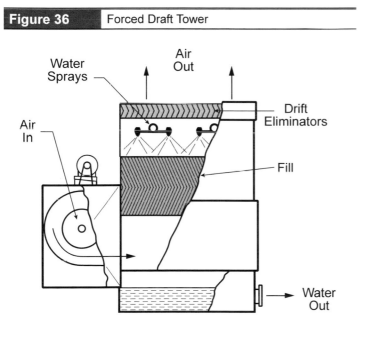

(Courtesy of Marley Cooling Technologies, Inc)

The fan forces ambient air into the tower below the packing (fill). It flows upward through the fill, where it meets the downward flowing water. Drift eliminators capture any entrained water from the air before it leaves the top of the tower.

With forced draft, vibration and noise are minimal since the fan is mounted on a solid foundation. The fans handle mostly dry air, which greatly reduces erosion and water condensation problems in the fan. However, forced draft towers are less suited to cold weather operation than induced draft towers. They must be closely monitored for ice build-up in cold weather. This is because the forced draft fan moves cold, ambient air and any moisture in the air may freeze on the fan blades, causing excessive vibration. Even though cooling towers are designed to avoid wet air recirculation from the top, it is impossible to prevent all.

Induced Draft Cooling Towers

The induced draft tower, illustrated in Figure 37, has one or more fans located at the top of the tower. The fans draw air upwards, against the downward flow of water in the fill. The fans at the top discharge the hot, moisture-laden air upward and away from the air entering at the bottom of the tower, thus preventing any recirculation of warm air. Warm water enters the distribution system located just under the drift eliminators and above the fill.

Figure 37	Counterflow Induced Draft Cooling Tower

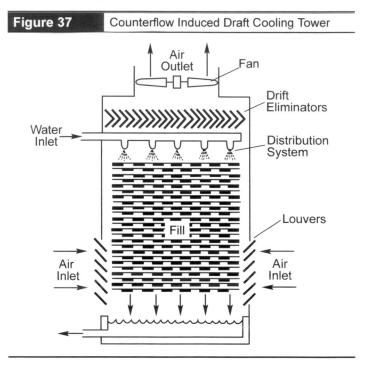

Counterflow Induced Draft Towers

Figures 38 and 39 show the components of counterflow, induced draft towers in more detail. These towers require large electric motors, due to the complex path that the air takes. The water is distributed over the fill by a distribution system that consists of headers and spray nozzles. The fill consists of wood or PVC slats that fit in a fiberglass framework. Side louvres direct the air evenly into the tower and preventing water loss. The drift eliminators change the direction of the airflow several times, which causes any water droplets to be left behind.

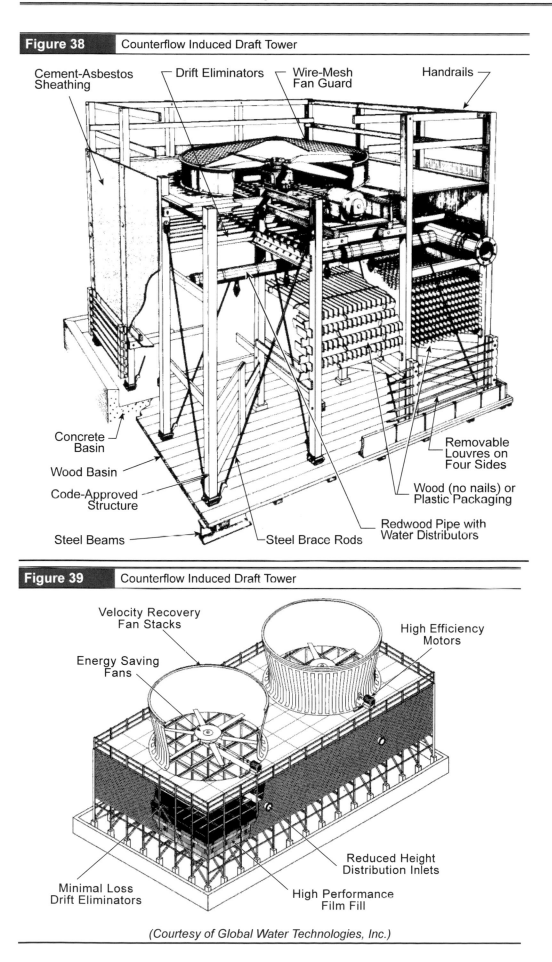

Figure 38   Counterflow Induced Draft Tower

Cement-Asbestos Sheathing — Drift Eliminators — Wire-Mesh Fan Guard — Handrails

Concrete Basin

Wood Basin

Code-Approved Structure

Steel Beams — Steel Brace Rods

Removable Louvres on Four Sides

Wood (no nails) or Plastic Packaging

Redwood Pipe with Water Distributors

Figure 39   Counterflow Induced Draft Tower

Velocity Recovery Fan Stacks

Energy Saving Fans

High Efficiency Motors

Minimal Loss Drift Eliminators

Reduced Height Distribution Inlets

High Performance Film Fill

(Courtesy of Global Water Technologies, Inc.)

Crossflow Induced Draft Towers

Figures 40 and 41 show a crossflow, induced draft cooling tower in which the air flows horizontally through the packing, while the water falls downward. With two sets of packing, this design is referred to as a two-cell cooling tower.

Figure 40	Crossflow Induced Draft Tower Design

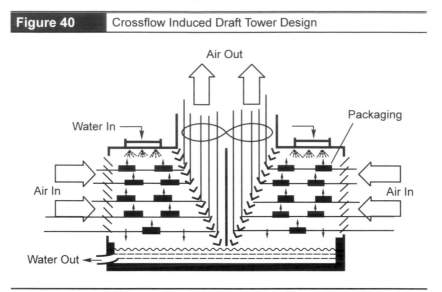

The fans draw air through cells and packing that are connected to a suction area beneath each fan. The water falls from a distribution system above each cell and cascades in small droplets over the packing. In the crossflow design, the total travel path of the air is longer and there is less resistance to airflow than in the counterflow design.

Figure 41	Crossflow Induced Draft Cooling Tower

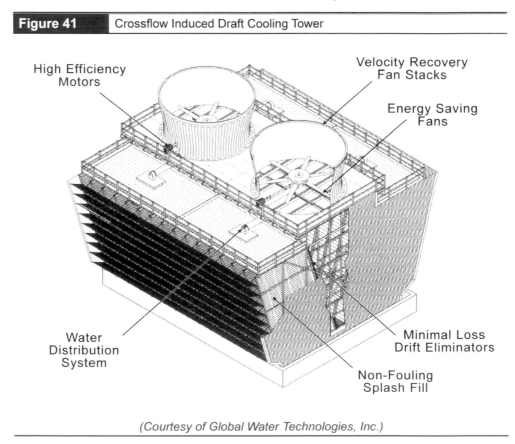

(Courtesy of Global Water Technologies, Inc.)

Figure 42 shows how a counterflow induced draft cooling tower is used in a power plant cycle with a condensing turbine.

The counterflow tower occupies less floor space than a crossflow tower but is taller for a given capacity. Advantages of the crossflow tower are the low-pressure drop (of the air flow) and low fan power requirement leading to lower energy costs.

| Figure 42 | Wet Evaporative Cooling System |

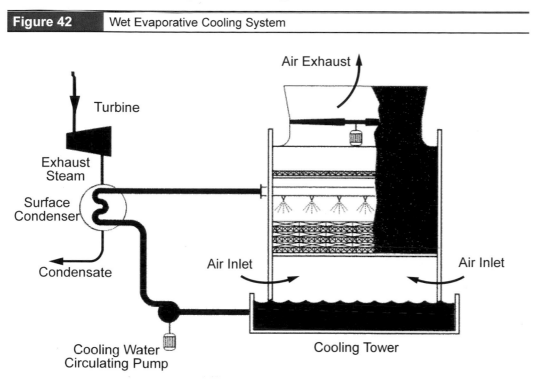

(Courtesy of Global Water Technologies, Inc.)

Mechanical draft towers must be located so that air intakes are not obstructed. The discharge air must diffuse freely into the atmosphere and must not recirculate through the tower. A cooling tower should be located as close as possible to the plant system it serves, to minimize pumping horsepower. Towers should be at a higher elevation than the condenser to prevent condenser water draining into the cooling tower after shutdown.

Cooling Tower Fill

Cooling tower efficiency is dependent upon the contact time between air and water in the fill material. The fill must promote maximum air contact time and minimum restriction of airflow.

Many cooling towers have been built with fill made of wood slats. The wood used is redwood or pressure treated Douglas fir.

Figure 42 shows wood fill, placed in a fiberglass grid.

Figure 43	Cooling Tower Wood Fill

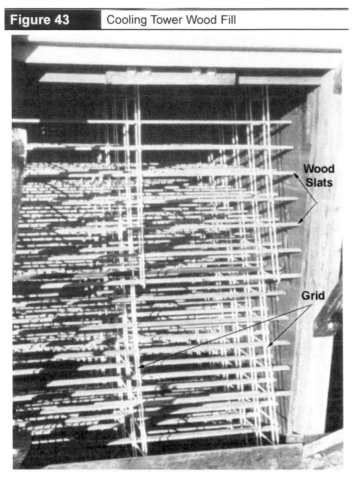

(Courtesy of Marley Cooling Technologies, Inc.)

The splash type fill material, shown in Figure 44, is constructed of PVC and is often a replacement for wood fill. The PVC is strong and chemical resistant. The bottom diagram shows how the fill breaks the water into droplets.

Figure 44	Cooling Tower Splash Fill–PVC

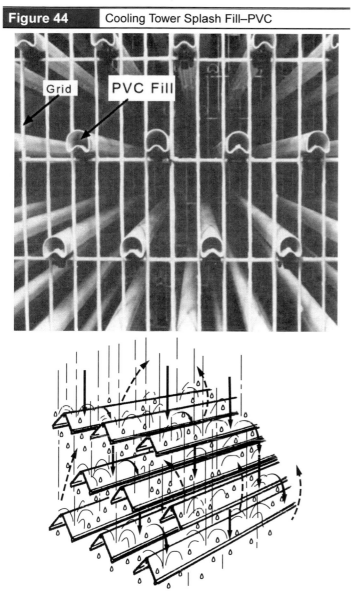

(Courtesy of Marley Cooling Technologies, Inc.)

Film Type Fill

Film type fill, as shown in Figure 44 is made of thin sheets spaced closely together. Film fill is made of PVC, because it is resistant to chemicals. The water spreads out on the sheets forming a thin film over a large surface area. The air flows up between the sheets.

Film fill provides more cooling than the same volume of splash fill, due to the larger surface. Uniform water distribution and spacing of the sheets is required to provide uniform airflows. Sections of film fill can be added to towers that already have splash fill to increase the cooling capacity.

Figure 45	Cooling Tower Louvres and Film Fill

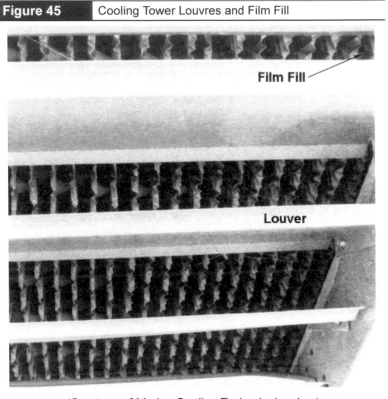

(Courtesy of Marley Cooling Technologies, Inc.)

CHAPTER 12 - QUESTIONS

1. Sketch a simple double-pipe exchanger. Describe its construction.

2. Sketch and describe a shell and tube heat exchanger, of the fixed straight tube design.

3. Sketch a low pressure feed water heater, showing the level control of the condensate in the shell.

4. What are the advantages of plate and shell heat exchangers? Why are they found mostly in lower pressure and clean service applications?

5. Sketch and describe an overhead aerial cooler.

6. Explain the operation precautions of operating an overhead aerial steam condenser in cold weather.

7. Sketch a natural draft cooling tower. Explain the water and air flows through the tower.

8. Explain the difference between a crossflow and a counterflow cooling tower.

ANSWERS: All answers are found within the content of the chapter.

Fired Heaters

LEARNING OUTCOME

When you complete this chapter you should be able to:

Describe the design, components, operation, and applications of direct-fired and indirect-fired natural draft process heaters.

LEARNING OBJECTIVES

Here is what you should be able to do when you complete each objective:

1. *Describe the common process applications for direct-fired heaters. Explain direct-fired heater designs and classifications.*

2. *Describe the design, identify the tube banks and explain the fluid and combustion gas flows through a multi-burner, vertical fired heater.*

3. *Describe typical burner designs and configurations, identifying burner components, including air registers, pilots, and flame scanners. Describe burner operation.*

4. *Describe the fuel gas supply system to the burners and explain the purpose of the major fittings.*

5. *Describe the monitoring, control, and shutdown devices on a typical heater.*

6. *Explain heater start-up procedure, including the lighting of additional burners once flame is established. Explain heater shutdown procedure.*

7. *Describe the design, components and operation of a typical horizontal, indirect-fired heater such as a salt bath heater.*

8. *Explain start-up and shutdown procedures for an indirect-fired heater.*

OBJECTIVE 1

Describe the common process applications for direct-fired heaters. Explain direct-fired heater designs and classifications.

USES OF DIRECT FIRED HEATER

Direct-fired heaters are common in refineries and chemical plants where they are used to heat process fluids. They are called "direct-fired" because the tubes carrying the process fluid are located inside a heater that has burners and the tubes are in direct contact with the heat from the burners. Some of the uses for direct-fired heaters are:

- Fractionator reboiling. They are used to heat fluid drawn off the bottom of a fractionator tower, so that the fluid can re-enter the fractionator tower in a partially vaporized state. This arrangement is shown in Figure 1.

Figure 1	Fractionator Reboiler

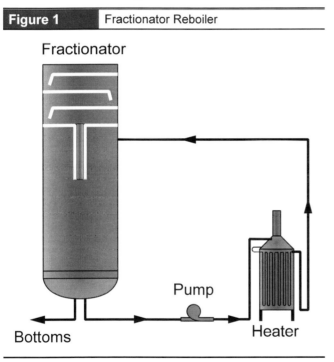

Fractionator

Pump

Bottoms

Heater

- Preheating the feed to a fractionator tower: The heater is used to heat the makeup to the fractionator tower (see Fig. 2).

Figure 2 | Fractionator Preheater

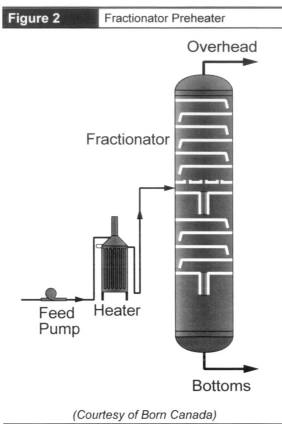

(Courtesy of Born Canada)

- Preheating the process feed to a reactor: The fluid must be hot enough for the reaction to occur. In some cases, start-up heaters are used only to get the chemical reaction started; when the reaction is self-sufficient, the heater may be shutdown. This arrangement is shown in Figure 3.

Figure 3 | Reactor Preheater

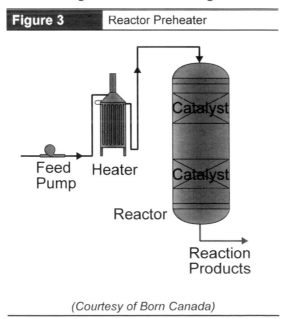

(Courtesy of Born Canada)

- For chemical reactions: The fired heater may be used to heat a fluid to promote a direct chemical reaction, where the reaction is temperature dependent. This reaction will occur inside the heater tubes when the correct temperature is reached.
- To heat a heat transfer medium: The heat transfer medium, such as hot oil, is used as the heat source in various heat exchangers throughout the process. The fired heater continuously heats the hot oil as it returns in a closed loop to the heater (Fig. 4).

Figure 4	Heating Medium Heater

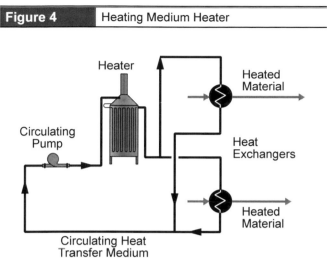

(Courtesy of Born Canada)

- Heating viscous fluids: Some fluids, at relatively cool temperatures, are too heavy or thick to pump or process. Fired heaters are often used to heat these fluids, thus lowering their viscosity.

Figure 5 shows a heater connected to a large storage tank. The fluid is taken from the bottom of the tank, heated in the heater tubes, then returned to the tank via a return distributor.

Figure 5	Fluid Heating

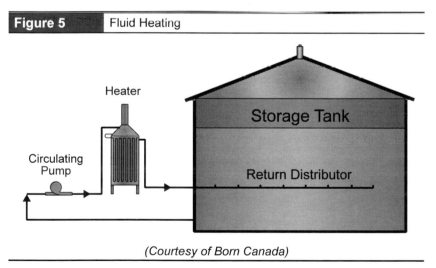

(Courtesy of Born Canada)

FIRED HEATER CLASSIFICATION

In terms of the method by which heat is transferred from the combustion zone to the tubes, there are three general classifications of fired heaters, namely radiant, convection and combination (radiant plus convection).

- In **radiant heaters** the heating surfaces (ie. the tubes) are in direct sight of the furnace. They are usually an integral part of the furnace, with the furnace walls completely surrounded by tubes. Heat from the combustion zone is transferred to the tubes by radiation through the furnace space. The heat then transfers by conduction through the tube metal to the process fluids flowing in the tubes. The flue gases pass out of the radiant area of the furnace and are discharged to the stack. Efficiencies for this type of heater are relatively low at 40 to 50%.

- In **convection heaters** the combustion gases flow across the tubes, which usually have fins on their outer surface. The heat from the combustion zone is thus carried to the tubes by convection. These heaters generally have an efficiency of 75 to 85%.

- **Combination radiant and convection heaters** are the most common. The bottom section of the heater contains the burners plus the radiant section, with tubes surrounding the furnace. Above the radiant section is a convection section, with one or more banks of tubes that receive heat from the combustion gases after they leave the furnace on their way to the stack.

FIRED HEATER DESIGNS

The most common fired heater design is the vertical heater. There are several configuration of vertical heaters. Some common designs are illustrated in Figure 6. In all three designs the burners are located in the furnace floor and fire upwards into the furnace.

- The **vertical**, cylindrical heater is the most common. The radiant section, containing vertical radiant tubes, is cylindrical. The convection section, with a horizontal tube bank, is mounted above the radiant section and is usually rectangular. The stack and outlet damper assembly are mounted on top of the convection section.

- The **cabin** heater is a vertical, rectangular design with a coil of horizontal radiant tubes surrounding the furnace. A sloping transition section joins the radiant section to the convection section, which contains one or more banks of horizontal convection tubes.

- The **central tube wall** design has radiant tubes around the outer walls, plus a central row of radiant tubes that divides the furnace vertically. This creates two furnace sections and is often referred to as a double fired design.

Figure 7 shows several other heater enclosure and coil configurations. In fact, virtually every heater is custom designed for its particular application in a process and for the required heat transfer duty. The term "box heater" refers to those heaters that have a rectangular shape in their radiant sections.

Figure 6 | Process Heater Designs

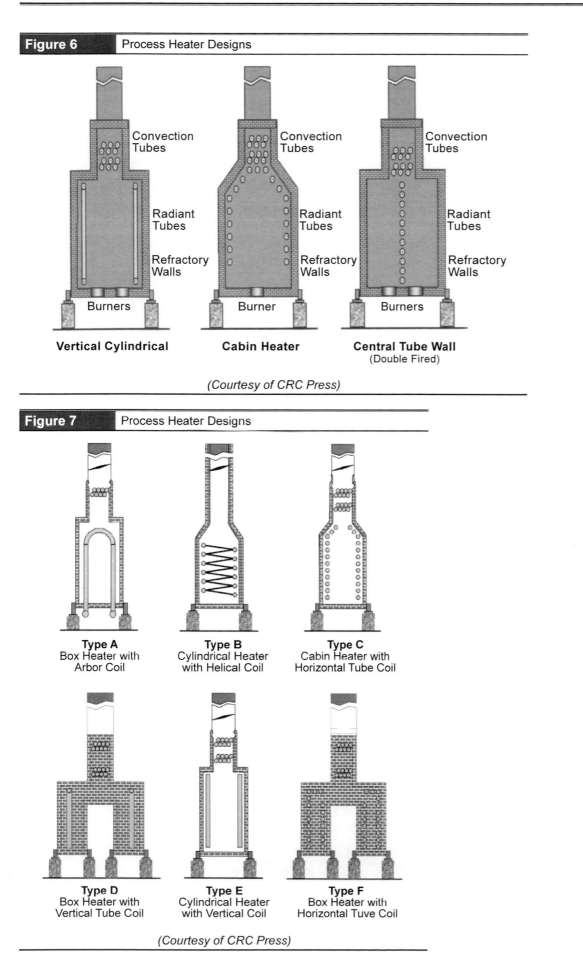

Vertical Cylindrical   **Cabin Heater**   **Central Tube Wall**
(Double Fired)

(Courtesy of CRC Press)

Figure 7 | Process Heater Designs

Type A
Box Heater with
Arbor Coil

Type B
Cylindrical Heater
with Helical Coil

Type C
Cabin Heater with
Horizontal Tube Coil

Type D
Box Heater with
Vertical Tube Coil

Type E
Cylindrical Heater
with Vertical Coil

Type F
Box Heater with
Horizontal Tuve Coil

(Courtesy of CRC Press)

OBJECTIVE 2

Describe the design, identify the tube banks and explain the fluid and combustion gas flows through a multi-burner, vertical fired heater.

VERTICAL HEATER CONSTRUCTION

Figure 8 shows the major components of a typical rectangular, vertical heater. The term "updraft" is often applied to this design, since the flow of combustion gases is upwards from the burners to the stack. Combustion air is received by natural draft, due to the height of the stack.

The process fluid enters the convection section and flows through the tubes in series in a descending direction. It then enters the radiant section tubes, which are located along the walls of the furnace. The heated process fluid leaves the lowest tubes on each wall and goes directly to the process equipment in the plant.

The vertical gas burners are mounted in the floor of the furnace and extend in a straight line from the front to the back of the furnace. The inner walls and floor are lined with refractory brick and other suitable insulating material to contain heat inside the furnace and prevent overheating of the exterior cladding. The heater is strengthened and supported by structural support beams mounted on reinforced concrete piers.

Figure 8	Horizontal Rectangular Heater

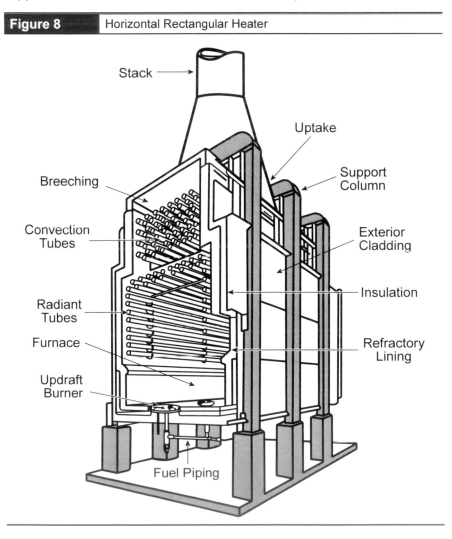

Figure 9 is a photograph of a typical vertical, cylindrical fired heater in a process plant. Figure 10 shows the same heater in a cutaway view.

These heaters are very common in chemical processing facilities. They are bottom fired, with a cylindrical radiant section, with vertical tubes, and a rectangular convection section. They are normally natural draft, but larger units may have draft fans. Ladders and platforms allow access to the convection section and stack damper.

Figure 9	Photo of Vertical Cylindrical Heater

Figure 10	Cutaway of Vertical Cylindrical Heater

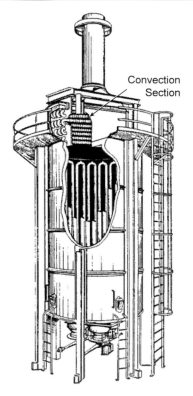

Convection Section

(Courtesy of Struthers Wells Corporation)

OBJECTIVE 3

Describe typical burner designs and configurations, identifying burner components, including air registers, pilots, and flame scanners. Describe burner operation.

BURNER DESIGNS

The burners on fired heaters are similar to those on boilers in that they have all the same major components. The most common fuels are gas, oil, or a combination of the two. Some heaters burn fuels that are a product or by-product of the process plant in which they operate. Most vertical fired heaters have natural draft burners, with no forced draft or induced draft fans.

Figure 11 illustrates a common gas burner for a vertically fired heater.

This design is called a premix, inspiriting gas burner. Primary air and gas flow through the central mixing tube and the mixture is ignited as it leaves the burner tip. Secondary air flows through adjustable air registers, located around the perimeter of the burner, and supplies secondary air to the combustion zone. The opening of the registers can be adjusted to modify the flame pattern and to keep the excess air within limits (usually between 10 and 30%). The pilot has a separate burner nozzle and gas supply line. The burner is set into the refractory on the furnace floor. The refractory protects the burner parts from the radiant heat of the furnace.

Figure 11	Gas Burner for Fired Heater

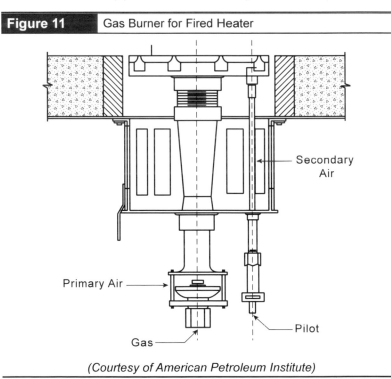

(Courtesy of American Petroleum Institute)

Figure 12 is a photograph of a natural gas burner for a bottom fired vertical heater.

In this design, the gas is not premixed with the air. The gas is piped to burner tips or nozzles for injection into the flame. Combustion air flow to each burner is controlled by an air register, which admits air to the burner through adjustable, rectangular holes. A small, gas fired pilot is used to ignite the main burner. A pressure gauge indicates the gas supply pressure to the burner.

| Figure 12 | Natural Gas Burner for a Vertical Heater |

(Courtesy of John Zink Company, LLC)

FLAME SCANNERS

Flame scanners, essential parts of the burner management system, ensure fuel to the burner is stopped if no stable flame is present. This prevents fuel from continuing to enter the furnace, which could cause an explosion if unburned fuel is ignited by the hot refractory.

The scanners monitor individual burners and respond to the presence or absence of a flame by producing an electrical output to the burner management system. They may also respond to the stability of the flame in each burner. The scanner must monitor the flame continuously and give quick output response if the flame changes. The scanner must be unaffected by radiation from neighboring burners or from the furnace background.

Figure 13 shows an ultraviolet flame scanner mounted on a burner. The scanner aims into the main body of the flame, but may require adjusting to suit firing conditions. If the scanner fails to see a flame for four seconds, the burner management system shuts off the fuel to the burner.

| Figure 13 | Burner with Flame Scanner |

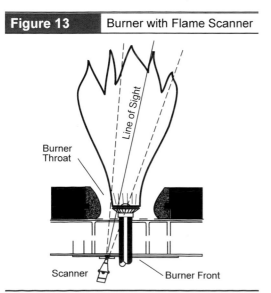

OBJECTIVE 4

Describe the fuel gas supply system to the burners and explain the purpose of the major fittings.

FUEL GAS SUPPLY SYSTEM

The fuel gas supply system consists of the piping, valves, and associated equipment required to deliver a stable fuel gas supply to the burners. It includes the main fuel control valve, burner safety shutoff valves and associated piping.

Figure 14 illustrates such a design, supplying 4 burners.

- The gas flows through a strainer "O" which removes any particulates or debris.
- There is a manual shutoff valve, T, which the field operator can use to isolate the supply. The gas can be vented using the manual vent V.
- The pressure regulator, "J", reduces the supply pressure and ensures a constant gas pressure to the main fuel control valves.
- Pressure gauge, "P1", allows monitoring of the pressure upstream of the main fuel control valve.
- Since the gas pressure is critical, there are high-pressure and low-pressure switches "Q" & "R", which trip the system off line if their respective pressure limits are exceeded.
- The safety valve, "K", protects this section from high pressure if the upstream regulator fails.
- The main fuel and bypass fuel control valves regulate the fuel pressure to the burners. They control the firing rate of the heater. Normally these valves are controlled by a remote system, located in the control room, but can also be controlled from a local field control panel, when starting or shutting down the unit. Downstream of the main fuel gas control valves the pressure is at burner supply pressure.
- A main shut off valve, "A", isolates all burners if a common shutdown condition arises (such as high-pressure or low-pressure) and the valve is "commanded" to close by the burner management system.
- A burner header vent valve, "C:, will also open to depressure the burner header.
- Each burner has a manual shutoff valve, labelled "SS" (which stands for supervisory shutoff valve) and a burner safety shutoff valve, "B". The latter is controlled by the burner management system and the individual flame scanner.

Figure 14 | Fuel Gas System for Multi-Burner Heater

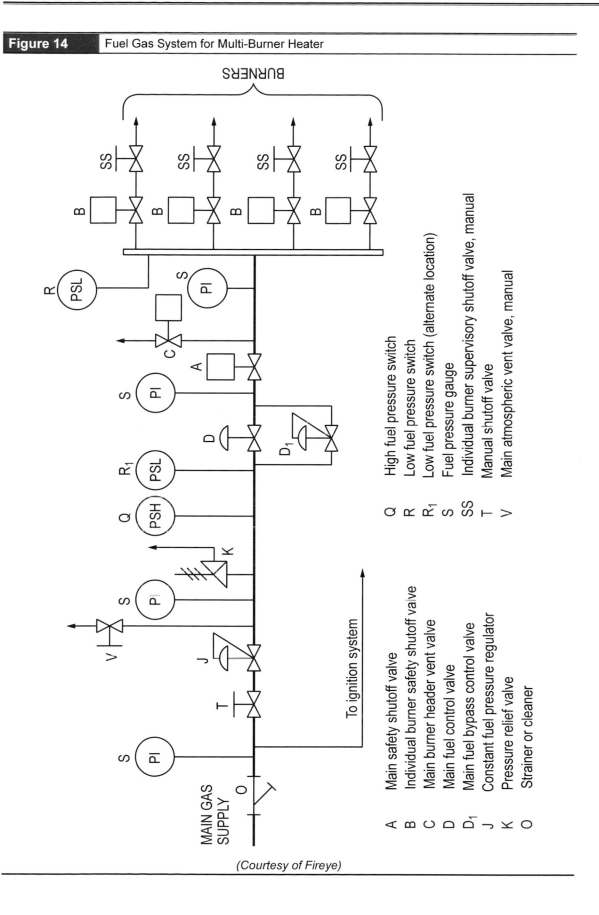

(Courtesy of Fireye)

A   Main safety shutoff valve
B   Individual burner safety shutoff valve
C   Main burner header vent valve
D   Main fuel control valve
D_1 Main fuel bypass control valve
J   Constant fuel pressure regulator
K   Pressure relief valve
O   Strainer or cleaner

Q   High fuel pressure switch
R   Low fuel pressure switch
R_1 Low fuel pressure switch (alternate location)
S   Fuel pressure gauge
SS   Individual burner supervisory shutoff valve, manual
T   Manual shutoff valve
V   Main atmospheric vent valve, manual

An example of a field control cabinet is shown in Figure 15. It normally contains the burner management controls, such as purge timers, and relays.

Figure 15	Fuel Gas System Piping with Field Control Cabinet

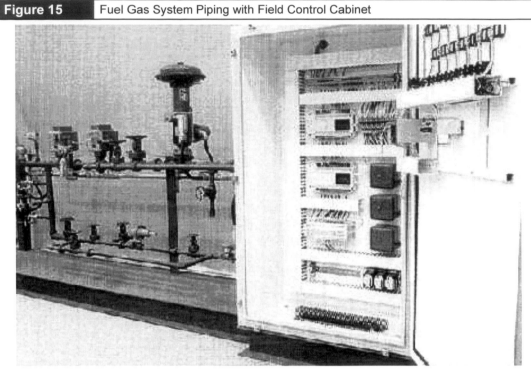

(Courtesy of Born Canada)

OBJECTIVE 5

Describe the monitoring, control, and shutdown devices on a typical heater.

HEATER MONITORING

Controlling heater operation requires knowledge of the heater temperatures, including the process fluid (in the various tube locations) and the flue gases. Most heaters have thermocouples permanently mounted in critical locations, which usually include:

- Process fluid at the inlet to the convection section.
- Process fluid between the convection section and radiant section.
- Process fluid at the outlet of the radiant section.
- Process fluid In multiple pass heaters, a common inlet thermocouple, plus an intermediate and outlet thermocouple in each pass.
- Flue gas above and below the convection section.
- Tubes in the hottest section of the furnace may have thermocouples attached to them to monitor metal temperatures.

Draft Monitoring

Draft is the difference in pressure between the inside of the heater and the outside. In natural draft heaters, the pressure inside the heater is lower than the outside. Draft is created in natural draft heaters by the heating of the flue gases, making them lighter and less dense. The flue gases then rise up the heater and out the stack. Flue gas leaving the stack is replaced by ambient air drawn in through the air registers.

The draft is very small, measured in fractions of an inch of water column or in millimeters of mercury. Draft measurement is done with draft gauges, special types of inclined manometers. An example is shown in Figure 16.

Figure 16	Draft Manometer

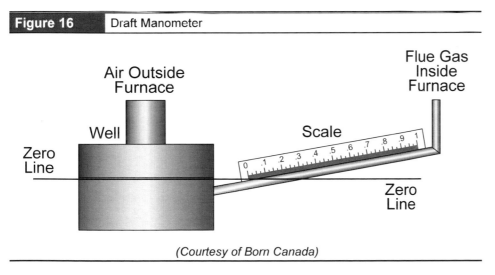

(Courtesy of Born Canada)

The draft sampling system must be air tight because of the very small pressures being measured. Any leakage into the sampling lines or tubes will cause a false reading. Normal areas to measure draft are near the floor of the firebox, just below the convection section, and in the duct above the convection section, as shown in Figure 17.

Figure 17	Draft Sample Points

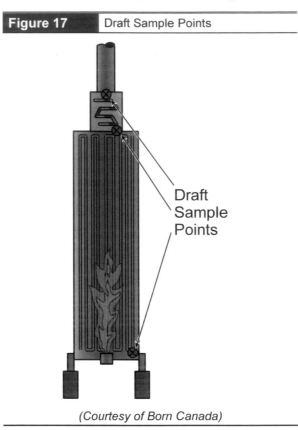

Draft Sample Points

(Courtesy of Born Canada)

Excess Air

To efficiently burn all of the fuel in a heater, the air flow must be optimized to the fuel flow. The burner registers control the amount of air entering the heater, while the stack damper (at the base of the stack) controls the draft. This determines the amount of flue gas leaving the heater. There should be excess air entering the heater to ensure that all fuel is burned. Excess air is air that is over and above what is needed for perfect combustion of the fuel.

Most fired heaters do not have sophisticated controls for excess air or draft. A reasonable estimate of whether there is sufficient excess air can be made by observing the burner flames. A good gas flame should be a translucent blue colour, with orange tips. Long yellow or orange flames indicate too little excess air. If the flame has no yellow or orange tip and is shorter than normal, there is too much excess air. To roughly set the air flow, reduce the air until the flame starts to turn orange, then increase the air slightly.

To more accurately determine the excess air, an oxygen analyzer should be used on the flue gas. After the oxygen percent is determined by the analyzer, the excess air can be obtained from a chart. For example, 4% oxygen in the flue gas gives about 23% excess air. An oxygen reading of 2% to 5% is typical, which equates to about 10% to 30% excess air.

In heaters with forced draft, the air flow is usually measured. The gas flow and the air flow can then be put on ratio control. This ratio is determined by oxygen analysis and flame observation, when the heater controls are initially set up. An online oxygen analyzer can be used to "fine-tune" the controls.

Figure 18 is a chart that illustrates the steps (procedure) required to adjust the draft and excess air on a natural draft furnace, bringing them both to their predetermined targets. The steps can be summarized as follows:

- Start the heater
- Check and adjust the draft: Depending on the reading follow the "high" or "Low" side of the chart. Check the oxygen and make adjustments to the damper or the air registers as shown. Repeat until the draft is on target.
- Check and adjust the oxygen: Adjust the air registers as indicated until the oxygen is on target.
- Return to the start and repeat adjustments if necessary to fine tune.

Figure 18	Draft Adjustment Chart

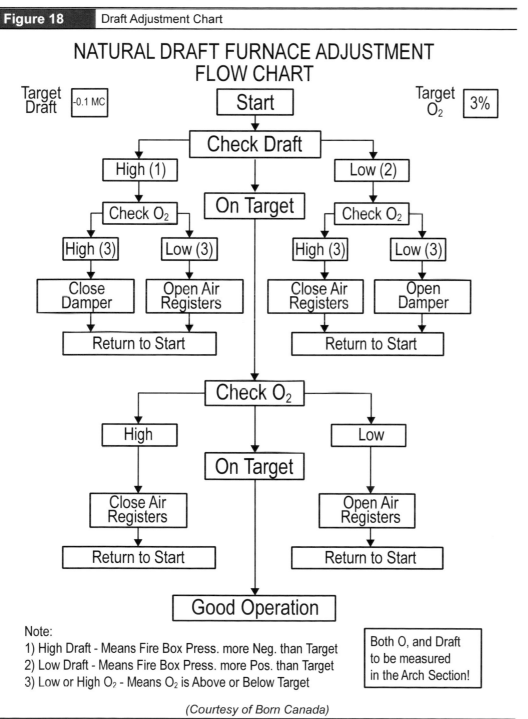

NATURAL DRAFT FURNACE ADJUSTMENT FLOW CHART

Note:
1) High Draft - Means Fire Box Press. more Neg. than Target
2) Low Draft - Means Fire Box Press. more Pos. than Target
3) Low or High O_2 - Means O_2 is Above or Below Target

Both O_2 and Draft to be measured in the Arch Section!

(Courtesy of Born Canada)

Protective Devices

Fired heaters require careful operation and properly functioning safety devices. The process liquid in the heater tubes is often flammable. An overheated tube could fail and spray flammable liquid into the furnace. If the process flow and the burners are not immediately stopped the heater could be destroyed and other equipment in the vicinity could be in danger.

To prevent such incidents, fired heaters are fitted with several shutdown devices. Also, there are pre-alarms, which alarm to the control room or a field panel before the actual trip is activated.

Shutdown devices that are common to most fired heaters include:

- Emergency shutdown switch: This is a manually activated switch that the operator can use in an emergency. There is usually a switch in the field and another in the control room.
- High or low fuel gas pressure shutdowns: These switches shut down the heater if the fuel gas pressure becomes too low or too high.
- Flame Failure: The burner flame scanners will shut off the fuel supply to individual burners if a stable flame is not seen.
- High stack temperature: This trip is set to guard against the overheating of the heater process coils. It is a signal that the heater is firing too hard. It also may indicate a tube leak inside the heater, with the leaking process fluid (if combustible) adding fuel to the furnace.
- Low process flow: If the flow of process fluid through the tubes is low or interrupted for some reason, the tubes could quickly overheat. The heater is shutdown until a normal minimum flow can be is re-established.

OBJECTIVE 6

Explain a heater start-up procedure, including the lighting of additional burners once flame is established. Explain heater shutdown procedure.

HEATER STARTUP PROCEDURE

A burner management system is attached to most process heaters to ensure that the burners will be lit and controlled safely. After lighting, control is transferred to the automatic control system only when safe to do so.

Figure 19 illustrates the start sequence of such a system.

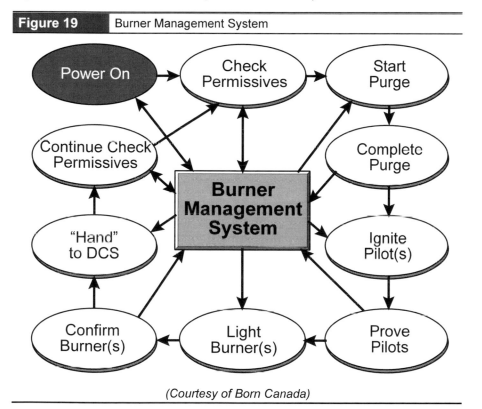

| Figure 19 | Burner Management System |

(Courtesy of Born Canada)

The sequence begins with the power being turned on to the burner management system, allowing the subsequent steps to proceed.

Permissives are checked before the purge can be started. Permissives are conditions that must be satisfied before the sequence can proceed. These include:

- Fuel valves to the pilots and burners must be in closed position
- The stack damper must be open
- The fuel gas supply pressure to the pilots and burners must be in acceptable operating range
- Other safety conditions specific to this heater must be met

When all permissives are confirmed, purging of the heater is initiated to ensure there are no combustibles in the furnace. Completion of the purge is determined by time or by testing of the stack gases for traces of combustibles.

When purge is complete, the burner management system will allow the pilots to be lit. When fuel enters the pilots, they are ignited by hand or by electric spark type igniters. Pilot ignition must be prompt to ensure unburned fuel gas does not accumulate in the furnace before ignition, causing a puff or explosion. Normally, if the flame scanners don't detect flame at the pilot burners within 10 seconds of the gas valves opening, the pilot gas will close. If this happens, the sequence must be restarted.

If the pilot flame is detected by the scanner, the burner management system opens the fuel valves to the main burner. The burner is ignited by the pilot flame. The main flame must be verified by the flame scanner within a certain time; otherwise the burner gas valve will close.

After the first burner is lit and the load on the heater is increasing (more flow through the process coils), more burners will be automatically lit.

When the main burners are proven and stable, the burner management system will allow control of the heater to be switched from hand to automatic. It will then continue to monitor all operating permissives.

HEATER SHUTDOWN PROCEDURE

As the process load is reduced, the firing rate of the heater is reduced. This causes the burner pressure to drop, unless individual burners are shut down. Therefore, when the burner pressure approaches the low-level trip setting a burner should be shut off. When only one burner remains and the burner pressure is low; the heater is on minimum firing.

When process conditions permit, the last burner may be shut off. The individual burner shutoff valves will be closed. The fuel supply system shutoff valve can now be closed.

The process flow should be maintained through the tubes until all burners are off.

Air flow through the heater may be maintained to cool the heater or, if the heater is to be restarted in a short time, the stack damper and air registers may be shut to keep the heater warm.

OBJECTIVE 7

Describe the design, components and operation of a typical horizontal, indirect-fired heater such as a salt bath heater.

Indirect fired heaters are heaters in which the flue gas never contacts the process heating tubes. The burner firetube is immersed in a bath containing an intermediate fluid. A process fluid heating coil is also immersed in the bath. The firetube transfers heat to the bath, which in turn heats the fluid flowing in the process tubes.

The three major components of an indirect fired heater are the shell or heat media reservoir, a burner and fire tube, and a process coil bundle. The shell usually operates at atmospheric pressure, although some steam bath heaters operate at a low pressure. An expansion tank or reservoir is attached to the top of the shell. The operating liquid level in the shell is maintained above the process tube bundle.

Figure 20 shows a heater with expansion tank and level glass.

Figure 20	Indirect Fired Heater and Coil Assemblies

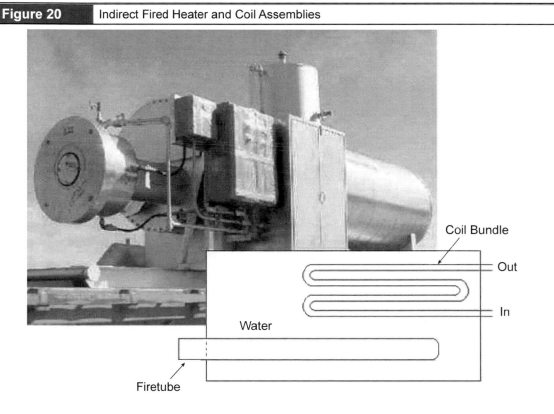

(Courtesy of Natco Canada Ltd.)

Figure 21 shows a firetube from an indirect heater. The firetube is immersed in the heat transfer fluid and the burner is connected to the inlet of the firetube. The end of the firetube protrudes from the top of the heater, forming an exhaust stack. The smooth bends of the firetube promote a low pressure drop and help create the required natural draft.

Figure 21	Heater Firetube

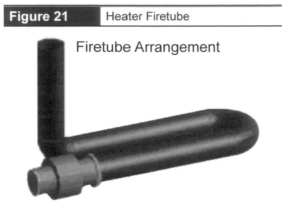

Firetube Arrangement

(Courtesy of Natco Canada Ltd.)

Indirect fired heaters use different heat transfer liquids or media for different temperature applications. The most common media are water, glycol, oil, and salt solutions.

Water bath heaters have a process outlet temperature range up to 90°C. In colder climates, glycol is mixed with water to reduce the freezing point of the media to -40°C. The outlet temperature range is also raised slightly to 110°C. The glycol also contains corrosion inhibitors, to protect the coils from corrosion and pitting.

Figure 22 shows a steam bath heater.

In the steam bath heater, only the fire tubes are immersed in the water bath. Saturated steam is produced as the firetube heat evaporates the water. The process coil is located in the steam space above the water level where it is heated by the steam. These systems operate safely with steam pressures up to 100 kPa and process outlet temperatures up to 100°C.

Figure 22	Steam Bath Heater

(Courtesy of Gas Tech Engineering)

Oil bath heaters are designed to use a variety of special heat transfer oils surrounding the firebox and the process heating coil. They provide uniform heat transfer to process fluids at medium temperatures. Process fluid outlet temperature range up to 260°C. The oil also protects the heating tubes from general corrosion and pitting.

Salt bath heaters use molten (melted) salt mixtures as the heat transfer media. Since the salt is stable at high temperatures, the salt bath can be operated at higher temperatures than oil, with process outlet temperatures up to 400°C. The salt is a mixture of sodium nitrite, potassium nitrite and potassium nitrate, which has a fairly low melting point, around 140°C. Salt baths are not corrosive to the coils or shell.

Figure 23 shows a typical salt bath heater arrangement.

Figure 23   Salt Bath Indirect Fired Heater

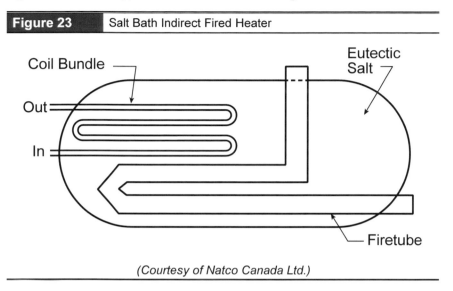

(Courtesy of Natco Canada Ltd.)

OBJECTIVE 8

Explain start-up and shutdown procedures for an indirect-fired heater.

INDIRECT FIRED HEATER - OPERATIONS

Indirect fired heaters have relatively simple firing systems. They are often located in remote areas, so are designed to operate with very limited supervision. They usually burn natural gas or propane. The fuel is often preheated by passing it through a heating coil inside the heater shell. From the preheat coil, the fuel goes to the pilot and main burners. The pilot operates continuously. The main burner is turned off and on by a thermostat, which senses the heater bath temperature. For a glycol heater, the temperature is set at 80 to 90°C.

Heater Start-Up
- Before starting the heater, check the condition of all heater components. Check all piping and tubing. Ensure that all fittings and connections are tight and leak fast.
- Check the electrical supply to the heater and ensure the power is on.
- Inspect fuel pressure regulator and the burner damper. Ensure the burner damper moves freely.
- Ensure proper operating level of the heat transfer fluid is established in the heater. This level is always above the process heating coils.
- Close the isolation valves upstream of the main burner and pilot.
- Open the main inlet gas valve to the fuel gas manifold. Adjust the main burner fuel pressure regulator for 35 kPa to 140 kPa gas pressure at the burner.
- The pilot is usually lit using a portable igniter or small rag saturated with fuel oil on the end of a wire. The rag is ignited, making a small torch, which is inserted through the pilot burner opening, and held in front of the pilot.
- Open the pilot valve to ignite the pilot. Adjust the pilot gas pressure for a stable flame.
- Open the fuel gas to the main burner, which allows the burner to light. Adjust the burner flame by adjusting the gas and the secondary air. Adjust the burner according to the specific instructions of the burner manufacturer. Set all controls to obtain a stable blue flame. A yellow flame indicates insufficient air and will result in sooting of the burner and the fire tube.
- If there is more than one main burner, repeat the steps for the remaining burners.
- The main burner will burn at full rate until the desired heat transfer fluid temperature is reached. When the temperature is reached, the main burner will cycle on and off to maintain this temperature.

Normal Operation
With the pilot and main burner in operation, start the process stream flowing through the heating coil. To regulate the temperature of the fluid passing through the coil, adjust the setting of the thermostat, which will change the bath (heat transfer fluid) temperature.

Check the burner operation and the process outlet temperature often. The level of the heat transfer fluid and the overall condition of the heater should be observed as well.

Heater Shutdown
The heater can be shutdown by turning off the fuel supply valve. All residual gas in the burner manifold will be burnt off and the main burner and pilot flames will go out. The process stream to the coils can now be blocked in. The air damper can be closed.

CHAPTER 13 - QUESTIONS

1. Briefly describe four uses for direct fired heaters.

2. Using a simple sketch, describe a vertical, cylindrical direct-fired heater with radiant and convection heating coils.

3. Explain the difference between an inspirating gas burner and a raw gas type of burner.

4. Explain the locations of thermocouples in a direct-fired heater.

5. How can an operator determine if a fired heater is operating with the correct amount of excess air? What can be done to increase the amount of excess air to the heater?

6. What are four permissives that must be satisfied before a purge can be initiated, when starting a fired heater?

7. Using a simple sketch, describe an indirect fired heater. Name three common heat transfer fluids that are used in indirect fired heaters.

8. List four things that an operator would inspect or check around an indirect fired heater before starting it up.

ANSWERS: All answers are found within the content of the chapter.

Wastewater Treatment

LEARNING OUTCOME

When you complete this chapter you should be able to:

Explain the purpose, designs, processes and control of industrial wastewater treatment.

LEARNING OBJECTIVES

Here is what you should be able to do when you complete each objective:

1. *State the purpose of wastewater treatment, list typical waste liquids, and explain the legislation and permitting, including parameters, for the disposal of wastewater.*

2. *Sketch an industrial wastewater treatment system and describe the processes that occur at each stage of treatment.*

3. *Describe the equipment and process involved in the removal of suspended solids from wastewater, including screening, flotation, and sedimentation.*

4. *Describe the equipment and process involved in the removal of colloidal solids from wastewater, including chemical coagulation, flocculation, and clarification.*

5. *Describe the equipment and process involved in the biological removal of solids from wastewater, including activated sludge, rotating biological contactors, and trickling filters.*

6. *Describe the control strategy for a wastewater treatment system. Define and explain the control of and sampling points for the main control parameters, including nutrients, BOD, COD, pH, and settle ability.*

OBJECTIVE 1

State the purpose of wastewater treatment, list typical waste liquids, and explain the legislation and permitting, including parameters, for the disposal of wastewater.

PURPOSE OF WASTEWATER TREATMENT

When water is used in our homes or industries, it can be mixed with undesirable materials. The water quality then becomes unacceptable for return to the environment until the contaminants are removed or reduced. The purpose of wastewater treatment is to remove and properly dispose of contaminants (pollutants) by the most practical and economic means, and then disinfect the wastewater before it is discharged to the receiving water.

WASTE LIQUIDS

The following is a list of typical waste liquids that can be found throughout industries and plants in Canada:

- Cooling tower blowdown water
- Storm water runoff from rain and melting snow
- Boiler blowdown water
- Water used for processing in industrial plants
- Agricultural pesticides

Wastewater Parameters

There are various factors that affect the quality of water:

- Toxicity
- Acidity
- Oxygen demand levels
- Temperature

Each of these must be controlled within certain parameters before the water can be discharged back into the environment.

Toxicity

Wastewater contains various chemicals that, in certain concentrations, cause adverse affects on the health and well being of human life. These effects are referred to as toxicity. Some of these chemicals and their maximum allowable concentrations are shown in Table 1.

Table 1	Chemical Concentrations
Chemical	**Maximum Allowable Concentration**
Cadmium	0.005 mg/L
Benzene	0.005 mg/L
Malathion	0.019 mg/L
Chromium	0.05 mg/L
Lead	0.010 mg/L

Acidity

Acidity of water is indicated by a pH value on a scale of zero to fourteen. A pH of seven (7) is neutral, less than seven is acidic, and above 7 is basic. The closer to zero pH, the more acidic is the water. The pH of wastewater must be between 6.5 and 8.5. If the wastewater has the ability to push the pH level of the receiving water beyond safe limits, then aquatic life may be adversely affected or the water may be unfit for other uses.

Oxygen Demand Levels

Oxygen levels in water are affected by the number of bacteria and protozoa that feed on organic waste in the water and by the chemicals that oxidize (use oxygen) in the water.

Biochemical oxygen demand (BOD) is the rate at which microorganisms consume oxygen in water at 20°C, while decomposing organic waste matter.

Chemical oxygen demand (COD) is the amount of oxygen consumed by chemical oxidants in the water. If BOD and COD rates are too high, oxygen levels in the water may be reduced enough to adversely affect fish and aquatic plant life.

Temperature

Temperature affects the ability of water to retain dissolved oxygen. High temperature water should not be dumped into receiving water since the increase in temperature deaerates (removes air) the water and increases oxygen demand. Where the temperature of a stream or lake will be affected by higher temperature wastewater, some method of cooling must be employed to reduce the wastewater temperature to near that of the receiving stream.

Retention ponds are used to allow wastewater to cool. Long serpentine channels are also useful, where the warm wastewater water may travel several kilometres before dumping into the stream. Cooling towers are also used. One advantage of cooling towers is that the wastewater is exposed to air, which increase the dissolved oxygen content of the water.

LEGISLATION

Government agencies establish guidelines for water quality and wastewater discharge. Following are a few of the commonly used acronyms that may be encountered when reviewing information on wastewater.

- CCME – Canadian Council of Ministers of the Environment
- CEQG – Canadian Environmental Quality Guidelines
- CWQG – Canadian Water Quality Guidelines
- US EPA – United States Environmental Protection Agency

In Canada, the Canadian Environmental Protection Act includes waste water quality regulations, which apply only to federal government operations, federal lands and aboriginal lands.

Each province and territory has its own environmental act and regulations. In Alberta, for example, the pertinent act is the Environmental Protection and Enhancement Act.

The Canadian Council of Ministers of the Environment (CCME) is a cooperative group of all provincial/territorial ministers with the intent of reaching a "common level of environmental quality across Canada". It is a recommending group only and does not have legislative authority.

Sketch an industrial wastewater treatment system and describe the processes that occur at each stage of treatment.

INDUSTRIAL WASTEWATER TREATMENT PLANT

Each industrial plant has its own unique wastewater treatment requirements, which depend upon the type of wastewater produced. However, Figure 1 illustrates one wastewater treatment system in a small to medium sized industrial plant, with components that are typical to most plants. The circled numbers in Figure 1 indicate various steps in the treatment process.

Figure 1	Industrial Wastewater Treatment Plant

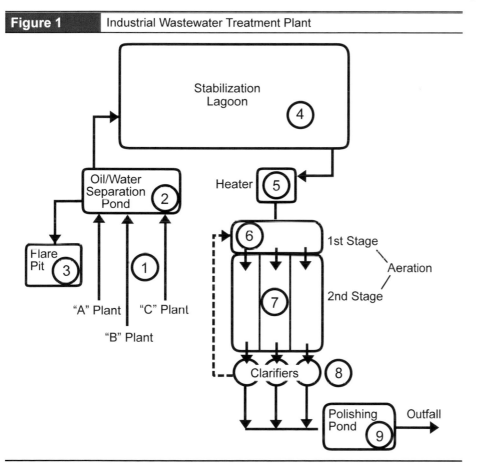

Collection System (1)

Wastewater from all plant components is drained by gravity to the oil/water separation pond. Piping must be large enough to handle flow from individual buildings. If the plant is not built on a slope, lift pumps may be required to raise wastewater from collection tanks to the oil/water separation pond.

Oil/Water Separation Pond (2)

Oil and scum float to the top of the pond where it is skimmed off and sent to the flare pit (3). Gravity causes heavy materials to settle to the bottom of the pond. The pond should be large enough to retain average flow for two to four days to allow reasonable separation. Effluent from the collection pond is drawn off halfway between the surface and the bottom, so that it does not collect floating material or sediment.

Flare Pit (3)

In the flare pit, waste hydrocarbons are burned off. The fire is assisted by a burner system for complete combustion.

Stabilization Lagoon (4)

Effluent from the oil/water separation pond either flows or is pumped to the stabilization lagoon, which is large enough to contain about one month's discharge from the plant. Compressed air is bubbled into the bottom of the lagoon through a grid system of pipes and diffuser heads. The rising bubbles circulate and diffuse dissolved oxygen through the liquid. Aerobic bacteria and other organisms use the dissolved oxygen to break down organic components in the wastewater.

Wastewater Heater (5)

The wastewater flows from the stabilizing lagoon to the wastewater heater. The heater increases the temperature of the water in preparation for the biological process that follows. The discharge from the heater flows to the first stage aeration tank.

First Stage Aeration Tank (6)

The incoming heated water mixes with activated sludge in the first stage aeration tank. Activated sludge has a high concentration of microorganisms that feed on the organic material in the flow. The wastewater remains in the first stage for three to six hours. Air diffusers in the bottom of the tank aerate and stir the wastewater continuously, supplying the oxygen required by the bacteria.

Second Stage Aeration Tank (7)

Flow enters one or more second stage aeration tanks where aeration and organic decomposition continues. Wastewater remains in these tanks for a much longer time (up to two days).

Clarifiers (8)

Clarifiers provide a location for the treated wastewater to separate by gravity from the sludge. A sludge pipe in the bottom of the clarifier removes a portion of the activated sludge and sends it back to the first stage aeration tank where microorganisms continue to break down any remaining organic material. The remainder of the sludge is sent to disposal. Plants with high sludge concentrations may further process the sludge. Clear water from the top of the clarifier flows to the polishing pond.

Polishing Pond (9)

The polishing pond is the final settling and aeration point for the effluent before it goes to the environment. Final adjustment of the clear water takes place over several days before it is sent to the outfall, which is the final discharge pipe.

OBJECTIVE 3

Describe the equipment and process involved in the removal of suspended solids from wastewater, including screening, flotation, and sedimentation.

GRIT REMOVAL

Grit includes sand and other heavy particles that settle out when the wastewater slows down. The grit is very abrasive and may cause wear and other damage to equipment, such as pumps.

A grit chamber is a tank that removes grit from the wastewater by allowing heavy particles to settle out. Heavy materials settle into a conical sump in the bottom of the grit chamber.

If the volume of grit is small enough that a conveyor system is not warranted, the grit chamber is usually cleaned whenever required by a vacuum truck. Alternatively, the chamber may be shut down and the material shoveled out by hand. If there is a substantial amount of grit, there may be an on-line method of handling the build up, such as a screw conveyer (auger) or a bucketed chain system that continuously or intermittently lifts the grit from the chamber. If the grit has a high organic content, it is washed as it is removed to a landfill for disposal.

SCREENS & SHREDDERS

If the wastewater is high in bulky or fibrous material, the material is either screened out or shredded, using a bar screen or a rotating screen. A bar screen consists of vertical or horizontal steel bars.

- A vertical unit, called a **barminutor**, has a high-speed shredder that traverses the bar screen, shredding any material that accumulates on the face of the screen. The bars can be manually cleaned if the quantity of trapped material is low, or mechanically cleaned if quantities are higher.

- With a rotating trash screen, called a **comminutor**, material accumulates on the screen face. It is intermittently rotated and a jet of water helps to clean the material off the screen. If the material on the screen is high in organics, it is not as acceptable as landfill material. If the material should be processed rather than disposed of, then the material is shredded rather than removed.

In municipal wastewater systems, the removal of cans, rags, sticks, plastics, sand, gravel and other inorganic material is carried out in grit chambers and screen sections. This removal section is often referred to as the **headworks**.

FLOTATION & SEDIMENTATION

Introducing small air bubbles causes suspended materials to rise and float to the surface of a liquid, from where they can be skimmed off. Sludge may also be subjected to gravity separation, which can be enhanced by adding chemicals that promote settling.

When air and water are combined under pressure, the air dissolves in the water. If this mixture is then depressurized, the air escapes as tiny bubbles (like carbon dioxide bubbling out of soda pop when the cap is removed). This principle is applied in a flotation tank.

Figure 2 shows a flotation tank.

- Clear effluent from the tank is returned to a dissolved air tank where it is pressurized with compressed air.
- The air/water mixture enters the flotation tank along with activated sludge influent.
- Tiny bubbles escape from the water and attach to suspended material, floating it to the top of the tank where the concentrated sludge is skimmed off by a slow moving skimmer.
- The concentrated sludge is then sent to a dewatering process or directly to disposal.

Figure 2	Flotation Tank

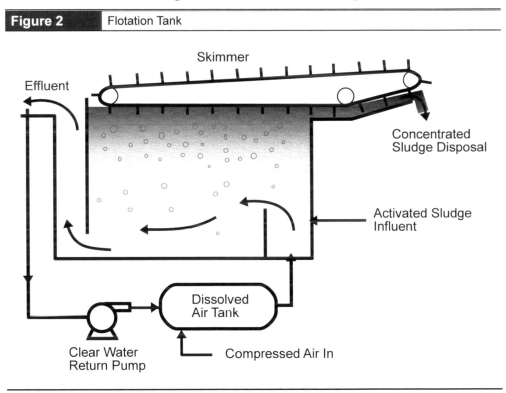

OBJECTIVE 4

Describe the equipment and process involved in the removal of colloidal solids from wastewater, including chemical coagulation, flocculation, and clarification.

COLLOIDAL MATERIALS

Colloidal particles are very small particles, ranging from 5 to 5000 ångström units in size. An ångström unit is 10^{-10} m (ie. 0.000 000 000 1 m). These particles are so small that they will not settle to the bottom or float to the top in water. They are too small for effective filtration. A high concentration of colloidal materials in water is unacceptable, especially if they are organic particles. For example, colloidal silica forms highly insulating, difficult to remove deposits in cooling water systems, boilers and turbines. Therefore, they must be removed.

COAGULATION

The tiny, colloidal particles in wastewater have the same (negative) charge and particles with the same charge repel each other. Unless the charges can be neutralized, the particles will remain tiny, suspended, and unable to settle out of the water. Coagulation is the process whereby the charges are neutralized, allowing the particles to attract each other and form heavier particles. Inorganic salts of aluminum (or iron) or organic polymers (polyeletrolytes) are added to the water and these chemicals, called "coagulants", interact with the particles to neutralize them. The particles then join together, forming larger particles, called "floc". This is the first step in wastewater clarification.

FLOCCULATION

The next step after coagulation is "flocculation". This brings together the floc that was formed in coagulation into even larger, heavier clumps, which can more readily settle out of the water. Often, additional chemicals, called flocculants (or coagulant aids), are added to the water, downstream of the coagulant, to enhance flocculation. Alternatively, a single chemical may be added, with the abilities of both a coagulant and a flocculant.

Figure 3 shows a simple clarifier, with a flash mixing section, where the coagulant is added and coagulation begins. This is followed by a flocculation section and, finally, a settling section. This overall combination of processes is called "clarification", with clear effluent being produced.

Figure 3	Simple Wastewater Clarifier

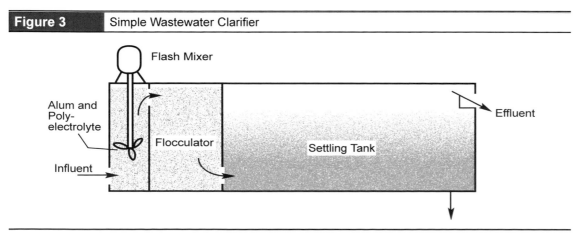

CLARIFIER

Figure 4 shows another design of clarifier, which may or may not have a flash mixer (Fig. 3) preceding it. If coagulant aids are used, then there is usually a flash mixer before the clarifier. The clarifier is a circular, cone-shaped vessel, as shown.

The conical clarifier described here is located downstream of the aeration tanks. One of its main purposes is to act as the final clarifier in the wastewater process, separating and settling out the sludge that carries out of the aeration tanks. It operates as follows:

- Mixed liquid from the aeration tanks enters the clarifier near the top and is directed downward by an internal baffle.
- Air is bubbled into one leg of the "U" tube syphon and acts as a "pump" to return scum or activated sludge from the top of the inlet section back to the aeration tanks.
- Sludge, being heavier, settles to the bottom of the cone and forms a sludge bed.
- Clear liquid rises to the top and spills over the edge of a central collection trough, which directs the clear, liquid effluent to the outlet.
- A portion of the sludge from the bottom of the cone is returned to the aeration tanks, since it is still 'activated' with bacteria and is still useful in the aeration process.
- Excess (waste) sludge that is not recycled as activated sludge is discharged from the bottom of the cone and is dewatered or directly disposed of.

Figure 4 Clarifier

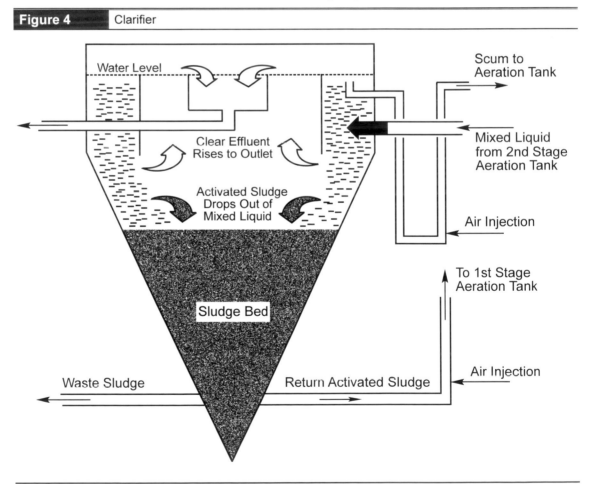

OBJECTIVE 5

Describe the equipment and process involved in the biological removal of solids from waste water, including activated sludge, rotating biological contactors, trickling filters.

BIOLOGICAL REMOVAL OF SOLIDS

Biological removal of solids means that microscopic living organisms are used to digest the solids from the wastewater. This can be achieved with the following processes:

- Activated sludge
- Rotating biological contactors
- Trickling filters

Activated Sludge

Wastewater is made to flow through a tank that contains a sludge bed composed of living bacteria. Air is injected into the tank and bubbles up through the water. The air bubbles provide the oxygen necessary for the bacteria in the activated sludge to live. These bacteria feed on the organic material in the wastewater and convert it to water and carbon dioxide.

The effluent from the activated sludge tanks enters secondary clarifiers (refer back to Fig. 4) and flows outward to effluent weirs along the edge of the clarifier. As the wastewater flows outward, the biological mass settles to the bottom of the clarifier. Collector arms rotate around the bottom of the clarifier collecting the biological mass (solids) that has settled. This biological mass contains active healthy growing bacteria that have developed in the aeration tanks.

Rotating Biological Contactors

A rotating biological contactor (RBC), shown in Figure 5, is an aeration device for reducing the biological oxygen demand (BOD) of a liquid effluent. The RBC consists of a series of discs, up to two meters long, made from stacks of pie-shaped plastic sheets. The sheets are spaced about 19 mm apart by cones on their surfaces. The discs are arranged radially around a shaft so that each section resembles a large drum. There may be up to four sections on one shaft. RBC units are usually contained in a covered structure, particularly in colder climates.

Figure 5	Rotating Biological Contactor

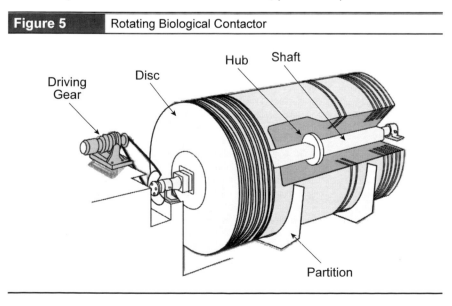

The shaft is mounted just above the level of the wastewater so that more than half of the RBC is exposed to air.

- The unit slowly rotates (one or two r/min), dipping the sheets into the wastewater and then out into the air again. Wastewater flows axially along the unit. The individual sections may be baffled from the adjacent sections to allow enough contact time and to prevent rapid flow-through of unprocessed material.
- A biological film of microscopic organisms develops on the surface of the sheets. The organisms consume organics in the wastewater. A layer of sludge forms and sloughs off when it becomes thick enough.
- The sludge is carried away in the effluent stream and is later separated by gravity settling.

An RBC can maintain a higher biological population than a conventional activated sludge plant. As a result an RBC can be relatively small, and the effluent may have a BOD value of less than 20 mg/L. Flow balancing and management systems are advisable if high quality effluents and, in particular, if low ammonia nitrogen values are to be achieved routinely.

Trickling Filters

A trickling filter, shown in Figure 6, consists of a permeable media bed of rock, slag, or plastic through which wastewater trickles. Rock or slag beds can be up to 70 metres in diameter and 1 to 3 metres deep with rock size varying from 25 mm to 100 mm. Packed plastic filters are narrower and deeper, 4 m to 12 m, more like towers.

- The organic material in the wastewater is absorbed by a population of microorganisms (fungi, algae and protozoa) attached to the media as a biological film or slime layer (approximately 0.1 to 0.2 mm thick). The film is formed by microorganisms in the water that gradually attach themselves to the media surface. The aerobic microorganism in the outer layer of the film degrades the organic material.
- As the layer thickens with microbial growth, oxygen can no longer penetrate to the media face, and anaerobic (don't require air to live) organisms develop.
- As the biological film continues to grow, the microorganisms next to the surface lose their ability to cling to the media, and a portion of the layer falls off. This is known as sloughing and is the main source of solids picked up by the underdrain system.
- This design includes an open drain system, which collects the filtrate as well as solids. This drain system also serves as a source of air for the microorganisms.
- The treated wastewater and solids are piped to a settling tank where the solids are separated. Some of the liquid is then recirculated back to the trickling filter to dilute the incoming wastewater and keep the filter moist.
- Successful operation requires that sufficient air be available, so large ventilation ports are located at the bottom of the filter to create natural draft.

Figure 6	Trickling Filter

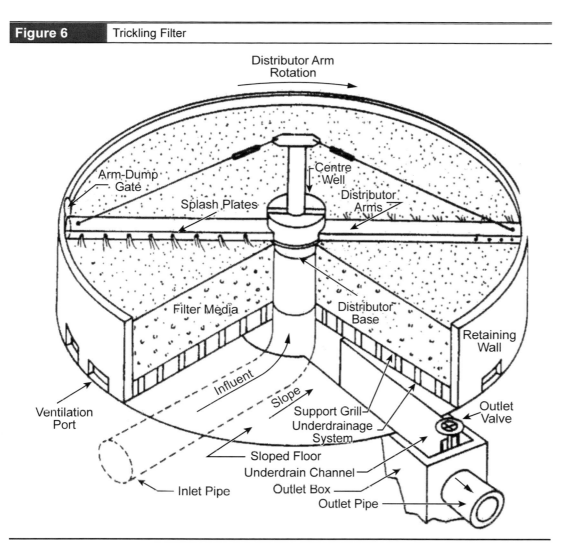

Anaerobic Digesters

In the anaerobic process, activated sludge and primary sludge are combined in a covered digester tank. The digesters must be heated since the process occurs at an optimal temperature around 37°C. The process takes about 25 days and can be used in conjunction with other treatments for more complete destruction. Naturally occurring anaerobic bacteria break down the organic contents of the sludge into stable substances such as water, carbon dioxide and methane. The digested sludge becomes less odorous, and most of the disease-causing organisms are destroyed. The methane gas produced can be used as fuel gas to heat the process. Any excess gas can be used in internal combustion engines to produce electrical power.

OBJECTIVE 6

Describe the control strategy for a wastewater treatment system. Define and explain the control of and sampling points for the main control parameters, including nutrients, BOD, COD, pH, and settleability.

CONTROL STRATEGY

Control strategies are as diverse as the types of treatment plants. If a plant operates in a steady-state condition, year in and year out, there won't be much variation in the treatment requirements. If the plant experiences seasonal, high load conditions, the wastewater will reflect these changes. Topographical features around the plant may cause storm water or snow melt to enter the wastewater flow. This will change the ratio of organic to inorganic material in the flow stream and also dilute the flow.

The wastewater treatment plant may be viewed as a "bug farm". If the "bugs" are happy, then the process is operating properly. If the nutrient supply in the water suddenly decreases, then the bugs will starve. The ideal occurs when new microorganisms (as in activated sludge) are introduced to a fresh flow of nutrient rich wastewater. When the quantity of material in the wastewater is properly matched to the right quantity and type of microorganisms, and conditions are optimized, then the wastewater treatment will meet or exceed the expectations for the plant.

SAMPLE POINTS

In most processes the usual sample point is at the end of a process to ensure that the desired conditions have been met. In a wastewater treatment plant it is also important that inlet samples be taken, since a change in inlet conditions may necessitate a change in the operating strategy of the plant.

Nutrients

Domestic wastewater is usually high in the nutrients required for plant growth. Phosphorus and nitrogen compounds are removed from the wastewater in a process known as the biological phosphorus and nitrogen removal process (BPNR). In the BPNR process, there are three different zones in which different naturally occurring microorganisms perform their function. The three zones are:

- Anaerobic, which has no dissolved oxygen
- Anoxic, which has no dissolved oxygen but does have nitrite
- Aerobic, which has dissolved oxygen

In the anaerobic chamber, bacteria release stored phosphorus. As the bacteria progress to the aerobic chamber they absorb more phosphorus than they release. When these bacteria are sent to waste along with the activated sludge, they carry off the excess phosphorus.

Nitrifying bacteria in the aerobic zone, through the nitrification process, convert ammonia (NH_3) to nitrite (NO_2) and further to nitrate (NO_3). Denitrifying bacteria in the anoxic zone convert the nitrate (NO_3) to nitrogen gas (N_2). The nitrogen gas then escapes into the atmosphere.

Oxygen Demand

The biochemical oxygen demand (BOD, also called biological oxygen demand) test is used to determine how much oxygen is being used by the aerobic microorganisms. The chemical oxygen demand (COD) is the amount of oxygen required to degrade the organic compounds in the wastewater. Tests for BOD and COD give a good indication of the effectiveness of the treatment process. If a sample has a high oxygen demand, there are still organic compounds in the wastewater that have not been degraded. If the discharged wastewater has a large COD it will demand more oxygen from the river or lake into which it flows.

In the BOD test, a measured amount of wastewater sample is placed in a bottle that is half-filled with buffered, nutrient enriched water. The top of the bottle contains air. A mercury manometer is attached to the bottle and the process is sealed. The bottle is incubated and stirred for five days. As the bacteria consume the organic material in the wastewater, oxygen from the air above the sample is removed, causing a reduction in pressure. A chemical contained in the bottle cap removes carbon dioxide, generated by the bacteria, and the pressure drop reflects the amount of oxygen consumed. The reduction of pressure in the bottle causes the mercury in the manometer to rise to produce the reading. The manometer is calibrated to read mg/L of BOD.

pH Control

Varying conditions and temperatures in each stage of treatment may cause a change in the pH level. The different reactions in each stage may require a change of pH for optimum process conditions. If, however, the flow becomes too acidic or too alkaline, it must be adjusted. If a sample showed that the pH had dropped too low (becoming too acidic), the addition of an alkaline solution such as sodium hydroxide would bring the flow back within parameters. Likewise, if the process became too alkaline, the addition of an acid would be necessary.

Settleability

Samples are drawn from the clarifier to determine if the sludge is separating properly from the flow stream. A sample is placed in a 1000 ml, graduated cylinder and left to stand. After 30 minutes, the sample is examined to determine if the sludge is settling with a clean, well defined line between sludge and clear water. The level of sludge in the cylinder also indicates the quantity of sludge settling out. If the settling is unacceptable, the process must be adjusted, either in aeration for a given time period, or in the food to microorganism ratio (which is adjusted by activated sludge return).

CHAPTER 14 - QUESTIONS

1. With the aid of a simple sketch, describe the various stages involved in the operation of a wastewater treatment system.

2. Explain how colloidal particles are removed from wastewater.

3. With the aid of a simple sketch, describe the operation of a clarifier.

4. Describe the floatation process for removal of material from wastewater.

5. What is a valuable by-product of anaerobic digestion and how is it utilized?

6. Explain the operation of a trickling filter.

ANSWERS: All answers are found within the content of the chapter.

Plant Maintenance & Administration

LEARNING OUTCOME

When you complete this chapter you should be able to:

> *Explain typical components of maintenance and administration programs for utilities and process facilities.*

LEARNING OBJECTIVES

Here is what you should be able to do when you complete each objective:

1. *Explain typical communication and accountability structures within a large facility, including the responsibilities for external communication.*

2. *Describe the typical components and responsibilities of scheduled and preventive maintenance management programs.*

3. *Explain the importance and extent of record keeping and describe the quality and content requirements for operating logbooks and records.*

4. *Using a complete boiler turnaround and inspection as an example, describe project management using two methods, Gantt Chart and critical path.*

5. *Explain the importance of procedures in the operation of a facility and describe the application of well-written procedures to personnel training and daily operation.*

6. *Explain typical environmental monitoring and management programs for operating facilities.*

OBJECTIVE 1

Explain typical communication and accountability structures within a large facility, including the responsibilities for external communication.

COMMUNICATIONS STRUCTURE

An effective communications structure within an organization is one of the key ingredients for effective and efficient operation. Effective communication is the orderly exchange of information, ideas, attitudes, thoughts, opinions, and instructions.

Internal Communications

There are many internal communication methods in an organization, but they can be divided into three groups:

- **Written Communication**: includes reports, letters, instructions, notices, circulars, email and manuals. Examples of manuals are the Standard Policies and Procedures Manual, and the Emergency Procedures Manual.
- **Verbal Communication**: in the form of speeches, lectures, telephone conversations, explanations or instructions to staff, or putting a case before a meeting. Meetings, in their various formats, play a large part in establishing and maintaining good communication.
- **Visual Communication**: includes posters, charts, films, exhibits, overheads, models and any information that is presented by visual means.

External Communications

The communications structure of an organization must include not only internal communications, but also external communications, which involves customers, vendors, contractors, inspectors, the public, etc.

A good external communication policy is important for several reasons.

- It facilitates and promotes successful relationships with customers and with vendors and contractors who provide the equipment, supplies and services that are essential to the everyday operational success of an organization.
- An open communication policy with inspectors and government officials is equally important to ensure understanding and compliance with all legislation, regulations, licensing, permitting, etc. that directly affect the organization. Such communication, provided it's open and honest, fosters a good relationship which has lasting and valuable benefits for an organization.
- Communication with the public must be open and timely, particularly where the operation of a facility has the potential to directly impact, whether positively or negatively, on the interests of the public. Support of the public can be a major asset toward the success of an organization and open communication fosters that support.

Figure 1 shows a simple internal communication chart for a large organization. This example is intended to demonstrate that effective communications must flow freely, in both directions, between management and the various departments. The line between Maintenance and Operations illustrates that direct communications between various departments is also mandatory. In fact, there could be direct lines drawn between all departments, since maximum operational efficiency requires continuous communications between all.

| **Figure 1** | Simple Internal Communications Chart |

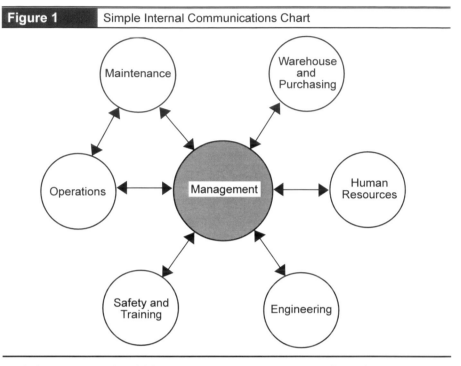

Each department should have its own communications flow chart. Some examples are shown in Figures 2 and 3. Both examples involve internal and external communication.

Referring to Figure 2, if the plant operator is having difficulty, for example, with the water treatment for the boilers, then the operator must relay this to the shift engineer (team leader). Depending on his/her level of authority, the team leader may then communicate with the water treatment consultant (vendor) to determine a solution and facilitate any ordering of chemicals with the warehouse and purchasing. The latter may be the responsibility of the Chief Engineer, who must be kept in the communication loop, along with the Production Superintendent, until the problem is resolved.

| **Figure 2** | Operations Communications Flow Chart |

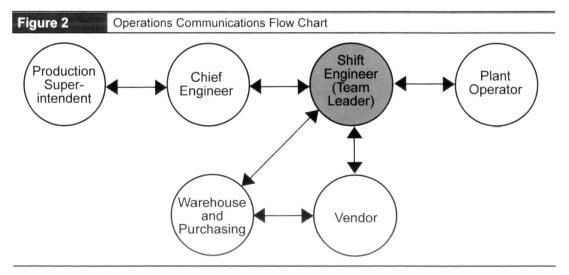

Referring to Figure 3, as an example, if a trades person discovers a problem during the preventive maintenance of a piece of equipment, he/she brings it to the attention of the trades team leader and the operations group. Together they should attempt to troubleshoot the problem, but if unsuccessful, the trades team leader will inform the maintenance superintendent and will contact the equipment vendor for assistance. The superintendent may ask the plant engineer for help, depending on the nature of the problem, and will have discussion with the production superintendent.   The same line of communication is followed if the original equipment problem is discovered by the operations personnel. It demonstrates the importance of good communications between operations and maintenance.

Figure 3	Maintenance Communications Flow Chart

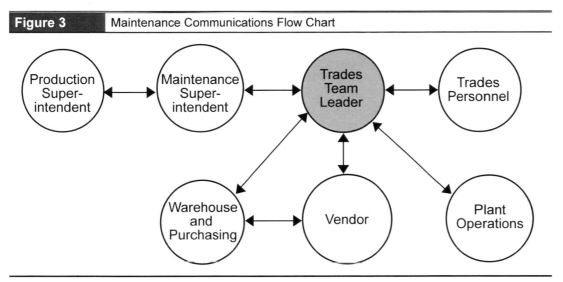

When a major piece of equipment must be overhauled or replaced the plant manger will become involved, since it will require the proper approvals for expenditure. If a plant is to be shut down for a turnaround, then those affected by the plant shut down (supply vendors, customers, contractors) must be notified.

In the event of an environmental issue, the environmental department must be made aware as soon as possible, so that the safety of the public can be ensured, and so regulatory authorities can be properly notified.

When a policy change or other key information must be communicated to everyone in the company, it is important that the communications structure allows timely and equal communication to all employees.

OBJECTIVE 2

Describe the typical components and responsibilities of scheduled and preventive maintenance management programs.

PREVENTIVE MAINTENANCE

The objective of a Preventive Maintenance (PM) program is to discover developing problems and to prevent equipment malfunctions and breakdowns. This is accomplished by the systematic inspection and servicing of the equipment. The main components of a PM program include, but are not limited to:

- List of all plant equipment
- PM inspection checklist for each piece of equipment
- Inspection frequency – monthly, bi-annually, annually, every two years, etc.
- Deficiency repairs and instrumentation adjustments and calibrations
- Record keeping
- Cost management policy

A successful PM program requires planning, estimating, scheduling, and controlling the maintenance work. Preventive maintenance work can be separated into two classifications:

1. **Mechanical work, consisting of:**
    - Inspecting
    - Adjusting
    - Tightening
    - Cleaning
    - Lubricating
    - Routine replacing of parts

2. **Paper work, consisting of:**
    - PM check lists
    - PM equipment history records
    - Preparing work orders
    - Parts inventory control

The overall maintenance program should include a list of all equipment requiring PM plus a PM inspection checklist for each. The checklist should allow the maintenance person to easily reference the listed items if mechanical repairs are determined to be necessary. The program should indicate the frequency of each PM, plus the frequency of regular, more extensive inspections. The latter are often reserved for times when the plant is shutdown or when standby equipment can be operated.

When the PM and/or any subsequent repairs are completed all related information should be entered into the PM Equipment History File. The history file is important, not only as a record-keeping exercise, but it allows trends to be observed, which can pinpoint recurrent problems. This allows adjustments to be made, if necessary, to the PM checklist and frequency.

Figure 4 is an example checklist for the PM of an air compressor. The major components of the compressor and checkpoints for each component are listed and space is provided to record the observations.

Figure 4	Preventive Maintenance Inspection Sheet

P. M. INSPECTION SHEET

Air Compressor _____ Check Sheet No. _____

Equipment No. S.P. 15 _____ Date _____

Monthly

1. Check V-Belt drive
2. Check lube oil
3. Check for vibration
4. Test high pressure cut out

   Low oil pressure cut out

   High temperature pressure cut out

   Low C. W. flow cut out
5. Check for noisy valves and proper unloader function
6. Clean air filter
7. Check motor bearing temperature and general condition

Inspected by: _____ Date _____

Remarks: _____

_____

_____

_____

Scheduled Maintenance Work

Scheduled maintenance is any maintenance, minor or major, that must be coordinated (ie. scheduled) between Maintenance and Operations departments. It may be the result of a regular schedule for that piece of equipment, a discovery made during a PM or during normal operation, or a sudden failure of the equipment. In all cases, it is assumed that there is time to plan and schedule the maintenance, following a preset and agreed program. The main components of a scheduled maintenance program include:

- **Work request system**: this is a system that formally requests maintenance on a specific piece of equipment. These requests are submitted to the maintenance team leader by operations or maintenance personnel. Figure 5 shows a simple work request form. Some are much more complicated than this.

- **Work order requisition system**: a work order requisition is created from a work request. It tracks all work done and all materials used for a particular repair, and connects the costs to the correct piece of equipment or cost center. It also facilitates ordering of all required replacement parts.

- **Scheduling system**: this is affected by the priority of the work request, and by availability of manpower. This is usually decided at a maintenance planning meeting, attended by operations and maintenance supervisors or team leaders, who discuss and agree on an appropriate schedule. Operations will have input into when the equipment can be taken out of service; Maintenance will have input into the availability of tradesmen and parts.

- **Record keeping system**: this system keeps a permanent record of all work done on each piece of equipment, plus associated costs. Cards are often kept for each piece of equipment. Examples are shown in Figures 6 and 7.

- **Cost management system**: this is where all operating and repair costs are tracked. This enables management to determine the cost effectiveness of a piece of equipment and whether it should be replaced or maintained.

Figure 5	Work Request Form

WORK REQUEST	
Date: _____	Cost Center: _____
Equipment Number: _____	
Submitted by: _____	Priority: _____
Description of Work Requested:	
Repaired by: _____	Hours: _____
Comments:	

Figure 6	Equipment Record Card

EQUIPMENT RECORD CARD

Card No.	Category	Equipment No.	
Requisition No.	Spec. No.	Reference Drawing Nos.	Date into Service
Function		Location	
Supplied		Purchase Cost	
Description			
Equipment Unit		Components	

Name

Model Type

Catalog No.
KW   Speed
Drive
Volt _____ Amp _____ Phase
Other specs.

Complete ins.
Remarks

Figure 7	Equipment Repair Record

EQUIPMENT REPAIR RECORD

COST OF REPAIRS - REPLACEMENT

Date	Name of Part	Supplied by	Repaired Installed by	Description of Repairs - Replacement	Labour Hours	Labour Cost	Material Cost

OBJECTIVE 3

Explain the importance and extent of record keeping and describe the quality and content requirements for operating logbooks and records.

RECORD KEEPING

Indexing, storage and retrieval of plant information are fundamental to records management. Equally important are establishing filing systems and deciding what must be filed, what can be discarded and how long files should be retained. Since records can be very extensive, the system must meet the requirements of the organization and be user friendly for the staff. Many companies store files electronically, but there is still a need to have hard copies for back-up.

Thorough and accurate record keeping is extremely important for the Power Engineer. Operationally, records provide documentation that allow analysis of operating conditions and helps make intelligent decisions that ensure operational integrity and efficiency. Perhaps more importantly, certain records are a legal, legislated requirement, particularly for all systems and equipment that are covered under the typical Boiler and Pressure Vessel legislation.

Legal Requirements

The Chief Power Engineer must maintain certain documentation to comply with the requirements of the following:

1. The jurisdictional Power Engineer Regulations.

2. The Provincial Worker's Compensation Board and Local Fire Marshall Regulations

3. The insurance companies

Operating Log Book

Of special interest to all power engineers, not just the chief engineer, is the operating logbook. In a large plant there may be more than one book, each dedicated to a specific section. In any case, the official logbooks are legal documents. Therefore, all information entered in a logbook must be thorough, accurate, legible, and easily understood by others.

Although the exact wording may vary, all jurisdictional "Boiler and Pressure Vessel Acts and Regulations" require that:

- "The chief engineer or building operator shall ensure that a log book is maintained to record any matters relating to the operation of the power plant. Records of the testing and servicing of safety valves and other safety devices and controls must also be kept".

While ultimately responsible for the record keeping, the chief engineer must ensure that the shift engineers (who are ultimately operating the equipment) maintain the required logbooks. They must date and sign their entries and the logbook(s) must be kept on file and made available at any time to a "Boiler Inspector". The book(s) may be used as evidence in inquiries and in courts of law.

As one example of legislation, the following is a direct quote from the *Alberta Safety Codes Act, Power Engineers Regulations, Section 6.*

"The chief power engineer of a power plant and the power engineer in charge of a heating plant or a thermal liquid heating system must ensure that a log book is updated and maintained to record

(a) matters relating to the operation and maintenance of that power plant, heating plant or thermal liquid heating system,

(b) the testing and servicing of safety valves and other safety devices and controls, and

(c) any other matter that may affect the safety of the power plant, heating plant or thermal liquid heating system."

In the Ontario legislation, *"Technical Standards and Safety Act, Operating Engineers Regulation (O.Reg. #219/01)"*, very precise regulations are stated for logbooks. The section is quoted here to illustrate the importance of the logbook and to provide a guideline as to the standard of its content, regardless of a power engineer's location in Canada.

37. (1) Every user of a plant shall keep in the plant a log in the form of a book or electronic log. O. Reg. 219/01, s. 37 (1).

(2) Subject to subsections (3) and (4), the logbook shall be bound and constructed so that the pages are numbered and cannot be removed and shall be large enough to accommodate all the required entries. O. Reg. 219/01, s. 37 (2).

(3) Where a user keeps an electronic log, the user shall ensure that a dated paper print-out of the log is created at the end of each shift, is entered into the logbook and signed by the chief operating engineer or chief operator the next business day. O. Reg. 219/01, s. 37 (3).

(4) An electronic log shall include information relating to equipment used, information produced, form produced, back up ability, ambient operating limits, and authorized pass code entry by only the chief engineer, chief operator, shift engineer or shift operator, and shall be kept so that any substations have read-only ability. O. Reg. 219/01, s. 37 (4).

(5) The names of the chief operating engineer, chief operator, relief chiefs, shift engineers and shift operators and their sample signatures shall be entered on the logbook's signature page. O. Reg. 219/01, s. 37 (5).

(6) No person except the chief operating engineer, chief operator, a shift engineer or a shift operator may make an entry in or sign the logbook. O. Reg. 219/01, s. 37 (6).

(7) Standing orders that are to be routinely followed shall be clearly documented in a location that is known and available to the persons to whom they apply and supplementary logs shall be registered in the log. O. Reg. 219/01, s. 37 (7).

(8) Shift entries to the log shall include,

(a) the date, the shift and the times at which the shift begins and ends; 14

(b) the names of all shift engineers, shift operators, assistant shift engineers, assistant shift operators, other staff and operating assistants or trainees on a shift and their periods of duty on the shift;

(c) any instructions for the shift operation or for staff, along with the name of the person giving the instructions;

(d) any change from normal operating procedure and the time of such change;

(e) any unusual or abnormal conditions observed in the plant and the time they were observed;

(f) the starting or stopping times of primary equipment not recorded in other logs;

(g) documentation of any repairs or maintenance, including that required under subsection 39 (9), to any part of the plant, the times the repair or maintenance took place, if they were completed and who attended at the repair or maintenance;

(h) any malfunction of any item or equipment, the time of the occurrence and any remedial action taken to correct the malfunction;

(i) any work performed by plant operating personnel outside the plant, the time spent and who attended at the work;

(j) the entry of any unauthorized person to the plant, together with the purpose of the entry and the time of entry and leaving;

(k) primary shift functions, including the times of at least the following functions:

   (i) boiler blow down,

   (ii) water column blow down,

   (iii) controls tests,

   (iv) safety valve tests,

   (v) sootblower operation, and

   (vi) water sampling and chemical treatment. O. Reg. 219/01, s. 37 (8).

(9) All logbook entries shall be in ink and any corrections shall not be erased but crossed out, corrected and initialled. O. Reg. 219/01, s. 37 (9).

(10) No person shall deface, damage, destroy or, without the permission of the owner or user, remove the logbook from the plant. O. Reg. 219/01, s. 37 (10).

(11) The chief operating engineer or chief operator shall read and sign the log at least once each business day. O. Reg. 219/01, s. 37 (11).

(12) The user shall ensure that the logbook is kept accessible in the plant for at least three years after the last entry is made and shall produce the logbook for examination upon the request of an inspector and, where an electronic log is kept by the user, the user shall retain the electronic log or hard copies for at least three years. O. Reg. 219/01, s. 37 (12).

Operating Log Sheets

Logsheets are separate forms that are used to regularly (every 2 hours or so) record critical, local operating parameters of individual equipment throughout a power plant. In larger plants there may be several logsheets, each pertaining to a different section or system in the plant. The logsheets are usually completed by the area operators, although control room operators may also have key items to record (in addition to logbook entries).

While the exact parameters to be logged are not specified, since all plants are different, most boiler and pressure vessel legislation requires that readings be logged. One example, again from the *"Alberta Safety Codes Act, Power Engineers Regulations, 2003, Section 6"*, states that:

> " The chief power engineer of a power plant and the power engineer in charge of a heating plant or a thermal liquid heating system must ensure that a log book is updated and maintained to record:
>
> (a) matters relating to the operation and maintenance of that power plant, heating plant or liquid thermal heating system,
>
> (b) the testing and servicing of safety valves and other safety devices and controls, and
>
> (c) any other matter that may affect the safety of the power plant, heating plant or thermal liquid heating system."

Besides being a regulated requirement, logsheet readings serve some extremely valuable operational functions.

- They allow the operators to recognize trends that may be leading to operating problems (eg. bearing temperatures increasing, storage levels dropping, boiler pH falling)
- They provide a cross-check of control room readings, which helps to maintain the accuracy of field instruments and controls.

Steam plant log sheets (often called "run sheets") should at least contain:

- critical temperatures, pressures and flows (especially those that are not already recorded in control room systems (such as DCS trends and historical data)
- steam production from boilers
- boiler water test results
- boiler chemical feed rates
- continuous blowdown settings
- water pre-treatment system production and quality
- equipment running hours
- boiler and Deaerator water levels
- oil levels, bearing temperatures, etc. of rotating equipment
- storage tank levels (water, fuel, chemicals)
- furnace conditions of fired equipment (damper positions, flame appearance, draft readings, etc.)

OBJECTIVE 4

Using a complete boiler turnaround and inspection as an example, describe project management using two methods, Gantt Chart and Critical Path.

PROJECT MANAGEMENT FUNCTIONS

"Project management" is, as the title implies, the systematic control (ie. management) of a major work project, from inception to completion. The system is designed to ensure that projects occur smoothly, in a logical sequence, and are completed on schedule. There are three basic functions in project management.

1. Planning
2. Implementation
3. Review

1. Planning

When a major project is scheduled, such as a boiler turnaround and inspection, very careful and thorough planning is required before the work begins. In fact, the key to the success of any project is the planning stage. Proper planning takes time. For example, a one-week boiler turnaround, involving annual inspection and repairs, will require several weeks of preparation. The project manager (planner) must develop a comprehensive plan for the project, which will require him to have specific information, including:

- Date the boiler will be shutdown and available for the project.
- The extent and complexity (in detail) of all intended work
- Project completion date (ie. date that the boiler must be back in service)
- Date that the internal inspection will be done

Given this information, the project manager can begin working with Operations, Maintenance, and Purchasing to establish a complete project plan, using a recognized project management system. This may be a computer-based system, a totally manual system, or a combination of the two. Using the boiler turnaround as an example, the planning stage should include the following, which must be completed before work can begin.

- Initiate the project management system (format) to be used (eg. Ghant Chart, Critical Path)
- Establish, with Operations and Maintenance, the exact order and timing of events
- Notify and confirm availability of inspectors (eg. Boiler Inspector, Water Treatment consultant)
- Determine internal manpower requirements from each trade and allot against each event. Include any requirements for extra safety personnel
- Determine external contractors required (eg. welders). Confirm and finalize contracts.
- Determine and arrange for any external shop repairs (eg. safety valve repairs)
- Determine required parts and supplies (eg. valves, gauge glasses, refractory, cleaning chemicals, etc); ensure all are ordered and delivery dates confirmed.
- Determine and confirm availability of tools, particularly specialty tools (eg. tube expanders, handhole cutters, tube cleaners)
- Determine and order rental equipment (eg. scaffolding, portable compressors)
- Confirm availability of safety equipment (eg. blinds, detectors, barricades)
- Establish laydown areas for equipment and parts

- Confirm responsibilities, including communication and reporting structures during the project.

2. Implementation

Implementation involves a Pre-Work Phase, in which the planning steps are finalized, followed by the Work Phase, during which the work is actually completed.

In the Pre-Work Phase, the project manager will continue to prepare and organize the project. He will maintain close communication with Maintenance, Operations, and Purchasing to ensure that the project schedule is still valid and that materials will be received on time. Contractors may require orientation to the site and to the safety rules, which can be done in advance. Meetings should be held with all those workers (or their team leaders) to review the entire project and ensure everyone understands their responsibilities and the project management system being used.

During the work phase the following major steps should be taken by the project manager:

- Daily meetings to discuss progress and challenges; agree on the scheduled jobs for each day.
- Constant updating of the project management "chart" so everyone is aware of the status, including plant management.
- Liaise with inspectors, contractors, safety personnel, etc. to ensure schedules are met.
- Confirm acceptance and sign-off of each project event.
- Revise the project schedule and/or order of events if necessary (and for good reason), with agreement from Operations, Maintenance and Management.

3. Review

During the implementation phase, as mentioned above, there is a process of constant review. This ensures the day to day progress of the project is being monitored and discussed and any unexpected challenges are being dealt with. The review may determine any changes in the system to make it work more smoothly or more efficiently.

Just as important is an overall project review, which is done after the project is completed. This honest, hindsight review of all aspects of the project will be beneficial to future similar projects. The benefits may be realized in better work efficiency, reduced project time, better work quality, improved safety, reduced costs, etc. Any mistakes or oversights in the overall project or individual jobs may be eliminated. The good points will be repeated.

PROJECT MANAGEMENT TOOLS

There are several management systems (tools) available to the project manager. The systems serve two purposes.

- First and foremost, they give the project manager a constant, visual tool for managing the project.
- Second, they act as a communication tool that keeps everyone informed of the project plan and status.

For larger projects, these tools are usually computerized and very complex. Their use requires a detailed understanding of the computer program and the more involved components of project management, including budgeting. Smaller projects may involve a more manual approach, with manually prepared charts. Two common and relatively simple systems are Gantt Charts and Critical Path.

1. Gantt Chart

The Gantt Chart lists the key planning steps and all implementation work (ie. the individual jobs) and identifies the exact timing and duration of each. Looking at the chart, one can see when each job will be done and its relationship to all other jobs in the same project. The amount of detail that the project manager puts into the chart is optional. Also, if an individual event within a project is itself fairly complicated, there may be a separate Gantt Chart for that event.

Figure 8 shows a Gantt Chart that has been prepared for a boiler turnaround.

- Each of the major jobs is listed in the left "Events" column. While not mandatory, it is beneficial if these are listed in order of expected starting time.
- The remaining columns are for the days and weeks during the project, including the planning and implementation stages. If a project is of short duration, the chart may break the time down into smaller increments (hours). In Figure 8, the total time of the boiler turnaround project is 3 weeks and the events are scheduled by days.
- Beside each event, in the time section, the start and end of the event is indicated and a straight line between them shows the duration of the event. It is easy to see the time relationship between all events. It is also easy to see where events will occur simultaneously. For example, on Thursday of Week 3 there are nine events scheduled.
- The progress of each event is shown by coloring its bar. Figure 8 shows that all events are on schedule up to the end of Tuesday in Week 3, except for "Repair 2 Safety Valves", which has not yet started for some reason.

Figure 8	Gantt Chart for Boiler Turnaround

Department _____

Project Number _____   Date _____

EVENTS	WEEK NO. 1							WEEK NO. 2							WEEK NO. 3						
	M	T	W	Th	F	S	S	M	T	W	Th	F	S	S	M	T	W	Th	F	S	S
Prepare list of shutdown items	▨	▨	▨																		
Notify Boiler & Insurance Inspectors				▨																	
Check for spare parts & order as needed				▨	▨	▨	▨	▨	▨	▨	▨	▨	▨	▨							
Estimate Maintenance hours by Trade								▨	▨												
Discuss schedule with Maintenance										▨											
Boiler shutdown & lockout 16:00 May 3															▨	▨	▨				
Complete boiler turn-over sheet for Maint.															⊓						
Clean boiler internally															▨						
Clean boiler fireside																▨					
Boiler instrumentation checks																⊓__⊓					
Boiler inspection																		⊓			
Overhaul B.F. pump No. 1																	⊓__⊓				
Repair 2 safety valves															⊓__⊓						
Check I.D. fan bearings																	⊓__⊓				
Repair refractory																	⊓__⊓				
Repack gauge glass isolation valves																	⊓				
Replace gauge glass																	⊓				
Repack non-return stop valve																	⊓				
Repair blowdown valves																▨					
Hydrostatic test																		⊓			
Check boiler shutdowns during start-up																			⊓		
Maint. sign-over of boiler to Operations																			⊓		

⌐ Start of work   ⌐ Work completed   ⌐‾‾‾‾⌐ Total time scheduled   ⌐▨▨▨⌐ Work done compared with schedule

2. Critical Path

While the Gantt Chart is sufficient for most projects in the steam plant, it does have some limitation, such as not forecasting troubles or delays until the event has already occurred and not clearly identifying which events MUST be completed before others. These problems are overcome with a more sophisticated project management tool, called Critical Path.

The objective of the critical path is to identify:

- a sequence of work activities, shown in a diagram (often called a network)
- the time relationship for the start and finish of the activities
- any spare time that occurs within the project
- Clearly show a "critical path" of activities, which is the sequence of activities that results in the longest project duration.
- Clearly show activities on "non-critical paths", which are paths that can be extended in duration (within limits) without increasing the overall project duration.

Critical Path Components

The main components of a critical path diagram (network) are "activities" and "milestones". The diagram uses arrows and circles to show the relationship between all activities and milestones in a project. The arrows represent activities; the circles represent events.

An **activity** is an individual job that must be completed as part of the project work. It has a start point and an end point. The critical path diagram is a series of activities (ie. connected arrows), which visually shows the relationship of all activities in the project.

A **milestone** is simply a point in the critical path. Think of it as a checkpoint. Activities occur between milestones, so each milestone has one or more activities before it and one or more activities after it. The activities before it must be completed before the activities after it can begin.

The activity arrow has the following characteristics:

- The tail represents the start of the activity
- The arrowhead represents the end of the activity

Activity

Start ⟶ End

- It is not drawn to scale and may be straight, curved, or bent
- It cannot be interrupted or broken by another activity
- An activity may be assigned a time value or have zero time value
- The start and end points of an activity are milestones, which have no time value

Milestone　　　　　　　　　　　　　Milestone

Each milestone in a network is assigned a unique number. Figure 9 shows milestone #3, with two activities before it and three activities after it.

Figure 9	Milestone Number

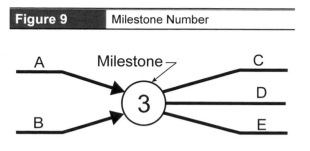

Figures 10 graphically explains the various arrow configurations in a critical path network. An explanation of each if given.

Figure 10	Network Arrow Interpretation

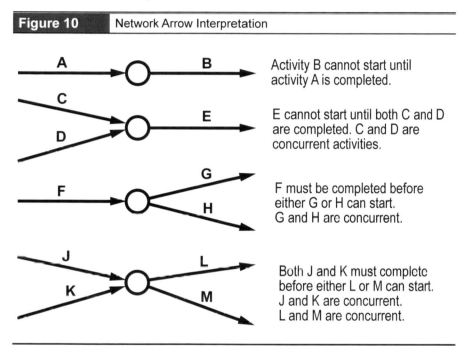

Activity B cannot start until activity A is completed.

E cannot start until both C and D are completed. C and D are concurrent activities.

F must be completed before either G or H can start. G and H are concurrent.

Both J and K must complete before either L or M can start. J and K are concurrent. L and M are concurrent.

Dummy Arrows

Figure 11 illustrates dummy arrows, which are used to fill gaps in the critical path diagram. They are shown by dotted lines. In Figure 11, activities K, L, and M all start when milestone number 9 is completed and they must all complete before milestone 12. Activity L is on the critical path. However, activities K and M are shorter duration than activity L and are on sub-critical paths. They also must be completed by milestone 12, but there is room for extra time if necessary. Dummy arrows complete the paths to milestone 12, indicating there is no activity occurring during that part of each path, unless activities K and M require extra time.

Figure 11	Dummy Arrows

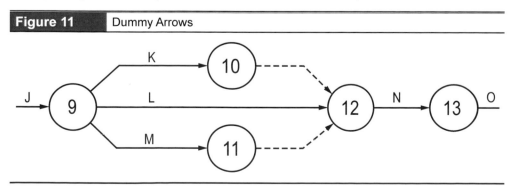

Constructing a Critical Path Diagram

To construct a critical path diagram, the project to be diagramed must first be divided into the many component activities. Then the activities are organized into a network, by answering the following questions for each activity.

- What activities (arrows) must be completed before this?
- What activities (arrows) can be concurrent with this one?
- What activities (arrows) cannot start until this one is finished?

Using the boiler turnaround project (Fig. 8) as an example, the following steps should be followed after the boiler has been made safe and turned over to maintenance.

- Make a Critical Path Work Description Sheet, which lists each activity that must occur during the turnaround. The sequence of events should be listed in logical order, without much detail. Short duration activities such as the repacking of the gauge glass isolation valves and the non-return valve, and the replacing of the gauge glass may be lumped together, as shown on the description work sheet in Figure 12.
- Number the activities on the worksheet (or use letters)
- Calculate the time that each activity will take to complete and show it in the right-hand column of the worksheet
- Using the worksheet information, construct the critical path diagram.
- Put the appropriate number (letter) and hours on each activity line.

Figure 12	Work Description Sheet for Boiler Turnaround

NO. 1 BOILER ANNUAL INSPECTION		
ACTIVITY NUMBER		**ESTIMATED JOB TIME IN HOURS**
	Boiler turned over to maintenance	
A	Remove and repair safety valves	6
B	Clean boiler internally	6
C	Clean boiler fireside	4
D	Boiler instrumentation checks	12
E	Boiler initial inspection	3
F	Overhaul Boiler feedpump No. 1	15
G	Check ID fan bearings	2
H	Repair Refractory	6
I	• Repack gauge glass isolation valves	8
	• Replace gauge glass	
	• Repack non-return stop valve	
J	Repair blowdown valves	4
K	Hydrostatic test and final inspection	10
L	Install safety valves	2
M	Boiler start-up	4
N	Check boiler shutdowns during start-up	2

Figure 13 shows a critical path diagram for the above worksheet.

| Figure 13 | Boiler Overhaul Critical Path |

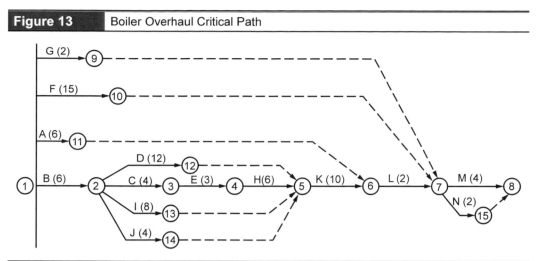

From Figure 13, the total duration for all jobs is 82 hours. However, by careful planning, the critical path is reduced to 35 hours. The critical path in this case is represented by the solid lines that run successively from milestone 1 to milestone 8.

Figure 14 shows how the critical path may change during the project. If, for example, during activity J, repairing the blowdown valves, one of the valves is found to be beyond repair and a new valve must be ordered, the duration of activity J must be revised. If it will take 24 hours to obtain a new valve, the critical path now changes, as shown, to 50 hours. This gives some additional time for activities, C, E, and H, if necessary. Normally, the project manager would not redraw the diagram, but would colour the new path and adjust the hours accordingly.

| Figure 14 | Boiler Overhaul Revised Critical Path |

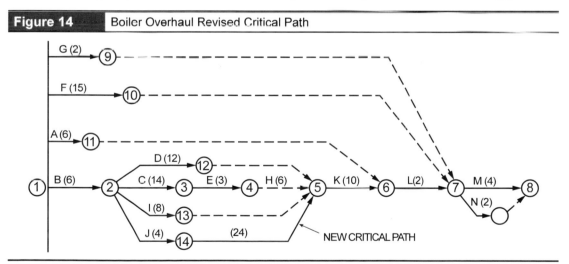

Updating the network, after work delays have occurred, is a powerful tool to reassess the progress of the work. It allows the programmer to make decisions, which deal with delays or other changes, in the most efficient way. It is especially useful in very complex construction projects and total plant shut downs.

After the shutdown is finished, it is important to review the shutdown activities. This is usually accompanied by a written record or summary, which is filed for future reference. An honest appraisal of the plan and its execution must be made and discussed with all the people involved. From this, valuable experience is gained for future programs.

It is very likely that if things went wrong the same mistakes will be repeated unless there has been a review and recommendations for improvement. The summary of the review and recommendations is distributed to the various participants and filed in a special place so it becomes part of the planning process.

OBJECTIVE 5

Explain the importance of procedures in the operation of a facility and describe the application of well-written procedures to personnel training and daily operation.

OPERATING PROCEDURES

Operating procedures are documents that show, in logical and progressive order, all the steps that are necessary to safely and accurately perform operational activities. The formats of these documents may vary greatly from company to company, some having much more detail than others. The format is usually standardized within a given company, but there may be some variation, depending on the purpose and complexity of the procedure. Regardless of their format, the importance of procedures can be recognized in the following purposes they serve within an operating facility.

1. Safety

Since safety must be the top priority of every company, the operating procedures must consider all safety issues that could impact on the employees, the public, and the company assets. This consideration will reduce the risk of accidents and incidents. A properly written procedure should mention all hazards associated with the procedure and state how to recognize and handle those hazards. Critical safety notes and steps must be included, such as isolation, purging, lockout, personal protective equipment required, etc.

2. Training

Procedures are invaluable in the training of personnel. This may include training a new employee in an initial operating area or a seasoned employee in a new operating area. It may also include training personnel to operate and maintain newly installed equipment or expanded processes. Training is enhanced when the procedures for an area are read and understood, then used as guidelines and checklists (for the trainee and the trainer) while performing the procedure for the first time.

3. Standardization

Having a procedure performed in the same way by all personnel Is important to the efficiency and integrity of many facilities. When procedures are written and available to all it is easier to enforce this standard, rather than allow each operator to "do it my own way". To support this, it is important that all operators have input into the procedure writing (plus any revisions) and that there be agreement and acceptance of the final version.

4. Competency Assurance and Review

For several purposes, besides training, written procedures are useful in assessing and ensuring the competence of employees. When a rarely-performed procedure must be undertaken, operators can review the procedure, which they have likely forgotten. If an operator is assigned to an area that he is qualified for, but hasn't work in for a long time, he can review the procedures as a refresher. A supervisor may use written procedures as guidelines when completing employee performance assessments.

5. Satisfy Regulations and Insurance

Companies that are ISO 9000 certified must complete a formal, annual review of all written procedures with every operator. In some jurisdictions, the Chief Power Engineer is required, by Regulation, to provide and maintain written operating procedures. Occupational Health and Safety Legislation Canada requires "Due Diligence" to be exercised by employers. This includes providing written procedures for all activities, particularly where safety is a factor. Most insurance companies require a company to have written procedures in place as part of their insurance contract.

6. Incident Investigations

Procedures are often the focus of any incident investigation, particularly serious incidents causing injury or death. Environmental incidents also require investigation. The focus will be on whether procedures exist, employees are trained in them, and they are accurate and enforced.

7. Emergencies

Critical emergency procedures are used if the integrity of an operation is threatened by an emergency situation, such as fire, explosion, gas release, etc. They clearly define all the responsibilities and steps that must be followed to handle the emergency.

OBJECTIVE 6

Explain typical environmental monitoring and management programs for operating facilities.

ENVIRONMENTAL MANAGEMENT PROGRAMS

Protection of the Environment

Protecting the environment (air, water and soil) requires a company to be familiar with all current government regulations pertaining to the environment. The company is then responsible to establish a program that will keep them in compliance with these regulations.

A typical environmental program will have three main components:

- **Training:** Employees who work in positions that could affect the environment must receive appropriate training in environmental regulations and procedures. Some of the training that the employees should receive include TDG (Transportation of Dangerous Goods) and HCS (Hazardous Communications Standard - OSHA)
- **Monitoring:** Effective monitoring of the air, water and soil qualities will require setting up air quality monitoring trailers, ground water observation wells, and a soil-sampling program.
- **Reporting:** A program must be established to meet government requirements for the reporting of all air, water and soil contamination. The company must ensure that all employees know the reporting procedures. It is also very important that all licensing agreements are in place and current.

Public Awareness

This may be the most difficult aspect of an environmental management program, since dealing with the public can be very stressful. It is important that the company maintain communications with the community around it. This can be accomplished by public information sessions or by mailing out information brochures. Their purpose is being able to share information about current and future operational issues that may impact the public or the environment.

The potentially hazardous nature of some facilities require that emergency telephone numbers be distributed to residents living within a certain radius of the facility. These numbers can be called if there are any concerns about the operation of the facility. There may also be an emergency evacuation plan that all nearby residents should know and follow in a serious environmental emergency.

Environmental Monitoring

When monitoring air quality the monitoring trailers must be checked regularly to determine if and when any air quality violations have occurred. This permits appropriate and timely reports to be submitted to the appropriate environmental agency.

In some cases, emissions are monitored hourly and a daily report is generated. The report is either kept for future reference or sent to the environmental agency for their records. These records indicate how close the operation is to exceeding the daily or monthly emissions limits and allows the operators to make knowledgeable process adjustments, if necessary, to remain within acceptable limits.

Asbestos contamination of the air is a major concern in many older facilities where asbestos was used for insulation. Any locations with asbestos insulation must be thoroughly sealed to prevent harmful asbestos fibers being released into the atmosphere. These locations must be inspected regularly to ensure that the seals are intact. Inspection personnel must wear proper protective clothing to prevent inhaling asbestos fibers. Seal repairs or removal of the asbestos must be undertaken only by personnel wearing appropriate protective clothing. An employer must ensure that all employees are familiar with the hazards and the safety procedures associated with asbestos.

Ground water quality is another important aspect of environmental monitoring. Ground water observation wells (also called Piezometer wells) are drilled in the vicinity of large holding ponds or underground storage tanks, where leaks or overflows may cause ground water contamination. The soil within a plant area is checked for contamination by taking soil samples from various locations and analyzing them for specific contaminants.

Another pollutant that can be just as irritating as any other pollution forms is noise. It can be particularly harmful to employees within the facility, but can be annoying to nearby residents. Sound decibel readings are regularly taken around the plant to monitor the noise levels.

CHAPTER 15 - QUESTIONS

1. What are the three main types of internal communication used in a large facility? What are the benefits of good external communications?

2. Draw the organization chart for the operating facility you are employed at and briefly describe the communication structure.

3. List the main components of a PM program.

4. Briefly describe how a PM program functions.

5. What three organizations require the Chief Steam Engineer to provide documentation upon request?

6. What items should the steam plant logbook contain?

7. What are the three basic functions of project management?

8. Explain how a Critical Path works.

9. Briefly describe the importance of procedures in the operation of a large operating facility.

10. List the two main focuses of an Environmental Management Program and describe one of them.

ANSWERS: All answers are found within the content of the chapter.